SPANISH VERB PIVOTS

UNLOCKING SPANISH GRAMMAR

FOR BEGINNER TO PRE-INTERMEDIATE LEARNERS

SENTENCE BUILDERS

A lexicogrammar approach

ISBN: 9783949651397

Imprint: Language Gym

Edited by:

Roberto Jover Soro

About the authors

Gianfranco Conti taught for 25 years at schools in Italy, the UK and in Kuala Lumpur, Malaysia. He has also been a university lecturer, holds a Master's degree in Applied Linguistics and a PhD in metacognitive strategies as applied to second language writing. He is now an author, a popular independent educational consultant and a professional development provider. He has written around 2,000 resources for the TES website, who awarded him the Best Resources Contributor in 2015. He has co-authored the best-selling and influential books for world languages teachers, "The Language Teacher Toolkit", "Breaking the sound barrier: Teaching learners how to listen", in which he puts forth his Listening As Modelling methodology and "Memory: what every language teacher should know". Last but not least, Gianfranco has created the instructional approach known as E.P.I. (Extensive Processing Instruction).

Dylan Viñales has taught for 17 years, in schools in Bath, Beijing and Kuala Lumpur in state, independent and international settings. He lives in Kuala Lumpur. He is fluent in five languages, and gets by in several more. Dylan is, besides a teacher, a professional development provider, specialising in E.P.I., metacognition, teaching languages through music (especially ukulele) and cognitive science. In the last five years, together with Dr Conti, he has driven the implementation of E.P.I. in one of the top international schools in the world: Garden International School. Dylan authors an influential blog on modern language pedagogy in which he supports the teaching of languages through E.P.I.

Esmeralda Salgado has taught for 22 years in schools in Bromley, Chatham and Ely, in both state and independent schools. She is an Advanced Skills Teacher and currently works at King's Ely, as Head of Modern Foreign Languages and Digital Learning Lead. Esmeralda is passionate about the use of digital technology to enhance the learning of languages, as well as using project based learning, all underpinned by E.P.I instruction. Esmeralda also authors her own influential pedagogical blog where she shares resources and reflects on her own practice supported by E.P.I and provides professional development workshops as a language consultant. Finally, Esmeralda is a Silver Winner of the Pearson National Teaching Awards 2022, under the category of Teacher of the Year in a secondary school.

Dedication

For Catrina

-Gianfranco

For Ariella & Leonard

-Dylan

For Indra, Otilia & Marina

-Esmeralda

Acknowledgements

Creating a book is a time-consuming yet rewarding endeavour.

We would like to thank our editor, Roberto Jover Soro for his tireless work, proofreading, editing and advising on this book. He is a talented, accomplished professional who always works at the highest possible level and adds value at every stage of the process. Not only this, but he is also a lovely, good-humoured colleague who goes above and beyond, and makes the hours of collaborating a real pleasure. ¡Gracias Bobby!

Our sincere gratitude to Ana Isabel del Casar Benítez & Apolinar García for your help in the recording of the listening audio files: your energy, enthusiasm and passion are clear in every recording and are the reason why the listening sections are such a successful and engaging resource, according to the many students who have been alpha and beta testing the book.

Thanks to Flaticon.com and Mockofun.com for providing access to a limitless library of engaging icons, clipart and images which we have used to make this book more user-friendly than any other Sentence Builders predecessor, with a view to be as engaging as possible for students.

Additionally, our gratitude to the MFL Twitterati for their ongoing support of E.P.I. and the Sentence Builders book series. In particular a shoutout to our team of incredible educators who helped in checking all the units: Imogen Brown, Susie Fernández Gómez, Tom Ball, David Dun, Thais López Martín, Paloma Lozano, Lewis Rees, Joe Barnes Moran, Pam Stallard, María Simon, Paddy McDevitt, Melissa Boyd, Jérôme Nogues, Inés Glowacka, Chris Pye, Simona Gravina, Aurélie Lethuilier and Sonja Fedrizzi. It is thanks to your time, patience, professionalism and detailed feedback that we have been able to produce such a refined and highly accurate product.

Gracias a todos,

Gianfranco, Dylan & Esmeralda

Introduction

Who is it for?

The Spanish Verb Pivots book is aimed at learners in the **A1-B1 proficiency range**. It was conceived both for classroom and independent use, whatever the method, setting or course, as it offers ample opportunities for practice through a wide range of activities designed to appeal to learners with a variety of cognitive styles and learning preferences.

It can be used to **introduce** the target verbs and associated grammar and lexicogrammar patterns to **absolute beginners**. It can also be useful if you teach **lower-to-intermediate learners** (years 9 to 11 in the U.K.) in order to consolidate, expand and deepen their mastery of those verbs and patterns. The latter learners, in my experience, are often able to master verb formation, but lack **depth of knowledge**, i.e. knowledge of verb **collocations** (which lexis the verbs partner with) and **colligations** (the rules which bind the verbs with what comes before and after them in a sentence).

Why this book?

Based on the premise that second language instruction should be first and foremost about **empowering learners with the ability to convey meaning in the real world** and not to learn grammar for grammar's sake, the book sets out to teach **lexicogrammar** (or pattern grammar), i.e.: the grammar glueing together the **sentence patterns** (or syntactic schemata) that we make use of in order to fulfil **a communicative purpose** (e.g. describing a person; comparing and contrasting people; making arrangements for an evening out; describing one's daily activities, etc.).

I conceived and created this book because **I felt the current trends in modern language teaching were too concerned with the teaching of isolated grammar rules as totally divorced from a communicative context.** Also, I have always found that textbooks, even when used in synergy with their associated workbooks, provide insufficient ***multimodal* practice**. This is a major shortcoming of traditional grammar instruction at large, as **research shows clearly that the learning of L2 grammar structures must be multimodal for them to be effectively learnt**. Multimodality is one of the most innovative features of this book: the target sentence patterns and morphemes are learnt **across all four language skills**, including speaking and listening, which are usually the most neglected skills.

Why is the book called "Spanish Verb Pivots"?

Verbs constitute the core of every sentence we utter and write. In other words, they are **the 'pivots' around which each sentence patterns develops**. Each verb one selects, as well as the social context and the purpose one selects it for, **constrains the range of lexical and grammatical choices we can make in producing a sentence**. So, for instance, using the verb *querer* to express what one wants someone to do will require the use of *querer + subject + present subjunctive* (e.g. quiero que tu vayas al supermercado).

This book aims at teaching how to use the most useful and frequent Spanish verbs in everyday communication in terms of how to:

- **manipulate them effectively** (inflectional morphology, e.g. how to conjugate the verbs in the present)
- **deal with the linguistic choices they trigger** (pattern grammar, i.e.: the constructions associated with each verb)
- **master the rules which bind words together** within a given syntactic pattern (colligations, i.e.: how each word affects the next; for instance how determiners or adjectives agree in gender and number with nouns)

As it is clear from (1), (2) and (3) above, exploring how a verb works also **entails learning a lot of other grammar and lexicogrammar rules which emerge organically from the communicative context at hand**. For instance, teaching the verb *ir* will lead to learning articled prepositions (e.g. voy/va/vamos/etc. **al** cine), possessives (e.g. con **mi/mis/su/sus**/etc. padres/amigos/hermanos/etc.) and even how to form a final clause (e.g. voy al centro comercial **para comprar un nuevo ordenador**).

What's in the Spanish book?

The book includes 8 macro-units, each focusing on a different verb or verb set in the present tense. The verbs are: *Tener, Ser, Hacer, Ir, Gustar, Estar, Jugar and Modal Verbs*. Each macro-unit centres on a key verb and explores and drills in, through a wide range of engaging and enjoyable **multimodal** tasks, all the possible patterns associated with it deemed to be learnable at this level of proficiency. Every macro-unit includes 7-8 sub-units for a total of 55 sub-units. For instance, the unit on *'Tener"* is broken down into the following sub-units:

1. Tener + un/una + noun: Introduction to masculine and feminine
2. Tengo + un/una + noun + adjective (colour)
3. Tener: full present conjugation
4. Tener: other uses
5. Tener + indefinite article + classroom object + adjective
6. Tener + indefinite article + clothing item + adjective
7. Tener + plural nouns + adjective

Each macro-unit **ends with a games unit that brings all the content of that unit together** and consolidates it through written and oral retrieval-practice tasks.

How does the book work?

Each macro-unit starts 'small' with the target verb being learnt within very basic sentence patterns and in the first person only. As each unit progresses **the target verbs are modelled in sentence patterns which gradually increase in length and complexity.** In order to enhance transferrability of learning and lexical depth, each verb is also practised with a variety of lexical sets. For instance, the verb *Tener* is practised with animals, classroom objects, clothes, physical description, emotional and physical states, age, etc.

Task-essentialness is pervasive: each unit contains a plethora of tasks which elicit the application of the target grammar structure multiple times.

Recycling is carefully engineered to allow for repeated receptive and productive processing of the target language items within the same units and across the whole book. As mentioned above, each new unit builds on the previous one in a 'what I know + 1" fashion, so that the stem of a new sentence builder was covered in the previous sub-unit. Also, every macro-unit ends with a massive recap of everything covered thus far.

Subconscious learning through input flood and repeated processing works in synergy with explicit learning in the way of (1) awareness-raising boxes at the beginning of each sub-unit, (2) tasks focusing the students' attention on the target features and (3) metacognitive activities eliciting self-reflection and self-evaluation.

Traditional grammar and lexicogrammar intersect throughout the whole book, as, in order for the learners to be able to become creative with each sentence pattern, they must also master the manipulation of the changeable items in each sentence such as verbs, adjectives, pronouns determiners, etc. **The teaching of grammar arises organically from the need to enhance the generative power of each target sentence pattern** – this is a major innovation of this book.

The book is very mindful of cognitive load. Hence, each instructional sequence gradually increases the cognitive challenge, with receptive activities in the initial section of each sub-unit paving the way for the productive ones located at the end and **with each task priming the next**. It goes without saying that the repeated processing and the constant recycling also makes it easier for the content to become effortlessly entrenched.

How can one supplement this book to enhance its impact?

Please note that this book is best used in synergy with language-gym.com and sentencebuilders.com. Both websites feature self-marking games and activities based on its content.

TABLE OF CONTENTS

THE LANGUAGE GYM

UNIT 1 – TENER

Yo	**Tengo**
Tú	**Tienes**
Él / Ella	**Tiene**
Nosotros / as	**Tenemos**
Vosotros / as	**Tenéis**
Ellos / as	**Tienen**

1.1 TENER + UN/UNA + NOUN + RELATIVE CLAUSE

(SAYING WHAT ANIMALS I HAVE)

Tener ***To have*** **– FIRST PERSON**			
		Masculine nouns	
Tengo *I have*	**un**	**caballo** *horse* **gato** *cat* **loro** *parrot* **pájaro** *bird* **perro** *dog* **pez*** *fish*	**que se llama Paco** *that is called Paco*
		Feminine nouns	
Tengo	**una**	**araña** *spider* **cobaya** *guinea pig* **gallina** *chicken* **iguana** *iguana* **serpiente*** *snake* **tortuga** *turtle*	**que se llama María** *that is called María*

LANGUAGE AWARENESS - NOUNS IN SPANISH

The verb ***tener*** (to have) is used in a similar way to English: to describe possession.

It is important to know that in Spanish, every noun (object/thing) is either **masculine** or **feminine**. The indefinite article "a" is translated as either *un* or *una* depending on the gender of the noun.

Sometimes, the gender of nouns is logical, for example when describing masculine or feminine people or things:

- **un hermano** *a brother* is masculine
- **una hermana** *a sister* is feminine

Sometimes, where equivalent nouns in English have no gender, such as inanimate objects or emotions, you can tell if a word is masculine or feminine by the ending of the word:

- **un teléfono** *a phone* is masculine
- **una regla** *a ruler* is feminine

Masculine nouns usually end with an **"o"** whereas **feminine** nouns usually end with an **"a"**, although there are a few exceptions!

*Some nouns do end in a letter different from "o" or "a". In these cases, we cannot know the gender by just looking at the word and must learn it!

Un pez *a fish* is a masculine noun, but we only know it thanks to *un*

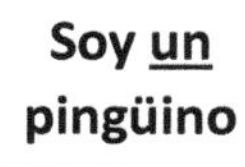

Una serpiente *a snake* is a feminine noun, but we only know it thanks to *una*

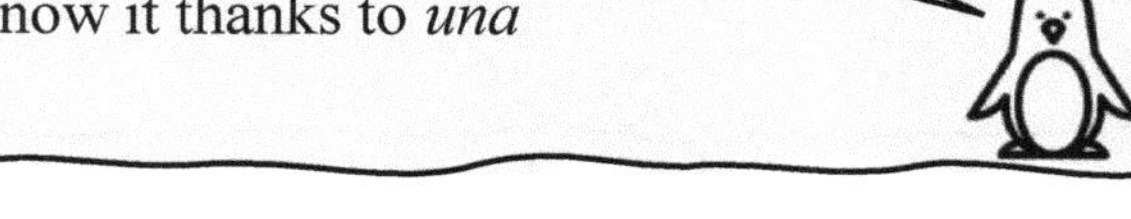

1. Match

Un pájaro	*A cat*
Una serpiente	*A bird*
Un pez	*A snake*
Una cobaya	*A fish*
Una iguana	*A guinea pig*
Una tortuga	*A dog*
Un caballo	*A spider*
Un perro	*An iguana*
Un gato	*A horse*
Una araña	*A turtle*

2. Listen and complete with the missing indefinite article (*un*/*una*)

a. Tengo ____ perro que se llama Raúl

b. Tengo ____ iguana que se llama Nana

c. Tengo ____ gato que se llama Félix

d. Tengo ____ gallina que se llama Amanda

e. Tengo ____ pez que se llama Rayo

f. Tengo ____ cobaya que se llama Juliana

g. Tengo ____ serpiente que se llama Clara

3. Break the flow

a. Tengounacobayayunloro

b. Tengoungatoyunatortuga

c. Tengounpezyunperro

d. Tengounaarañayungato

e. Tengoungatoyunagallina

f. Tengounpezyunpájaro

g. Tengounperroyunacobaya

h. Tengounaiguanayunaserpiente

4. Spot and correct the errors

a. Tengo una caballo que se llama Paco

b. Tengo un perro que se llamo Patricio

c. Tengo un tortuga que se llama Rex

d. Tengo una loro que se llama Tuno

e. Tengo una pez que se llama Ringo

f. Tengo un iguana que se llama Gian

g. Tengo un serpiente que se llama Clara

h. Tengo un gato que me llama Simba

5. Listen and complete the table following the same pattern in the example

	Verb	Indefinite Article	Noun
e.g.	***Tengo***	***una***	***cobaya***
a.			
b.			
c.			
d.			
e.			
f.			

6. Guess the missing words, then listen to check if you got them correct

a. Tengo u__ c__ __ __ __ __ __

b. Tengo u__ p__ __ __ __

c. Tengo u__ __ a__ __ __ __

d. Tengo u__ __ t__ __ __ __ __ __

e. Tengo u__ g__ __ __

f. Tengo u__ __ c__ __ __ __ __

g. Tengo u__ __ g__ __ __ __ __ __

h. Tengo u__ l__ __ __

7. Complete with '*o*' or '*a*'

a. Tengo un caball__ y un lor__

b. Tengo una tortug__ y un perr__

c. Tengo una cobay__ y un conej__

d. Tengo un gat__ y un pájar__

e. Tengo un lor__ y un perr_

f. Tengo una iguan__ y una arañ__

g. Tengo un perr__ , un gat__ y un pájar__

h. Tengo una arañ__, una iguan__ y una cobay__

8. Guided translation

a. *I have a dog and a cat* T________ u__ p_______ y u__ g_______

b. *I have a parrot and a fish* T________ u__ l______ y u__ p______

c. *I have a horse and a snake* T_________ u__ c_________ y u____ s______________

d. *I have a spider and an iguana* T_________ u____ a________ y u___ i_____________

e. *I have a cat, a dog and a bird* T_______ u__ g______, u__ p________ y u__ p__________

f. *I have a turtle, a spider and a cat* T_______ u____ t________, u__ a________ y u___ g_______

g. *I have a snake and a horse* T_______ u____ s____________ y u__ c______________

9. Translate into Spanish, then listen and check your answers

a. I have a dog called Felipe and a parrot called Antonio

b. I have a cat called Zorro and a dog called Julián

c. I have a guinea pig called Silvia and an iguana called Nicola

d. I have a rabbit called Mario and a cat called Luigi

e. I have a parrot called Dylan and a snake called Dan

f. I have a turtle called Marina and a bird called Conti

g. I have a horse called Francisco and a dog called Rex

h. I have a snake called Luna and a spider called Muerte

1.2 TENGO + UN/UNA + NOUN + ADJECTIVE + RELATIVE CLAUSE

(SAYING WHAT ANIMAL I HAVE AND ITS COLOUR)

<table>
<tr>
<td rowspan="3">Tengo
I have</td>
<td>un</td>
<td>caballo horse
conejo rabbit
gato cat
pájaro bird
pato duck
perro dog
pez fish</td>
<td>amarillo yellow
blanco white
negro black
rojo red</td>
<td rowspan="3">que se llama</td>
<td>Mario</td>
</tr>
<tr>
<td colspan="2">These colours stay the same in masculine & feminine</td>
<td>azul blue
marrón brown
naranja orange
rosa pink
verde green</td>
<td rowspan="2">Marina</td>
</tr>
<tr>
<td>una</td>
<td>araña spider
cobaya guinea pig
gallina chicken
rata rat
serpiente snake
tortuga turtle</td>
<td>amarilla yellow
blanca white
negra black
roja red</td>
</tr>
</table>

LANGUAGE AWARENESS – ADJECTIVAL AGREEMENT (GENDER)

As mentioned in the last section, in Spanish all nouns are either **masculine** or **feminine.**

- **Un** caballo or **una** tortuga

Depending on whether a noun is masculine or feminine, the adjective that follows usually needs to change its ending. **"O"** is usually the **masculine** ending and **"A"** is usually the **feminine** ending:

- **Un** caballo amarill**o**
- **Una** tortuga amarill**a**

This notion is called **gender agreement.**

Adjectives ending in a different letter from **"o"**, like *verde, marrón* or *azul* do not change their ending:

- **Un** perro verd**e,** marró**n y** azul
- **Una** tortuga verd**e,** marró**n y** azul

This rule also applies to adjectives ending in **"a"** like *naranja* and *rosa*, which do not change their ending either!

- **Un** gato naranj**a**
- **Un** pájaro ros**a**

Adjectives in Spanish are placed after the noun!

Soy un conejo blanco

¿Sabesss que todo el libro está en blanco y negro?

Sí, sí, es verdad...

1. Match

Un pájaro amarillo	*A yellow bird*
Una gallina roja	*A white rabbit*
Una serpiente verde	*A red chicken*
Un pez rojo	*A green snake*
Una cobaya blanca	*A red fish*
Una iguana verde	*A grey rat*
Una araña amarilla	*A white guinea pig*
Un caballo negro	*A green iguana*
Un perro blanco	*A yellow spider*
Una tortuga verde	*A green turtle*
Un conejo blanco	*A black horse*
Una rata gris	*A white dog*

2. Select the correct adjective

	Masculine Adjective	**Feminine Adjective**
Un pájaro	amarillo	amarilla
Un pez	rojo	roja
Una rata	negro	negra
Un perro	blanco	blanca
Una gallina	negro	negra
Una iguana	amarillo	amarilla
Un conejo	blanco	blanca
Una serpiente	negro	negra
Una araña	rojo y negro	roja y negra
Un caballo	blanco y negro	blanca y negra

3. Faulty translation: fix the English

a. Una serpiente verde	*A blue snake*
b. Un pez azul	*A blue cat*
c. Un conejo marrón	*A red rabbit*
d. Una iguana blanca	*A green iguana*
e. Un gato blanco	*A white dog*
f. Una tortuga verde	*A brown turtle*
g. Una rata gris	*A green rat*
h. Una araña negra	*A black cat*
i. Una gallina roja	*A pink chicken*

4. Likely or Unlikely: write L or U depending on whether you are likely to find animals of that colour

a. Tengo un perro azul y verde

b. Tengo un gato blanco y negro

c. Tengo un caballo rosa y naranja

d. Tengo una araña blanca y negra

e. Tengo un pingüino blanco y negro

f. Tengo una cobaya rosa y azul

g. Tengo una iguana roja, blanca y verde

h. Tengo una tortuga azul y blanca

i. Tengo una serpiente verde

5. Listen and complete the gaps with *un* or *una* 

a. Tengo ________ cobaya marrón

b. Tengo ________ conejo blanco

c. Tengo ________ serpiente negra y marrón

d. Tengo ________ tortuga verde

e. Tengo ________ pez rojo y azul

f. Tengo ________ rata blanca

g. Tengo ________ iguana azul y blanca

6. Translate into English

a. Tengo un pez rojo y azul

b. Tengo una tortuga verde y marrón

c. Tengo una cobaya marrón y blanca

d. Tengo un conejo blanco y negro

e. Tengo una araña negra y azul

f. Tengo una rata blanca y negra

g. Tengo una serpiente negra, blanca y gris

h. Tengo un caballo blanco y marrón

7. Spot and correct the mistakes

a. Tengo una rata blanco

b. Tengo un serpiente roja

c. Tengo una araña verda

d. Tengo un gallina roja

e. Tengo una iguana azula

f. Tengo un gato blanco y negra

g. Tengo una pájaro amarillo

h. Tengo una pez rosa

i. Teno un pingüino blano y negro

8. Listen and cross out the wrong words 

a. Tengo un **perro/perra** negro

b. Tengo **un/una** pájaro azul

c. Tengo **un/una** rata verde

d. Tengo un pingüino **blanco/blanca** y **negro/negra**

e. Tengo **un/una** serpiente verde

f. Tengo una cobaya **blanco/blanca**

g. Tengo una iguana azul y **negro/negra**

h. Tengo una tortuga **verde/verda**

i. Tengo un caballo **azula/azul**

9. Insert *un* or *una* as appropriate

a. Tengo _____ gallina blanca

b. Tengo _____ pájaro rojo

c. Tengo _____ iguana verde y azul

d. Tengo _____ gato blanco

e. Tengo _____ cobaya marrón

f. Tengo _____ araña negra

g. Tengo _____ serpiente negra, blanca y gris

h. Tengo _____ gato naranja

10. Missing letter challenge

a. Tengo un caballo negr__ que se llama Jesús

b. Tengo un pájaro ros__ que se llama David

c. Tengo una cobaya naranj__ que se llama Laura

d. Tengo un perro blanc__ que se llama Alfonso

e. Tengo una tortuga verd__ que se llama Lily

f. Tengo un gato amarill__ que se llama Roberto

g. Tengo un pato verd__ que se llama Donald

11. Slalom listening: follow the speaker from top to bottom and connect the boxes accordingly. You'll need to listen till the end to complete each one as the word order is different in Spanish :) 

e.g. Me llamo Juan, tengo un perro rojo y una tortuga

***e.g.* Juan**	**a - Ana**	**b - Mario**	**c - Esmeralda**	**d - Felipe**
My name is Juan.	My name is Ana.	My name is Mario.	My name is Esmeralda.	My name is Felipe.
I have a yellow	**I have a red**	I have a black	I have a white	I have an orange
cat and a	parrot and a	**dog**	snake and a	horse and a
pink	**and a**	black & white	yellow	blue
penguin	bird	**turtle**	iguana	fish

12. Guided translation

a. T __ __ __ __ u __ pájaro n __ __ __ __
I have a black bird

b. T __ __ __ __ u __ loro a __ __ __
I have a blue parrot

c. T __ __ __ __ u __ gato bla __ __ __...
I have a white cat...

d. ...q __ e s__ ll __ __ __ Miau
...that is called Miau

e. T __ __ __ __ u __ pingüino negro y a__ __ __
I have a black and blue penguin

f. T __ __ __ __ u __ __ serpiente verde
I have a green snake

g. T __ __ __ __ u __ __ rata b__ __ __ __ __
I have a white rat

13. Listen and complete

	Verb	Indefinite article	Noun	Adjective
a.	Tengo			
b.	Tengo			
c.	Tengo			
d.	Tengo			
e.	Tengo			
f.	Tengo			
g.	Tengo			
h.	Tengo			

14. Tangled translation: translate into Spanish

a. ***I have*** un ***dog*** que se llama Rafa

b. Tengo ***a cat that*** se llama María

c. Tengo ***a snake*** verde y ***white***

d. Tengo ***a*** cobaya blanca ***and black***

e. ***I have*** una iguana ***green*** que ***is called*** Bob

f. Tengo un pájaro ***blue and*** amarillo

g. Tengo ***a*** pez ***orange*** y rosa ***that*** se llama Dory

h. Tengo ***two*** animales: ***a*** araña y ***a*** caballo

i. Tengo un ***rabbit*** blanco y ***a*** cobaya ***brown***

15. Translate into Spanish, then listen to check your answers

a. I have a green snake

b. I have a yellow bird

c. I have a black dog

d. I have a red and yellow fish

e. I have a white duck

f. I have a rat that is called Lola

g. I have a black horse that is called Paco

h. I have a blue snake that is called Sisi

16. Reflection: now make some notes, in your own words, about what you have learnt so far

I use "un" for...

I use "una" for...

I change an adjective ending from "o" to "a" when...

Adjectives like "verde" and "naranja"...

I have also learnt...

1.3 ALL PERSONS OF TENER + UN/UNA + NOUN + RELATIVE CLAUSE

(SAYING WHAT ANIMAL ONE HAS)

(*Yo) Tengo	*I have*	**Masculine nouns**			
(Tú) Tienes	*You have*	**un**	**amigo**	*friend*	**que se llama Paco**
(Él) Tiene	*He has*		**caballo**	*horse*	
(Ella) Tiene	*She has*		**gato**	*cat*	
(Nosotros) Tenemos	*We have*		**loro**	*parrot*	
(Nosotras) Tenemos	*We have (f)*		**pájaro**	*bird*	
(Vosotros) Tenéis	*You guys have*		**perro**	*dog*	
(Vosotras) Tenéis	*You girls have*		**pez**	*fish*	
(Ellos) Tienen	*They have*	**Feminine nouns**			
(Ellas) Tienen	*They have (f)*	**una**	**amiga**	*friend*	**que se llama María**
			araña	*spider*	
			cobaya	*guinea pig*	
			gallina	*chicken*	
			iguana	*iguana*	
			serpiente	*snake*	
			tortuga	*turtle*	

LANGUAGE AWARENESS

CONJUGATING *TENER*

The verb ***tener*** (to have) has different forms (or **conjugations**) depending on whom we are talking about.

e.g. ***Tengo*** means "I have" whereas ***tienes*** means "you have". This is different from English where you only have two options: "have" or "has".

NOSOTRAS, VOSOTRAS & ELLAS

These are **feminine subject pronouns.** They are used if talking about a group made up **entirely** of girls. For example:

- **Nosotras tenemos un perro**
  We (group of girls) have a dog
- **¿Vosotras tenéis un perro?**
  Do you girls have a dog?
- **Ellas tienen un perro**
  They (girls) have a dog

If the group is masculine or mixed then we use the masculine subject pronouns: ***nosotros***, ***vosotros*** and ***ellos***.

SUBJECT PRONOUNS

*The words in brackets (*yo, tú, él, ella, nosotros/as, vosotros/as, ellos/as*) are called **subject pronouns**. In many cases they are optional and not used/needed. This is because both ***tengo*** and ***yo tengo*** mean "I have".

When are **subject pronouns** necessary?

1) We sometimes need them in **3rd person (he/she) sentences** to be clear who you are talking about:

e.g. ***Tiene*** means "He/she has". So, to be more specific you add the subject pronoun *Él tiene* (he has) or *Ella tiene* (she has)

2) To add **emphasis** to a sentence:

e.g. ***Yo*** *tengo un perro* is the equivalent of **"I** have a dog" with strong emphasis on the "I".

1. Match

Tienes	*You guys have*
Tenéis	*I have*
Tiene	*We have*
Tienen	*You have*
Tengo	*They have*
Tenemos	*He/She has*

2. One of three

	1	2	3
Yo	tenemos	tengo	tienen
Mi hermano	tiene	tengo	tienen
Ellos	tengo	tenéis	tienen
Vosotros	tengo	tenéis	tienes
Él	tenemos	tienen	tiene
Nosotras	tenemos	tengo	tiene
Ellas	tiene	tienen	tenemos
Tú	tienes	tenéis	tienen

3. Translate into English

a. Tengo una tortuga verde y marrón

b. ¿Tienes un perro?

c. Tenemos un gato blanco

d. ¿Tenéis un caballo?

e. Tienen una serpiente negra

f. ¿Tienen una araña?

g. No tengo una rata

h. ¿Qué animales tienes?

i. Tenemos un pato y un conejo

4. Faulty translation: fix the English translation

a. Tenemos un caballo	*They have a horse*
b. Tengo una cobaya	*He has a guinea pig*
c. Tiene una tortuga	*They have a turtle*
d. Tiene una serpiente	*I have a snake*
e. ¿Tienes una araña?	*Do I have a spider?*
f. Tengo un pato	*We have a duck*
g. Tienen un perro	*I have a dog*
h. ¿Tenéis un animal?	*Do we have an animal?*
i. Tienen un gato y un perro	*You have a cat and a dog*

5. Listen and complete

a. Tenemo_ un gato

b. No t__enen un conejo

c. ¿Ten__is una tortuga?

d. No ten__o un gato

e. ¿T__enes una serpiente?

f. Mis padres tiene__ un gato negro

g. Mi hermana tien__ una araña

h. ¿Qué animal tiene__ tú?

i. Ellas no tiene__ animales

j. Teng__ un perro blanco, Lily

6. Spot and correct the mistakes

a. Tienemos una araña	*We have a spider*
b. Teno un conejo	*I have a rabbit*
c. Tenen un gato negro	*They have a black cat*
d. ¿Tenes un perro?	*Do you have a dog?*
e. Ellas tenéis una rata	*They have a rat*
f. Él no tengo animales	*He doesn't have animals*
g. ¿Qué animales tiene?	*What animals do you have?*
h. Mi tío tienen un caballo	*My uncle has a horse*
i. Tene un pez azul	*He has a blue fish*

7. Find the Spanish translation and write it next to the English prompts

a. We have a dog
b. I have a cat
c. He has a duck
d. They have a fish
e. You have a rabbit
f. You guys have a horse
g. They have a bird
h. We have a spider

o	t	r	a	p	l	t	t	i	e	n	e	s	u	n	c	o	n	e	j	o	n
p	e	i	n	t	i	e	n	e	n	u	n	p	á	j	a	r	o	c	n	m	o
i	a	z	e	a	t	n	a	p	e	r	e	z	o	s	o	l	e	n	t	o	t
f	t	e	a	n	r	g	t	e	n	e	m	o	s	u	n	p	e	r	r	o	t
l	i	r	m	c	e	o	n	a	r	d	r	e	p	e	z	b	a	c	a	v	a
t	e	n	é	i	s	u	n	c	a	b	a	l	l	o	t	i	e	g	r	o	g
e	m	t	a	e	r	n	n	b	g	r	z	e	p	n	u	n	e	n	e	i	t
s	p	i	s	t	i	g	s	p	i	n	m	o	n	i	ü	g	n	i	p	e	z
r	o	b	e	r	n	a	a	ñ	a	r	a	a	n	u	s	o	m	e	n	e	t
a	l	u	n	r	a	t	ñ	r	t	t	r	t	a	j	á	p	o	l	a	a	l
e	a	t	i	o	s	o	a	i	e	n	o	i	r	s	i	e	n	g	o	c	b

8. Put the correct pronouns *yo, tú, él, nosotros, vosotros, ellos* in the brackets

a. (_____) no tenemos un gato

b. (_____) tiene una serpiente

c. ¿(_____) tenéis un perro en casa?

d. (_____) no tengo una araña

e. ¿(________) tienes un caballo?

f. ¿(_____) tiene un animal en casa?

g. ¿(________) tienen una rata y un gato?

Remember:

Yo	*I*
Tú	*You*
Él/Ella	*He/She*
Nosotros/as	*We*
Vosotros/as	*You guys*
Ellos/Ellas	*They*

9. Provide the correct form of *TENER*

a. Yo _ _ _ _ _

b. Tú _ _ _ _ _ _

c. Ella _ _ _ _ _

d. Nosotras _ _ _ _ _ _ _

e. Vosotras _ _ _ _ _ _

f. Ellas _ _ _ _ _ _

10. Dictation: complete with the missing forms of *TENER*

a. __ __ __ __ __ un amigo que se llama Patricio

b. __ __ __ __ __ __ __ una tortuga que se llama Lola

c. __ __ __ __ __ __ un perro que se llama Paco

d. __ __ __ __ __ una serpiente que se llama Susi

e. ¿ __ __ __ __ __ __ un caballo?

f. __ __ __ __ __ __ __ una cobaya

g. __ __ __ __ __ un pájaro azul y amarillo

h. __ __ __ __ __ __ un perro y un gato en casa

i. __ __ __ __ __ un pingüino que se llama Pepe

11. Translate into Spanish

a. He has a white cat

b. I have a black horse

c. You have a yellow fish

d. He has a green snake

e. She has a blue spider

f. We have a red iguana

g. They have a white guinea pig

h. We have a black and white rabbit

i. Do you guys have an animal?

1.4 TENER + NOUN *(SAYING HOW ONE FEELS)*

	Real meaning		Literal Translation
(*Yo) Tengo **(Tú) Tienes** **(Él) Tiene** **(Ella) Tiene** **Mi hermano tiene** **Mi hermana tiene** **(Nosotros) Tenemos** **(Nosotras) Tenemos** **(Vosotros) Tenéis** **(Vosotras) Tenéis** **(Ellos) Tienen** **(Ellas) Tienen**			
	calor	*to be hot*	*to have heat*
	frío	*to be cold*	*to have cold*
	hambre	*to be hungry*	*to have hunger*
	miedo	*to be scared*	*to have fear*
	sed	*to be thirsty*	*to have thirst*
	sueño	*to be sleepy*	*to have dream*
	***dolor de cabeza** **dolor de estómago** **dolor de muelas**	*a headache* *stomachache* *toothache*	*to have 'pain of head'* *to have 'pain of stomach'* *to have 'pain of teeth'*

Author's note: *Tengo dolor de cabeza / estómago / muelas* actually means *"I have"* a headache / stomachache / toothache, as opposed to the other expressions above (*calor / frío / hambre*) which translate into English as *"I am…"*

LANGUAGE AWARENESS

¿TENER O NO TENER? *TO "BE" OR NOT TO "BE"?*

The expressions above are very useful, idiomatic and commonly used. They all take the verb *tener* in Spanish, but they nearly all translate in English as "to be".

• **Tengo hambre**	*I **am** hungry*	literally:	*I have hunger*
• **¿Tienes frío?**	***Are** you cold?*	literally:	*Do you have cold?*
• **Mi perro tiene sed**	*My dog **is** thirsty*	literally:	*My dog has thirst*
• **Tenemos miedo**	*We **are** scared*	literally:	*We have fear*
• **Ellos tienen sueño**	*They **are** sleepy*	literally:	*They have dream*

1. Match

Tengo miedo	*I am cold*
Tengo hambre	*I am thirsty*
Tenemos calor	*I am hungry*
Tengo sed	*We are hot*
Tenemos sueño	*We are hungry*
Tengo frío	*I am sleepy*
Tenemos miedo	*We are sleepy*
Tengo calor	*I am hot*
Tengo sueño	*We are scared*
Tenemos hambre	*I am scared*

2. Cross out the wrong verb

e.g.* Mi madre tiene/~~tengo~~ hambre** ***My mother is hungry

a. Tengo/tenemos sed *I am thirsty*

b. Hoy tiene/tenemos sueño *Today we are sleepy*

c. ¿Tienes/tienen frío? *Are you cold?*

d. Tengo/tiene miedo *I am scared*

e. Mis padres tenemos/tienen calor *My parents are hot*

f. ¿Tienes/tenéis sueño? *Are you guys sleepy?*

g. Tengo/tiene hambre *I am hungry*

3. Missing letter challenge

a. Tenemo_ miedo

b. No t__enen sed

c. ¿Ten__is hambre?

d. No ten__o miedo

e. ¿T__enes frío?

f. Mis padres siempre tiene__ calor

g. Ten__o miedo de las arañas

h. ¿Ti__nes sueño?

i. Ellas no tiene__ frío

4. Faulty translation: fix the English translation

a. ¿Tenéis sed? *Are you hungry?*

b. Tengo miedo *He is scared*

c. David tiene calor *David is cold*

d. María tiene frío *María is sleepy*

e. ¿Tienes hambre? *Are you guys hungry?*

f. Tenemos sueño *We are hot*

g. No tengo calor *I am not sleepy*

h. ¿Tenéis frío? *Are they cold?*

i. Tienen hambre *Are they scared?*

5. Multiple choice: select which one you hear, then translate the sentence into English 

a. Tenemos **hambre / miedo / sed**

b. Tengo **sueño / calor / frío**

c. ¿Tenéis **frío / miedo / hambre?**

d. María siempre tiene **frío / miedo / calor**

e. Tenemos **frío / calor / sueño**

f. Mis abuelos siempre tienen **calor / sueño / frío**

g. Mi tía tiene **sueño / hambre / miedo**

h. ¿Tiene **calor / sed / miedo?**

6. Gapped translation: listen and complete the translation

a. My aunt Gina is very _______________of cats

b. Today we are very _________________

c. My friends are always very __________

d. My dad is often ________________

e. I am sometimes ________________ at school

f. We are really __________________ today

g. Are you guys __________________?

7. Spot and correct the mistakes

a. Tienemos miedo

b. Tengo harambe

c. Tenen sed

d. ¿Tenes frío?

e. Vosotros tenéis color

f. David no tiene sueno

g. ¿Tú tienes jambre?

8. Complete with the missing forms of *TENER*

a. (Yo) __ __ __ __ __ miedo de las arañas

b. (Nosotros) __ __ __ __ __ __ __ hambre hoy

c. (Ellos) __ __ __ __ __ __ frío

d. Mi hermano __ __ __ __ __ calor

e. (Tú) ¿__ __ __ __ __ __ sueño?

f. (Nosotras) __ __ __ __ __ __ __ hambre

g. (Ella) __ __ __ __ __ sueño

h. (Ellos) __ __ __ __ __ __ miedo de la oscuridad

i. (Yo) __ __ __ __ __ calor

9. Guided translation

a. T __ __ __ __ m __ __ __ __

I am scared

b. T __ __ __ __ __ __ h __ __ __ __ __

We are hungry

c. T __ __ __ __ c __ __ __ __

He is hot

d. T __ __ __ __ __ s __ __ __ __

They are sleepy

e. T __ __ __ __ __ s __ __

Are you guys thirsty?

f. T __ __ __ __ c __ __ __ __

He is hot

10. Translate into Spanish, then listen to check your answers

a. I am hungry

b. Pablo is thirsty

c. We are scared

d. They (m) are hot

e. You are sleepy

f. I am cold

g. They are thirsty (f)

h. We are hungry

11. Match

Tengo dolor de cabeza	*I have toothache*
Tengo dolor de estómago	*I have headache*
Tengo dolor de muelas	*I have stomachache*
Tengo frío	*I am thirsty*
Tengo calor	*I am hungry*
Tengo miedo	*I am cold*
Tengo hambre	*I am scared*
Tengo sed	*I am hot*

12. Cross out the wrong verb

e.g. Mi madre **tiene/~~tengo~~** dolor de cabeza
My mother has a headache

a. **Tengo/tenemos** dolor de estómago
I have a stomachache

b. Hoy **tiene/tenemos** dolor de muelas
Today he has a toothache

c. **¿Tienes/tienen** dolor de cabeza?
Do you have a headache?

d. **Tengo/tiene** dolor de estómago
I have a stomachache

e. Mis padres **tenemos/tienen** dolor de muelas
My parents have toothache

13. Missing letter challenge

a. Tenemo__ dolor de cabeza

b. No t__ene dolor de muelas

c. ¿Ten__is dolor de estómago?

d. No tenem__s dolor de cabeza

e. ¿T__enes dolor de cabeza?

f. Mi amigo tie__e dolor de muelas

g. Ten__o dolor de cabeza

h. Ellos tien__n dolor de muelas

i. Ellas no tiene__ dolor de estómago

14. Faulty translation: fix the Spanish translation

a. *Are you hungry?* ¿Tenéis dolor de muelas?

b. *He is scared* Tiene dolor de cabeza

c. *Gian is cold* Gian tiene calor

d. *Lisa has a headache* Lisa tiene dolor de estómago

e. *Do you have a toothache?* ¿Tienes dolor de cabeza?

f. *We have a headache* Tenemos dolor de muelas

g. *He is sleepy* Tiene calor

h. *Are you guys hot?* ¿Tenéis hambre?

i. *We have a headache* Tienen dolor de cabeza

15. Translate into Spanish

a. My mum is cold and has stomachache

b. I am sleepy and have a headache

c. My parents have a headache and are hot

d. María is hot and has a headache

e. We have toothache

f. My sister has stomachache and is cold

g. My dad is hot and has a headache

16. Listen and translate into English

a.

b.

c.

d.

e.

f.

g.

h.

1.5 TENER + INDEFINITE ARTICLE + CLASSROOM OBJECTS + ADJECTIVE

(SAYING WHAT SCHOOL ITEMS ONE HAS)

Subject + verb	Noun	Meaning	Adjective	Meaning
(*Yo) Tengo	**una carpeta**	*a folder*	**amarilla**	*yellow*
(Tú) Tienes	**una goma**	*a rubber*	**blanca**	*white*
(Él) Tiene	**una mochila**	*a schoolbag*	**negra**	*black*
(Ella) Tiene	**una pluma**	*an ink pen*	**roja**	*red*
Mi hermano/a tiene	**una regla**	*a ruler*		
(Nosotros) Tenemos	These colours stay the same in masculine & feminine		**azul**	*blue*
(Nosotras) Tenemos			**naranja**	*orange*
(Vosotros) Tenéis			**rosa**	*pink*
(Vosotras) Tenéis			**verde**	*green*
(Ellos) Tienen	**un bolígrafo**	*a pen*	**amarillo**	*yellow*
(Ellas) Tienen	**un cuaderno**	*an exercise book*	**blanco**	*white*
	un estuche	*a pencilcase*	**negro**	*black*
	un lápiz	*a pencil*	**rojo**	*red*
	un libro	*a book*		
	un rotulador	*a marker*		

LANGUAGE AWARENESS

ADJECTIVAL GENDER AGREEMENT IN SPANISH

All nouns in Spanish are either masculine (generally ending in -o) or feminine (generally ending in -a).

- **Un bolígrafo**
- **Una goma**

When we want to describe a noun (such as colours), we must use an **adjective**.

Gender Agreement means that if a noun is masculine, the adjective describing it, must be in the masculine form too. Similarly, if a noun is feminine its adjective must be in the feminine form too:

HOW DO WE MAKE ADJECTIVES AGREE?

If an adjective ends in **-o** we change it to **-a** to make it agree with a feminine word.

- Tengo **un bolígrafo** blanco
- Tengo **una goma** blanca

If it ends in any other letter (vowel or consonant), it is good news! It remains the same for both masculine and feminine nouns:

- Tengo **un** lápiz **azul**
- Tengo **una** regla **azul**
- Tengo **un** bolígrafo **naranja**
- Tengo **una** pluma **naranja**
- Tengo **un** cuaderno **verde**
- Tengo **una** mochila **verde**

In these examples, ***azul, naranja*** and ***verde*** do not change as they do not end in -o.

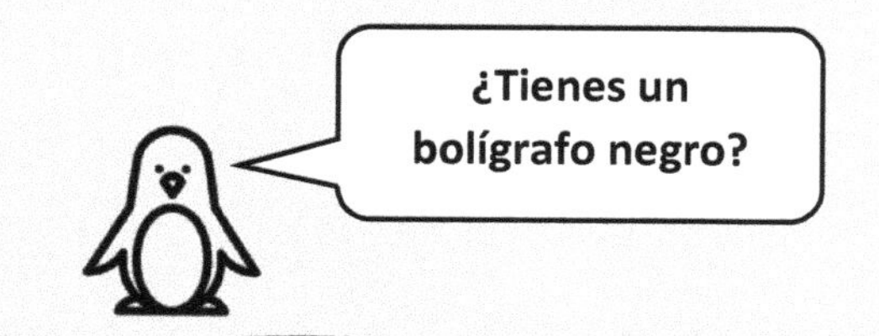

Los osos polares no tienen bolígrafos

1. Complete with the missing verb

a. (Yo) T__________ una carpeta marrón

b. (Él) T___________ un bolígrafo rojo

c. (Nosotros) T_________ una regla blanca

d. (Tú) ¿T___________ una regla?

e. (Vosotros) ¿Qué t________ en vuestra mochila?

f. (Nosotras) T_________ un libro blanco y negro

g. (Él) T_______ una goma blanca

2. Spot and correct the grammar mistakes: then listen and check your answers

a. Tengo un goma amarilla

b. Tenemos una regla blanco

c. Tienen un negro estuche

d. Tiene un libro naranjo

e. Tengo un lápiz roso

f. Mi hermano tiene una mochila verda

g. Tienen un rosa cuaderno

3. Guess the sentences

a. T__ __ __m__ __ u__ __ g__ __ __ b__ __ __ __ __

b. E__ __ __ t__ __ __ __ u__ b__ __ __ __ __ __ __ __ n__ __ __ __

c. É__ t__ __ __ __ u__ e__ __ __ __ __ __ a__ __ __ __ __ __ __

d. ¿T__ __ __ __ __ u__ __ p__ __ __ __ r__ __ __?

e. N__ t__ __ __ __ u__ __ m__ __ __ __ __ __ v__ __ __ __

f. ¿T__ __ __e__ u__ __ c__ __ __ __ __ __ n__ __ __ __ __ __?

g. E__ __a__ t__ __ __ __ __ u__ __ r__ __ __ __ b__ __ __ __ __

4. Translate into Spanish, then listen and check your answers

a. We have a white rubber

b. I have a white schoolbag

c. She has a red pencil case

d. They have a pink folder

e. He has a red pen

f. Do you have a green exercise book?

g. We don't have a white and blue schoolbag

h. Do you guys have an orange exercise book?

1.6 TENER + INDEFINITE ARTICLE + CLOTHING ITEM + ADJECTIVE

(SAYING WHAT CLOTHES ONE HAS)

(Yo) Tengo	**una camisa**	*a shirt*	**amarilla**	*yellow*		
(Tú) Tienes	**una camiseta**	*a t-shirt*	**blanca**	*white*		
(Él) Tiene	**una chaqueta**	*a jacket*	**negra**	*black*		
(Ella) Tiene	**una corbata**	*a tie*	**roja**	*red*		
Mi hermano tiene	**una falda**	*a skirt*				
Mi hermana tiene	**una gorra**	*a cap*				
(Nosotros) Tenemos	These colours stay the same in masculine & feminine		**azul**	*blue*	**naranja**	*orange*
(Nosotras) Tenemos			**gris**	*grey*	**rosa**	*pink*
			marrón	*brown*	**verde**	*green*
(Vosotros) Tenéis	**un abrigo**	*a coat*	**amarillo**	*yellow*		
(Vosotras) Tenéis	**un cinturón**	*a belt*	**blanco**	*white*		
(Ellos) Tienen	**un sombrero**	*a hat*	**negro**	*black*		
(Ellas) Tienen	**un traje**	*a suit*	**rojo**	*red*		
Mis padres tienen	**un uniforme**	*a uniform*				
	un vestido	*a dress*				

1. Translate into English

a. Tengo una camiseta roja

b. Tiene un abrigo negro

c. Tenemos una gorra azul y amarilla

d. Tienen una camisa negra

e. ¿Tienes un vestido naranja?

f. Tenemos una corbata verde

g. ¿Tenéis un uniforme negro?

2. Complete with *yo, tú, ella, nosotras, vosotras* or *ellas* as appropriate

a. ___________ tiene una falda roja

b. ___________ tenemos un uniforme verde y blanco

c. ___________ tienen un cinturón negro

d. ¿__________ tienes una falda azul?

e. ___________ tengo una corbata verde

f. ¿__________ tenéis un sombrero amarillo?

g. ___________ tenemos un vestido rosa

3. Correct the errors, then listen and check

a. Tenemos un amarillo uniforme

b. No tengo una corbata negro

c. Mi madre tiene un rojo vestido

d. ¿Tienes una falda azula?

e. Tenemos una chaqueta verda

f. ¿Tenéis una sombrero blanco?

g. No tengo una camisa grisa

4. Translate into Spanish

a. I have a blue and white tie

b. She has a black and white hat

c. We have a green and brown belt

d. They have an orange and green dress

e. Do you have a grey and black coat?

f. He has a white and red t-shirt

g. Do you guys have a green and white uniform?

1.7 TENER + NUMBER + PLURAL NOUNS + ADJECTIVES

(SAYING HOW MANY THINGS ONE HAS)

Subject	Number		Noun		Adjective	
(Yo) Tengo	**unos**	*Some*	**caballos**	*horses*	**amarillos**	*yellow*
(Tú) Tienes	**dos**	*2*	**gatos**	*cats*	**blancos**	*white*
(Él) Tiene	**tres**	*3*	**peces**	*fish*	**negros**	*black*
(Ella) Tiene	**cuatro**	*4*	**bolígrafos**	*pens*	**rojos**	*red*
Mi hermano tiene	**cinco**	*5*	**estuches**	*pencil cases*		
Mi hermana tiene	**seis**	*6*	**lápices**	*pencils*		
(Nosotros) Tenemos	**siete**	*7*	**pantalones**	*trousers*		
(Nosotras) Tenemos	**ocho**	*8*	**vaqueros**	*jeans*		
	nueve	*9*	**vestidos**	*dresses*		
	diez	*10*	**zapatos**	*shoes*		
	These colours stay the same in masculine & feminine plural		**azules** *blue*	**naranjas** *orange*	**rosas** *pink*	**verdes** *green*
(Vosotros) Tenéis	**unas**	*Some*	**arañas**	*spiders*	**amarillas**	*yellow*
(Vosotras) Tenéis	**dos**	*2*	**cobayas**	*guinea pigs*	**blancas**	*white*
(Ellos) Tienen	**tres**	*3*	**gallinas**	*chickens (hens)*	**negras**	*black*
(Ellas) Tienen	**cuatro**	*4*	**serpientes**	*snakes*	**rojas**	*red*
Mis padres tienen	**cinco**	*5*	**tortugas**	*turtles*		
	seis	*6*	**gomas**	*rubbers*		
	siete	*7*	**mochilas**	*school bags*		
	ocho	*8*	**reglas**	*rulers*		
	nueve	*9*	**camisas**	*shirts*		
	diez	*10*	**camisetas**	*t-shirts*		
			corbatas	*ties*		
			botas	*boots*		

LANGUAGE AWARENESS

NUMBER AGREEMENT: MAKING NOUNS & ADJECTIVES PLURAL

In Spanish, like in English, when we talk about more than one item, we need to make the noun plural.

To make a noun plural, if it ends in a vowel (*a,e,i,o,u*), we just add **-s**

- Tengo **una** araña
- Tengo **dos** arañas

NOUNS ENDING IN A CONSONANT

If the noun ends in a consonant, we add **-es**

- Tengo **un** *pantal**ó**n
- Tengo **unos** pantalones/ **dos** pantalones

*Note that the accent on *pantalón* disappears in the plural form. The same always applies for any word ending in "*-ón*" when they change from singular to plural.

As you can see from the word lists above, nouns usually end in o/a/e. Nouns ending in n/z or other consonants are not as common.

LANGUAGE AWARENESS

Number agreement: adjectives must also become plural!

To make an adjective plural and make it agree with the noun, we follow the same rules as per nouns (add an **-s**, if it ends in a vowel or **-es**, if it ends in a consonant)

· Tengo **un** pantalón blanc**o** y azul

becomes:

· Tengo **dos** pantalon**es** blanc**os** y azul**es**

This means that adjectives must **agree in gender** (masculine / feminine) **and number** (singular / plural) with the nouns they describe.

MAKING A <u>Z</u> PLURAL

If a word ends in *z*, such as ***lápiz*** or ***pez***, when we make it plural and add **-es**, the **z** changes into a **c**.

• Tengo un lápi**z**

•Tengo dos lápi**ces**

•Tengo un pe**z**

•Tengo tres pe**ces**

1. Faulty translation: fix the English translation

a. Tenemos dos pájaros amarillos	*They have two yellow birds*
b. Tienen unos pantalones marrones	*They have some brown boots*
c. Tiene dos estuches rojos	*He has two red pencils*
d. Tengo dos arañas negras	*I have two black snakes*
e. Tienen unas gallinas blancas	*They have some white cats*
f. Tenéis dos peces verdes	*You guys have some red fish*
g. Tiene unas reglas blancas	*She has some white rubbers*
h. Tengo nueve corbatas rojas	*We have eight red shirts*

2. Spot and correct the mistakes, then listen to check

a. Tengo unas camisetas azulas

b. Tiene cinco lápices negras

c. Tenemos tres gomas blancos

d. Tienen ocho gallina marrones

e. Tenéis tres vestido rosas

f. No tengo zapatos negro

g. Mi hermano tiene unos botas verdes

3. Complete with the correct option

amarillos	negros	azules	blancas	rosas	blancas	negras	rojas	amarillas	marrones

a. Tengo unas botas ____________________ *I have some black boots*

b. Tenemos seis peces _______________ *We have six blue fish*

c. Tiene unos vaqueros ___________________ *He has some black jeans*

d. Tienen dos gallinas _______________ *They have two white chickens*

e. Tenéis dos mochilas _______________ *You guys have two pink schoolbags*

f. Tiene dos loros __________________ *He has two yellow parrots*

g. Tiene tres lápices ____________________ *He has three brown pencils*

h. Tenemos cinco camisetas _______________ *We have five yellow t-shirts*

i. Tengo dos faldas _____________________ *I have two red skirts*

j. Tiene tres camisas ____________________ *He has three white shirts*

4. Listen and translate into English

a.

b.

c.

d.

e.

f.

g.

h.

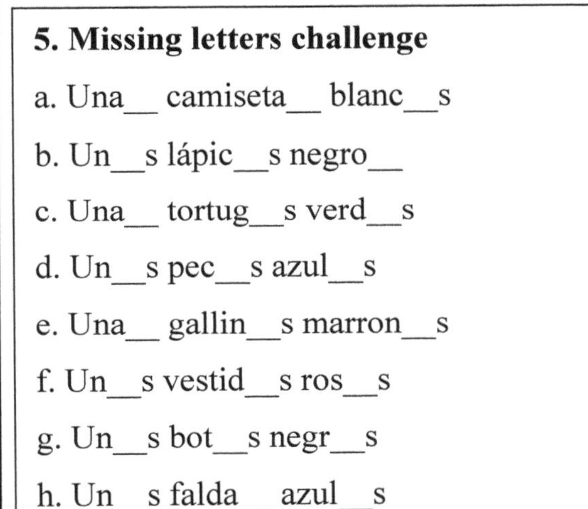

5. Missing letters challenge

a. Una__ camiseta__ blanc__s

b. Un__s lápic__s negro__

c. Una__ tortug__s verd__s

d. Un__s pec__s azul__s

e. Una__ gallin__s marron__s

f. Un__s vestid__s ros__s

g. Un__s bot__s negr__s

h. Un__s falda__ azul__s

6. Tangled translation into Spanish

a. ***We have*** dos ***chickens*** blancas

b. (He) ***Has*** cinco camisetas ***blue***

c. Tengo ***two*** arañas ***black***

d. Mi hermano ***has*** dos ***schoolbags*** rosas

e. No tengo camisas ***yellow***

f. Mis padres ***have*** dos perros ***black***

g. Tiene ***ten*** rotuladores ***green***

h. ¿Tienes unos ***trousers white***?

7. Anagrams

e.g. Dos lápices **maalloris = Dos lápices amarillos**

a. Unos **líbogrosaf** negros

b. Cinco peces **zuaels**

c. Unas **tasmacise** blancas

d. **nUas** tortugas **reesvd**

e. Ocho **llgianas labnasc**

f. **oDs** mochilas **osars**

g. Unos **pnaeosnlta rromasne**

8. Slalom translation: use one item from each row of the table to translate each sentence

Tenemos	Tengo	Tiene	Tienen	Tienes	No
cuatro	tres	dos	seis	tenéis	ocho
rotuladores	camisetas	camisas	perros	peces	gallinas
rosas	blancas	negros	azules	amarillas	verdes

a. I have two blue fish

b. We have three black dogs

c. He has six white chickens

d. They have four green shirts

e. You have eight yellow t-shirts

f. You guys don't have pink felt tips

9. Complete with the missing letters

a. Unas gomas __ __ __ __ __ __ — *Some blue rubbers*

b. __ __ __ __ vestidos rosas — *Some pink dresses*

c. Tres peces __ __ __ __ __ __ — *Three green fish*

d. Unos __ __ __ __ __ __ __ negros — *Some black shoes*

e. Seis rotuladores __ __ __ __ __ — *Six red markers*

f. Diez camisetas __ __ __ __ __ __ __ — *Ten white t-shirts*

g. Unas __ __ __ __ __ __ __ __ marrones — *Some brown chickens*

h. Dos pájaros __ __ __ __ __ __ __ __ __ — *Two yellow birds*

i. Unos __ __ __ __ __ __ __ __ azules — *Some blue jeans*

10. Complete the grid

English	Español
Shoes	
Pencils	
	Amarillos
	Rosas
Chickens	
Trousers	
	Vaqueros
Fishes	
Parrots	

11. Guided translation

a. T____________ d____ v____________ n____________ — *We have two pairs of black jeans*

b. T_________ t______ p__________ b___________ — *They have three white dogs*

c. E______ t_________ s______ v___________ r____________ — *She has six red dresses*

d. T____________ u_____ p________ a_________ — *We have some blue fish*

e. T__________ c_________ a___________ n__________ — *I have five black spiders*

f. T__________ c_________ l__________ v__________ — *He has four green pencils*

g. T__________ d______ b_____________ r___________ — *You guys have ten red pens*

h. T__ t_________ d____ m____________ r__________ — *You have two pink schoolbags*

12. Change the phrases from singular to plural

Singular	Plural
Una camiseta verde	***Unas camisetas verdes***
Un perro blanco	
Un lápiz marrón	
Un pez azul	
Una gorra negra	
Una rata blanca	
Un zapato amarillo	
Una mochila rosa	
Una corbata amarilla	
Un vestido rojo	
Una araña negra	
Un pájaro negro	

13. Translate into Spanish

a. I have two blue fish

b. We have some white t-shirts

c. They have six yellow shirts

d. He has two pink schoolbags

e. You guys have three black spiders

f. My brother has six green turtles

g. Do you have ten red caps?

h. My parents have two brown dogs

i. She has four white rats

j. They have eight or nine yellow ties

1.8 TENER + NUMBER + AÑOS *(TELLING ONE'S AGE)*

Saying your age

(Yo) Tengo	un *1*	año
(Tú) Tienes (Él) Tiene (Ella) Tiene Mi hermano tiene Mi hermana tiene (Nosotros) Tenemos (Nosotras) Tenemos (Vosotros) Tenéis (Vosotras) Tenéis (Ellos) Tienen (Ellas) Tienen Mis padres tienen	Dos *2* Tres *3* Cuatro *4* Cinco *5* Seis *6* Siete *7* Ocho *8* Nueve *9* Diez *10* Once *11* Doce *12* Trece *13* Catorce *14* Quince *15* Etc.	años

1. Translate into English

a. Tenemos quince años

b. Tiene cuatro años

c. ¿Cuántos años tenéis?

d. Tienen doce años

e. Tengo once años

f. Tiene trece años

g. ¿Cuántos años tienen?

h. Tiene doce años

i. ¿Cuántos años tienes?

j. Tenemos catorce años

LANGUAGE AWARENESS

TELLING ONE'S AGE IN SPANISH

In Spanish, to tell one's age we use the verb ***tener*** (to have) as opposed to using ***ser*** (to be) like we do in English. Therefore, in Spanish we are literally saying "I have 12 years [old]" when we say ***tengo 12 años.***

Most Latin languages (such as Italian and French) also use their version of the verb **to have** to talk about age. Germanic languages (such as German, of course) usually use **to be** when talking about age.

¿Cuántos años tienes?

Tengo quince años

2. Complete the verbs below

a. T _ _ _ _ _ _ _ doce años *We are 12*

b. T _ _ _ _ cinco años *I am 5*

c. T _ _ _ _ _ quince años *They are 15*

d. ¿Cuántos años t _ _ _ _ _? *How old are you?*

e. Mi hermano t _ _ _ _ once años *My brother is 11*

f. T _ _ _ _ _ ocho años *They are 8*

g. T _ _ _ _ _ veinte años *They are 20*

h. T _ _ _ _ _ _ dieciséis años *We are 16*

i. ¿Cuántos años _ _ _ _ _? *How old is he?*

j. ¿Ti _ _ _ _ dieciocho años? *Are you 18?*

3. Listen: Choose one in three

a.	**Tenemos**	doce años	once años	tres años
b.	**Tienes**	dos años	quince años	cinco años
c.	**Tengo**	cuatro años	trece años	diez años
d.	**Tenéis**	seis años	siete años	dieciséis años
e.	**Tiene**	catorce años	nueve años	un año
f.	**Tienen**	diez años	ocho años	diecisiete años

4. Find the Spanish translation and write it next to the English prompts

a. I am 15 b. We are 12 c. She is 6 d. We are 15 e. You are 9 f. We are 3 g. You are 12

t	e	n	g	o	q	u	i	n	c	e	a	ñ	o	s	t	u	a	n	a	i	g
a	h	f	e	u	s	a	s	o	ñ	a	e	c	o	d	s	e	n	e	i	t	r
p	c	t	n	r	a	o	r	q	t	e	i	n	e	r	o	c	u	t	e	n	o
t	i	e	n	e	s	n	u	e	v	e	a	ñ	o	s	a	l	i	l	y	p	m
a	o	m	u	a	o	v	i	g	s	o	ñ	a	s	i	e	s	e	n	e	i	t
t	e	n	e	m	o	s	q	u	i	n	c	e	a	ñ	o	s	m	l	u	n	q
m	u	y	n	e	r	t	o	m	c	t	i	a	n	i	n	o	r	a	a	g	u
t	a	e	b	n	t	e	n	e	m	o	s	d	o	c	e	a	ñ	o	s	ü	i
n	i	o	l	u	c	h	a	s	t	a	l	d	t	f	d	e	t	e	u	i	n
b	r	m	o	n	s	t	r	m	e	r	f	a	b	r	a	n	e	l	p	n	t
t	e	n	e	m	o	s	t	r	e	s	a	ñ	o	s	a	n	t	o	s	o	a

5. Guided translation

a. T__________ q________ a________ *We are 15*

b. T________ t________ a________ *I am 13*

c. T________ c__________ a_______ *She is 14*

d. T__________ t_______ a_______ *They are 3*

e. ¿T________ d____________ a_____? *Are you 18?*

f. N__ t________ d________ a_______ *He isn't 10*

g. T___________ n_________ a______ *We are 9*

h. T_________ d___________ a_______ *They are 17*

6. Translate into Spanish

a. She is fifteen

b. I am thirteen

c. We are twelve

d. How old are you?

e. You guys are eighteen

f. She is not fourteen

g. How old is he?

h. I am not eighteen

ORAL PING PONG

TENER

A

ENGLISH 1	SPANISH 1	ENGLISH 2	SPANISH 2
I have a turtle that is called Manola.	(Yo) Tengo una tortuga que se llama Manola.	My iguana is thirsty.	
I have a snake that is called Rodolfa.	(Yo) Tengo una serpiente que se llama Rodolfa.	I have a red and green chicken that is called Sandra.	
They have a horse, a snake and a guinea pig.	(Ellos/ellas) Tienen un caballo, una serpiente y una cobaya.	We have a white and brown dog who is four.	
She has a white shirt and a pink dress.	(Ella) Tiene una camisa blanca y un vestido rosa.	Do you have a green pen?	
We have a black belt and two red ties.	(Nosotros/as) Tenemos un cinturón negro y dos corbatas rojas.	I have stomachache and I am sleepy.	
You have six red dresses and two pairs of jeans.	(Tú) Tienes seis vestidos rojos y dos vaqueros.	My black horse has toothache.	
I am hungry and thirsty.	(Yo) Tengo hambre y sed.	Do you have two orange books?	
My cat is sleepy.	Mi gato tiene sueño.	They have a white rubber.	

INSTRUCTIONS - You are **PARTNER A.** Work in pairs. Each of you has two sets of sentences - one set has already been translated for you. You will ask your partner to translate these. The other set of sentences have not been translated. Your partner will ask you to translate these.
HOW TO PLAY - Partner A starts by reading out his/her/their first sentence in English. Partner B must translate. Partner A must check the answer and award the following points: **3 points** = perfect, **2 points** = 1 mistake, **1 point** = mistakes but the verb is accurate. If they cannot translate correctly, Partner A will read out the sentence so that Partner B can learn what the correct translation is.
Then Partner B reads out his/her/their first sentence, and so on.
OBJECTIVE - Try to win more points than your partner by translating correctly as many sentences as possible.

B

ORAL PING PONG

TENER

ENGLISH 1	SPANISH 1	ENGLISH 2	SPANISH 2
I have a turtle that is called Manola.		My iguana is thirsty.	Mi iguana tiene sed.
I have a snake that is called Rodolfa.		I have a red and green chicken that is called Sandra.	(Yo) Tengo una gallina roja y verde que se llama Sandra.
They have a horse, a snake and a guinea pig.		We have a white and brown dog who is four.	(Nosotros/as) Tenemos un perro blanco y marrón que tiene cuatro años.
She has a white shirt and a pink dress.		Do you have a green pen?	¿(Tú) Tienes un bolígrafo verde?
We have a black belt and two red ties.		I have stomachache and I am sleepy.	(Yo) Tengo dolor de estómago y tengo sueño.
You have six red dresses and two pairs of jeans.		My black horse has toothache.	Mi caballo negro tiene dolor de muelas.
I am hungry and thirsty.		Do you have two orange books?	¿(Tú) Tienes dos libros naranjas?
My cat is sleepy.		They have a white rubber.	(Ellos/as) Tienen una goma blanca.

INSTRUCTIONS - You are **PARTNER B.** Work in pairs. Each of you has two sets of sentences - one set has already been translated for you. You will ask your partner to translate these. The other set of sentences have not been translated. Your partner will ask you to translate these.
HOW TO PLAY - Partner A starts by reading out his/her/their first sentence in English. Partner B must translate. Partner A must check the answer and award the following points: **3 points** = perfect, **2 points** = 1 mistake, **1 point** = mistakes but the verb is accurate. If they cannot translate correctly, Partner A will read out the sentence so that Partner B can learn what the correct translation is.
Then Partner B reads out his/her/their first sentence, and so on.
OBJECTIVE - Try to win more points than your partner by translating correctly as many sentences as possible.

TENER

No Snakes No Ladders

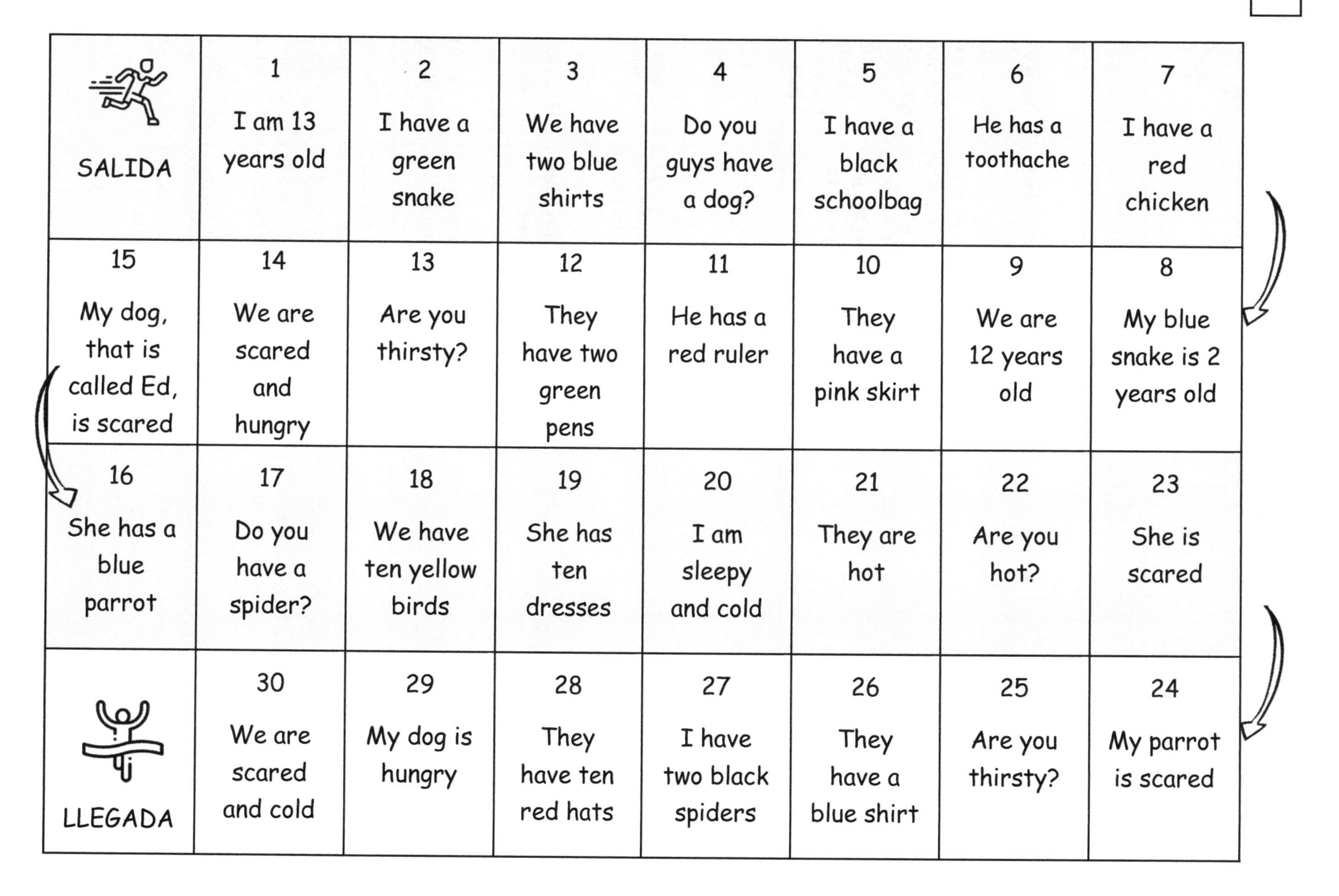

SALIDA	1 I am 13 years old	2 I have a green snake	3 We have two blue shirts	4 Do you guys have a dog?	5 I have a black schoolbag	6 He has a toothache	7 I have a red chicken
15 My dog, that is called Ed, is scared	14 We are scared and hungry	13 Are you thirsty?	12 They have two green pens	11 He has a red ruler	10 They have a pink skirt	9 We are 12 years old	8 My blue snake is 2 years old
16 She has a blue parrot	17 Do you have a spider?	18 We have ten yellow birds	19 She has ten dresses	20 I am sleepy and cold	21 They are hot	22 Are you hot?	23 She is scared
LLEGADA	30 We are scared and cold	29 My dog is hungry	28 They have ten red hats	27 I have two black spiders	26 They have a blue shirt	25 Are you thirsty?	24 My parrot is scared

No Snakes No Ladders

SALIDA	1 Tengo trece años	2 Tengo una serpiente verde	3 Tenemos dos camisas azules	4 ¿Tenéis un perro?	5 Tengo una mochila negra	6 (Él) Tiene dolor de muelas	7 Tengo una gallina roja
15 Mi perro, que se llama Pepe, tiene miedo	14 (Nosotros/as) Tenemos miedo y hambre	13 ¿Tienes sed?	12 (Ellos/as) Tienen dos bolígrafos verdes	11 (Él) Tiene una regla roja	10 (Ellos/as) Tienen una camisa rosa	9 Tenemos doce años	8 Mi serpiente azul tiene dos años
16 (Ella) tiene un loro azul	17 ¿Tienes una araña?	18 Tenemos diez pájaros amarillos	19 (Ella) Tiene diez vestidos	20 Tengo sueño y frío	21 (Ellos/as) Tienen calor	22 ¿Tienes calor?	23 (Ella) Tiene miedo
LLEGADA	30 Tenemos miedo y frío	29 Mi perro tiene hambre	28 (Ellos/as) Tienen diez sombreros rojos	27 Tengo dos arañas negras	26 (Ellos/as) tienen una camisa azul	25 ¿Tienes sed?	24 Mi loro tiene miedo

PYRAMID TRANSLATION

Unit 1 - Tener

Translate each part of the pyramid out loud with your partner, then write it into the spaces provided below.

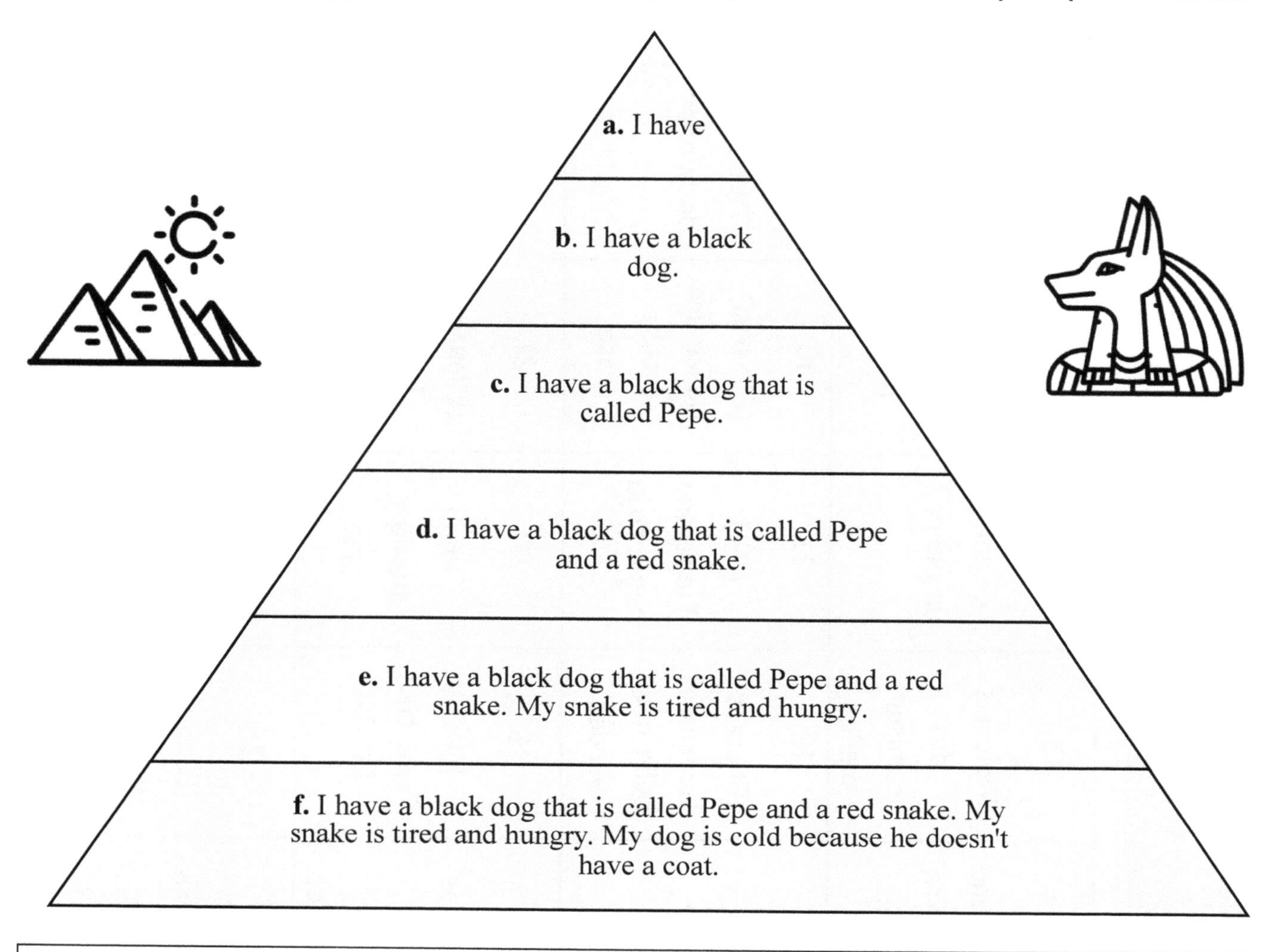

Write your translation here

SOLUTION: *Tengo un perro negro que se llama Pepe y una serpiente roja. Mi serpiente está cansada y tiene hambre. Mi perro tiene frío porque no tiene un abrigo.*

UNIT 2 – SER

Yo	**Soy**
Tú	**Eres**
Él / Ella	**Es**
Nosotros / as	**Somos**
Vosotros / as	**Sois**
Ellos / as	**Son**

2.1 SER + ADJECTIVE
(DESCRIBING PEOPLE'S PERSONALITY AND APPEARANCE)

Masculine					
Verb		**Physical description**		**Character description**	
(Yo) Soy	*I am*	**alto**	*tall*	**aburrido**	*boring*
(Tú) Eres	*You are*	**bajo**	*short*	**antipático**	*mean*
(Él) Es	*He is*	**delgado**	*slim*	**divertido**	*fun*
Mi hermano es	*My brother is*	**fuerte**	*strong*	**gracioso**	*funny*
Mi padre es	*My father is*	**gordo**	*fat*	**inteligente**	*intelligent*
		grande	*big*	**listo**	*clever*
		guapo	*handsome*	**perezoso**	*lazy*
		musculoso	*muscular*	**pesado**	*annoying*
		pequeño	*small*	**simpático**	*nice*
				trabajador	*hard-working*

Feminine			
Verb		**Physical description**	**Character description**
(Yo) Soy	*I am*	**alta**	**aburrida**
(Tú) Eres	*You are*	**baja**	**antipática**
(Ella) Es	*She is*	**delgada**	**divertida**
Mi hermana es	*My sister is*	**fuerte**	**graciosa**
Mi madre es	*My mother is*	**gorda**	**inteligente**
		grande	**lista**
		guapa	**perezosa**
		musculosa	**pesada**
		pequeña	**simpática**
			trabajadora

LANGUAGE AWARENESS

SER – TO BE

There are two Spanish verbs to express the idea "to be", these are ***ser*** and ***estar***. This unit will look into how and when we use the verb ***ser***. The first three parts which we will practise in this sub-unit are ***soy/eres/es.***

Ser in Spanish is one of the main verbs for expressing "to be". One of its main uses is for describing people and things in terms of **physical appearance** and **personality/character**.

- **Soy alto** — *I **am** tall (m)*
- **Soy simpática** — *I **am** nice (f)*
- **Mi hermana es lista** — *My sister **is** clever (f)*
- **Mi profe es divertido** — *My teacher **is** fun (m)*

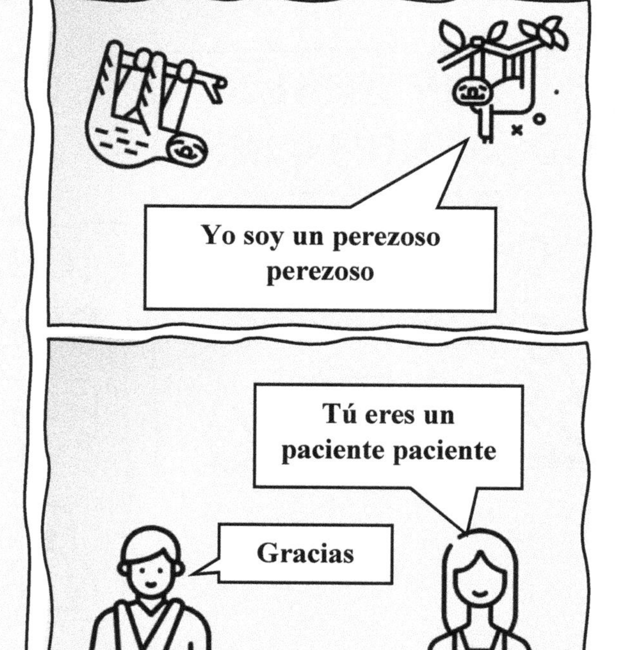

1. Match

Soy alto	*I am nice*
Es divertido	*He is mean*
Soy simpático	*You are handsome*
Eres guapo	*I am muscular*
Es antipático	*I am tall*
Soy musculoso	*You are hard-working*
Soy fuerte	*He is slim*
Eres gordo	*He is fun*
Es delgado	*I am strong*
Eres trabajador	*You are lazy*
Eres perezoso	*You are fat*

2. Complete the box

Masculine	Feminine
Soy alto	
	Soy trabajadora
	Eres gorda
Es perezoso	
Soy bajo	
	Es antipática
	Es simpática
Eres guapo	

3. Faulty translation: fix the English translation

a. Soy delgado — *He is slim*

b. Es antipático — *He is tall*

c. Eres aburrido — *You are tall*

d. Es guapa — *She is funny*

e. Soy bajo y musculoso — *I am fun and muscular*

f. Es simpático y divertido — *He is strong and fun*

g. Es guapo y fuerte — *He is short and weak*

h. Soy perezoso — *I am hard-working*

4. Dictation: listen and complete the words

a. S _ _ g _ _ _ _ — *I am fat (m)*

b. E _ d _ _ _ _ _ _ _ — *She is slim*

c. E _ _ _ f _ _ _ _ _ _ — *You are strong*

d. E _ a _ _ _ _ _ _ _ _ _ _ _ — *She is mean*

e. N _ s _ _ a _ _ _ — *I am not tall (f)*

f. E _ p _ _ _ _ _ _ _ _ _ — *He is lazy*

g. E _ _ _ a _ _ _ — *You are tall (m)*

h. E _ g _ _ _ _ — *He is handsome*

5. Tangled translation: translate to Spanish, then listen & check

a. ***I am*** alto ***and*** delgado

b. ***He is*** perezoso y ***mean***

c. Es ***short*** y pesado

d. ***You are small and*** aburrido

e. Es ***small***, pero ***very*** simpática

f. Mi ***mother*** es ***very*** trabajadora

g. Soy musculoso ***and handsome***

h. ***She is*** alta y ***slim***

6. Guided translation

a. M___ h__________ e__ g__________ y l___________

My sister is big and clever

b. M___ m________ e__ a______ y t________________

My mum is tall and hard-working

c. M___ a______ e__ m___________, p____ m______ b_____

My friend is muscular but very short

d. M___ p________ e__ b_______ y d______________

My dad is short and fun

e. M__ h_________ e_ i___________, p______ p_________

My brother is intelligent but annoying

7. Slalom translation: use one item from each row of the table to translate each sentence

Mi hermana	Yo	Mi madre	Mi hermano	Mi amigo	Tú
soy	eres	es	es	es	es
grande	pesada	musculoso	listo	guapa	antipático
pero divertida	pero antipático	pero listo	y alto	y baja	y simpático

a. *My friend is mean but clever*

b. *My sister is annoying but fun*

c. *You are muscular and tall*

d. *My mum is good-looking and short*

e. *I am big and nice*

f. *My brother is clever but mean*

8. Slalom listening: listen and then use one item per row to create a sentence 

Mi hermana	Yo	Mi madre	Mi hermana mayor	Mi amigo	Tú	Mi hermano mayor
soy	eres	es	es	es	es	es
trabajadora	simpático	musculosa	listo	guapa	antipático	trabajador
alto	bajo	grande	guapa	y baja,	y pequeño,	y guapo,
pero divertida	pero antipático	pero listo	y perezoso	y lista	y grande	y lista

a.

b.

c.

d.

e.

f.

g.

2.2 ALL PERSONS OF SER + INTENSIFIER + SINGULAR NOUN + ADJECTIVE
(DESCRIBING PEOPLE)

Subject	Intensifiers	Physical adjectives		Personality adjectives	
		Masculine			
(Yo) Soy (Tú) Eres	**bastante** *quite* **demasiado** *too* **muy** *very* **un poco** *a bit*	**alto** **bajo** **delgado** **fuerte** **gordo** **grande** **guapo** **pequeño** **joven** **viejo**	*tall* *short* *slim* *strong* *fat* *big* *good-looking* *small* *young* *old*	**aburrido** **alegre** **callado** **divertido** **gracioso** **hablador** **listo** **perezoso** **pesado** **simpático** **trabajador**	*boring* *cheerful* *reserved, quiet* *fun* *funny* *talkative* *clever* *lazy* *annoying* *nice* *hard-working*
(Él) Es **Mi abuelo es** **Mi hermano es** **Mi hermano mayor es** **Mi hermano menor es** **Mi padre es** **Mi tío Paco es**					
		Feminine			
(Ella) Es **Mi abuela es** **Mi hermana es** **Mi hermana mayor es** **Mi hermana menor es** **Mi madre es** **Mi tía Marta es**		**alta** **baja** **delgada** **fuerte** **gorda** **grande** **guapa** **pequeña** **joven** **vieja**		**aburrida** **alegre** **callada** **divertida** **graciosa** **habladora** **lista** **perezosa** **pesada** **simpática** **trabajadora**	

LANGUAGE AWARENESS
WHAT ARE INTENSIFIERS?

Intensifiers are **adverbs** such as *too, very, quite* and *a bit*. They are used to intensify the meaning of other words such as adjectives and verbs. In Spanish, the most frequently used **intensifiers** are:

- **bastante** *quite, enough*
- **demasiado** *too*
- **muy** *very*
- **un poco** *a bit*

Just as in English, **intensifiers** go before **adjectives**.

- Mi padre es **bastante** alto
- Mi madre es **muy** inteligente
- Mi hermana es **un poco** perezosa
- Mi hermano es **demasiado** hablador

1. Gapped translation: complete the translation

a. Mi madre es bastante alta y guapa	*My mother is _______ tall and good-looking*
b. Mi padre es un poco gordo y listo	*My father is ________ fat and clever*
c. Mi hermano es demasiado perezoso	*My brother is ________ lazy*
d. Mi hermano mayor no es muy musculoso	*My older brother is not very __________*
e. Mi abuelo materno es muy viejo	*My maternal grandfather is very _________*
f. Mi abuela paterna no es muy alegre	*My paternal grandmother is not __________ cheerful*
g. Mi tío Felipe es demasiado hablador	*My uncle Felipe is too ____________*
h. Mi tía Clara es muy callada	*My aunt Clara is very _____________*

2. Listen and arrange the words in the correct order: then translate into English

a. madre Mi habladora bastante es

b. materna abuela Mi muy es alegre

c. trabajador padre Mi demasiado es

d. perezoso es un Mi poco abuelo

e. hermano Mi inteligente menor muy es

f. Mi musculosa Marta tía bastante es

g. es Mi hermana gorda un poco

h. no muy Yo soy alto

3. Tangled translation: translate into Spanish

a. Mi ***grandfather*** materno ***is very*** viejo

b. ***My*** tía Marina es ***quite talkative***

c. Mi ***father*** es muy ***tall*** y ***muscular***

d. ***My*** hermana ***younger*** es ***a bit lazy***

e. Mi madre es ***very quiet*** y tímida

f. Mi abuelo materno ***is too*** hablador

g. Mi gato es ***very fat*** y perezoso

4. Broken translation: complete with the missing letters

a. M__ __ simp__ __ __ __ __	*Very nice (f)*
b. Bast__ __ __ __ gu__ __ __	*Quite handsome*
c. U__ po__ __ pere__ __ __ __	*A bit lazy (f)*
d. N__ m__ __ al__ __	*Not very tall (f)*
e. Dema __ __ __ __ __li __ __ __	*Too clever (m)*
f. __ __ __ __ __ante aburrido	*Quite boring*
g. __n p__ __ __ go__ __ __	*A bit fat (f)*
h. Ba__ __ __ __ __ __ __ ba__ __	*Quite short (f)*

5. Listen and translate into Spanish

a. My aunt is very tall

b. My brother is too talkative

c. My sister is quite lazy

d. My grandfather is very old

e. My grandmother is very quiet

f. I am a bit fat but muscular

g. My mother is very cheerful

h. My dog is very strong

6. Find the Spanish translation and write it next to the English prompts

u	u	d	e	m	a	s	i	a	d	o	f	u	e	r	t	e
u	n	p	o	c	o	a	l	t	o	t	j	o	n	b	n	a
a	e	p	m	u	y	b	a	j	o	i	n	v	t	a	j	o
t	s	r	o	j	a	b	e	t	n	a	t	s	a	b	e	d
u	n	p	o	c	o	d	e	l	g	a	d	o	d	i	m	a
a	l	n	i	e	o	j	e	i	v	o	c	o	p	n	u	s
b	i	e	r	n	u	g	a	s	m	i	e	r	d	b	k	l
r	l	v	u	e	g	n	u	n	p	o	c	o	b	a	j	o
i	y	o	f	t	m	u	y	a	l	t	a	n	u	g	b	u
g	p	j	i	n	e	s	i	d	p	c	b	l	e	o	n	f
o	a	y	o	p	i	n	g	n	u	o	a	l	l	p	e	d
g	t	u	d	e	m	a	s	i	a	d	o	g	u	a	p	a
d	e	m	a	s	i	a	d	o	a	l	t	o	m	o	n	o

a. Very tall (f)

b. A bit good-looking (m)

c. A bit short (m)

d. Too strong (m)

e. Too tall (m)

f. Quite short (m)

g. A bit tall (m)

h. A bit old (m)

i. Very young (f)

j. Very short (m)

k. Too good-looking (f)

l. A bit slim (m)

7. Staircase translation: translate each sentence from memory and then listen to check

a.	My mother is	very tall.				
b.	My father is	quite short	and slim.			
c.	My brother is	very good-looking,	but a bit fat.	He is very lazy!		
d.	My sister is	quite slim	and muscular.	She is very intelligent	and hard-working.	
e.	My grandfather is	very old,	but quite strong.	He is very cheerful	and fun	but too talkative.

a. ____________________

b. ____________________

c. ____________________

d. ____________________

e. ____________________

2.3 PRONOUN/NOUN + SER + SINGULAR/PLURAL NOUN + ADJECTIVE
(DESCRIBING PEOPLE)

<table>
<tr><th colspan="6">Masculine</th></tr>
<tr><td>(Yo)</td><td>I</td><td>Soy</td><td>I am</td><td rowspan="3">antipático
delgado
divertido
fuerte
grande
joven
pequeño
pesado
trabajador
viejo</td><td rowspan="3">mean
slim
fun
strong
big
young
small
annoying
hard-working
old</td></tr>
<tr><td>(Tú)</td><td>You</td><td>Eres</td><td>You are</td></tr>
<tr><td>(Él)
(Mi hermano)
(Mi padre)</td><td>He
My brother
My father</td><td>Es</td><td>He is</td></tr>
<tr><td>(Nosotros)
(Mi padre y yo)</td><td>We
My father and I</td><td>Somos</td><td>We are</td><td rowspan="3">aburridos
callados
gordos
inteligentes
jóvenes
perezosos
simpáticos
trabajadores
viejos</td><td rowspan="3">boring
quiet
fat
intelligent
young
lazy
nice
hard-working
old</td></tr>
<tr><td>(Vosotros)</td><td>You guys</td><td>Sois</td><td>You guys are</td></tr>
<tr><td>(Ellos)
(Mis hermanos)
(Mis padres)</td><td>They
My brothers/siblings
My parents</td><td>Son</td><td>They are</td></tr>
<tr><th colspan="6">Feminine</th></tr>
<tr><td>(Yo)</td><td>I</td><td>Soy</td><td>I am</td><td rowspan="3">antipática
delgada
divertida
fuerte
graciosa
joven
pesada
pequeña
trabajadora
vieja</td><td rowspan="3">mean
slim
fun
strong
funny
young
annoying
small
hard-working
old</td></tr>
<tr><td>(Tú)</td><td>You</td><td>Eres</td><td>You are</td></tr>
<tr><td>(Ella)
(Mi hermana)
(Mi madre)</td><td>She
My sister
My mother</td><td>Es</td><td>She is</td></tr>
<tr><td>(Nosotras)
(Mi madre y yo)</td><td>We
My mother and I</td><td>Somos</td><td>We are</td><td rowspan="3">aburridas
calladas
gordas
graciosas
inteligentes
perezosas
simpáticas
trabajadoras
viejas</td><td rowspan="3">boring
quiet
fat
funny
intelligent
lazy
nice
hard-working
old</td></tr>
<tr><td>(Vosotras)</td><td>You ladies</td><td>Sois</td><td>You ladies are</td></tr>
<tr><td>(Ellas)
(Mis hermanas)
(Mis tías)</td><td>They
My sisters
My aunts</td><td>Son</td><td>They are</td></tr>
</table>

LANGUAGE AWARENESS

ADJECTIVAL AGREEMENT – GENDER & PLURALS

As we mentioned in the previous unit, in Spanish the adjective (describing word) must agree with the noun it describes:

- Mi hermano es divertido (*My brother is fun*).

Divertido is masculine and singular as it agrees with *hermano*.

Masculine Singular

- Mis hermanos son divertidos (*My brother/siblings are fun*).

Divertidos is masculine and plural as it agrees with *hermanos*.

Masculine Plural

- Mi hermana es aburrida (*My sister is boring*).

Aburrida is feminine and singular as it agrees with *hermana*.

Feminine Singular

- Mis hermanas son aburridas (*My sisters are boring*).

Aburridas is feminine and plural as it agrees with *hermanas*.

Feminine Plural

ADJECTIVAL AGREEMENT: GENDER – RECAP

If an adjective ends in **-o** (masculine form) we turn the **-o** into **-a** (feminine form) to make it agree with a feminine noun:

- Mi padre es **perezoso**
  My father is lazy
- Mi madre es **perezosa**
  My mother is lazy

If an adjective ends in any other letter different from **-o**, it stays the same for the masculine and feminine forms:

- Mi pez es **grande y azul**
  My fish is big and blue
- Mi tortuga es **grande y azul**
  My turtle is big and blue

ADJECTIVES ENDING IN "OR"

If an adjective ends in ***-or*** (*trabajador*) it becomes ***-ora*** in the feminine form:

- Mi padre es **trabajador**
  My father is hard-working
- Mi madre es **trabajadora**
  My mother is hard-working

MAKING ADJECTIVES PLURAL:

If a noun ends in…

… a **vowel**, to make it plural we just add **-s**

- Mis padres son **perezosos**
- Mis hermanas son **perezosas**

… **-or** we add **-es** (masculine) or **-as** (feminine)

- Mis padres son **trabajadores**
- Mis hermanas son **trabajadoras**

… most other **consonants** (such as **–d, -j, -l, -n, -r, -s, -z, -ch**) we add **-es**

- Los elefantes son **grises**
- Las tortugas son **grises**

Adjective	Masculine singular	Feminine singular	Masculine plural	Feminine plural
alto ending in **-o**	Mi padre es **alto**	Mi madre es **alta**	Mis padres son **altos**	Mis tías son **altas**
grande ending in **other vowels -a/-e/-i/-u**	Mi padre es **grande**	Mi madre es **grande**	Mis padres son **grandes**	Mis tías son **grandes**
gris ending in a **consonant**	Mi elefante es **gris**	Mi tortuga es **gris**	Mis elefantes son **grises**	Mis tortugas son **grises**
trabajador adjective ending in **-or**	Mi padre es **trabajador**	Mi madre es **trabajadora**	Mis padres son **trabajadores**	Mis tías son **trabajadoras**

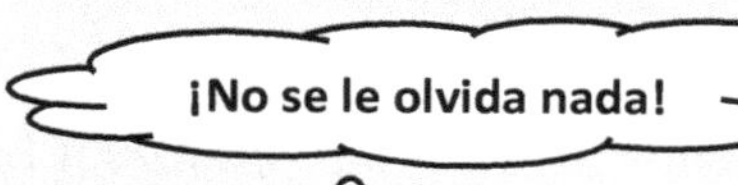

Mis padres son grises y muy grandes, pero yo soy muy pequeño.

¿Yo por qué soy gris?

1. Listening dictation

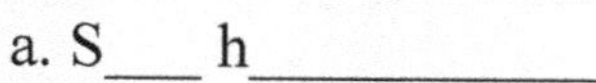

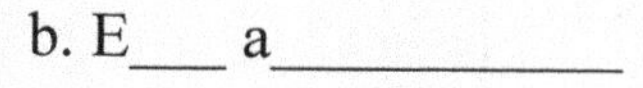

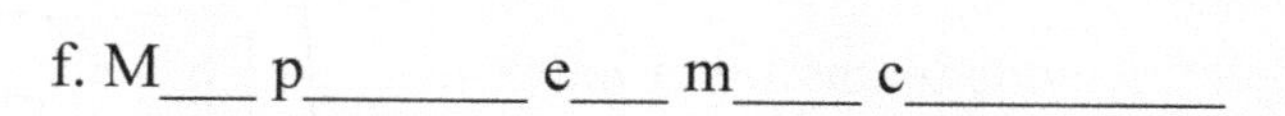

a. S___ h___________

b. E___ a___________

c. S___ p___________

d. S______ s___________

e. E___ a___________

f. M___ p_______ e___ m____ c___________

g. M___ h___________ e___ g___________

h. S______ d___________

i. E_____ m_____ p___________

j. M____ p________ s______ t______________

2. Complete the table

Español	English
aburrido	
	fun
	nice
	clever
pesado	
bajo	
	hard-working
viejo	
	muscular
joven	

3. Complete with the endings *-o*, *-a*, *-os*, *-es* or *-as*, then listen and check

a. Mi hermana es demasiado perezos__

b Mi padre es alt__

c. Mis padres son bastante baj__ __

d. Mi hermano mayor es guap__

e. Mis tías son muy pesad__ __

f. Mi abuela materna es muy callad__

g. Mis abuelos paternos son muy viej__ __

h. Mis amigos Pedro y Paco son muy fuert__ __

i. Mis hermanas son muy inteligent__ __

j. Mi profesor de matemáticas es muy list__

4. Correct the mistakes:

a. Mi madre es muy alto

b. Mis padres son bastante bajas

c. Mis hermanos son muy guapas

d. Mi tía es muy hablador

e. Mis tíos son muy trabajadoros

f. Mis abuelos son muy divertidas

g. Mis amigas son muy simpáticos

h. Mi amigo Mario es muy pesada

i. Mis primas son muy jóvenas

j. Mi pingüino es muy fuerto

5. Gapped translation: complete the translation

a. Soy muy a__ __ __ — *I'm very tall (m)*

b. Somos bastante b__ __ __ __ __ — *We're quite short (f)*

c. Son demas__ __ __ __ p__ __ __ __ __ __ __ — *They are too annoying (m)*

d. Sois muy f__ __ __ __ __ __ __ — *You guys are very strong*

e. Soy muy t__ __ __ __ __ __ __ __ __ __ __ __ — *I'm very hard-working (f)*

f. Es muy g__ __ __ __ __ — *She is very pretty*

g. Mis abuelos son v__ __ __ __ __ __ — *My grandparents are old*

h. Mi hermano es dem__ __ __ __ __ __ __s__ __ __ __ __ __ __ __ __ — *My brother is too nice*

REVISION QUICKIE: FAMILY; PRESENT OF SER; ADJECTIVES; AGREEMENT; POSSESSIVES

1. Faulty translation: fix the English translation

a. Soy muy callado	*I am quite tall*
b. Somos un poco gordos	*We are very fat*
c. Son demasiado habladores	*They are too lazy*
d. Sois muy perezosos	*They are very lazy*
e. Sois bastante delgados	*We are quite short*
f. Soy un poco aburrida	*She is a bit boring*
g. Ellos son muy tontos	*They are very clever*

2. Each Spanish sentence contains TWO mistakes: spot and correct them

a. Mi madre eres alto
My mother is tall

b. Mi hermanas son bajos
My sisters are short

c. No son perezosos
I am not lazy

d. Tú es muy trabajadores
You are very hard-working

e. Ellas sois inteligentas
They are intelligent

f. Mi amigo Marco son bastante gracioso
My friend Marco is a bit funny

3. Sentence Puzzle

a. Mi muy es alta, madre delgada bastante y un tímida poco
My mother is very tall, quite slim and a bit shy

b. padre Mi bastante es bajo, guapo muy y un perezoso poco
My father is quite short, very good-looking and a bit lazy

c. Mis graciosos son hermanos habladores, muy y simpáticos
My brothers are talkative, friendly and very funny

d. tonto Mi Paco amigo musculoso, muy es pero es muy y pesado
My friend Paco is very muscular, but he is very stupid and annoying

4. Complete with the missing letters

a. Mis padres s__ __ m__ __ trabajad__ __ __ __

b. Mi madre es bast__ __ __ __ al__ __

c. Mis hermanos s__ __ muy perez__ __ __ __

d. Yo no s__ __ m__ __ l __ __ __ __

e. ¡Tú er__ __ m__ __ fue__ __ __ !

f. Vosotros sois demas__ __ __ __ call__ __ __ __

g. Mi hermana e__ b__ __ __ __nte divertida

h. Mi tío e__ muy hablad __ __ y divert __ __ __

5. Translate into Spanish

a. My dog is quite strong and a bit fat

b. My mother is tall, slim and quite muscular

c. My father is quite handsome and fun

d. You are very intelligent and hard-working

e. You guys are very young and lazy

f. She is very funny, talkative and nice

g. My uncle Paco is quite shy and quiet

2.4 SER + COMPARATIVES *(COMPARING PEOPLE)*

Part 1 - SINGULAR

(Yo) Soy *I am* **(Tú) Eres** *You are* **(Él / Ella) Es** *He/She is* **Mi amiga Ana es** *My friend Ana is* **Mi amigo Paco es** *My friend Paco is* **Mi hermano/hermana es** *My brother/sister is* **Mi madre es** *My mother is* **Mi padre es** *My dad is* **Mi tía es** *My aunt is* **Mi tío es** *My uncle is*	**más** more **menos** less **tan** as	**aburrido/a** *boring* **alto/a** *tall* **amable** *kind* **antipático/a** *mean* **bajo/a** *short* **cariñoso/a** *affectionate* **débil** *weak* **delgado/a** *slim* **deportista** *sporty* **divertido/a** *fun* **fuerte** *strong* **gordo/a** *fat* **gracioso/a** *funny* **guapo/a** *good-looking* **hablador/a** *talkative* **inteligente** *intelligent* **jóven** *young* **listo/a** *clever* **perezoso/a** *lazy* **ruidoso/a** *noisy* **serio/a** *serious* **simpático/a** *nice* **terco/a** *stubborn* **tonto/a** *stupid* **trabajador/a** *hard-working* **tranquilo/a** *calm* **viejo/a** *old*	**que** than **que** than **como** as	**yo** *I, me* **tú** *you* **él / ella** *him/her* **nosotros / nosotras** *us* **vosotros / vosotras** *you* **ellos / ellas** *them* **mi abuela** **mi abuelo** **mis abuelas** **mis abuelos** **mi amiga Ana** **mi amigo Paco** **mis amigas** **mis amigos** **mi hermana** **mi hermano** **mis hermanas** **mis hermanos** **mi madre** **mi padre** **mis padres** **mi tía** **mi tío** **mis tíos** **mi perro**

2.4 SER + COMPARATIVES *(COMPARING PEOPLE)*

Part 2 - PLURAL

		aburridos/as *boring*		**yo** *I, me*
		altos/as *tall*		**tú** *you*
(Nosotros / Nosotras) Somos		**amables** *kind*		**él / ella** *him/her*
We are		**antipáticos/as** *mean*		**nosotros / nosotras** *us*
(Vosotros / Vosotras) Sois		**bajos/as** *short*		**vosotros / vosotras** *you*
You guys/ladies are		**cariñosos/as** *affectionate*		**ellos / ellas** *them*
(Ellos / Ellas) Son		**débiles** *weak*		**mi abuela**
They are		**delgados/as** *slim*		**mi abuelo**
Mis abuelas son	**más**	**deportistas** *sporty*		**mis abuelas**
My grandmothers are	more	**divertidos/as** *fun*	**que**	**mis abuelos**
Mis abuelos son		**fuertes** *strong*	than	
My grandparents are		**gordos/as** *fat*		**mi amiga Ana**
		graciosos/as *funny*		**mi amigo Paco**
Mis amigos/amigas son	**menos**	**guapos/as** *good-looking*	**que**	**mis amigas**
My friends are	less	**habladores/as** *talkative*	than	**mis amigos**
Mis hermanas son		**inteligentes** *intelligent*		**mi hermana**
My sisters are		**jóvenes** *young*		**mi hermano**
Mis hermanos son	**tan**	**listos/as** *clever*	**como**	**mis hermanas**
My brothers/siblings are	as	**perezosos/as** *lazy*	as	**mis hermanos**
		ruidosos/as *noisy*		
Mis padres son		**serios/as** *serious*		**mi madre**
My parents are		**simpáticos/as** *nice*		**mi padre**
Mis tíos son		**tercos/as** *stubborn*		**mis padres**
My aunts & uncles are		**tontos/as** *stupid*		**mi tía**
		trabajadores/as *hard-working*		**mi tío**
		tranquilos/as *calm*		**mis tíos**
		viejos/as *old*		
				mi perro

1. Match English and Spanish

más aburrido que	*less clever than*
más terco que	*less noisy than*
menos listo que	*stronger than*
tan callado como	*as tall as*
menos ruidoso que	*as stupid as*
tan tonto como	*more boring than*
más fuerte que	*shorter than*
más bajo que	*more stubborn than*
tan alto como	*as quiet as*

2. Sentence Puzzle

a. Mi es baja hermana más yo que

b. Mis son hermanos yo altos más que

c. tías Mis son padres tan como estrictas mis

d. Mis son amigos ellos menos musculosos que

e. amigas Mis menos son delgadas que yo

f. Yo como tan guapo él soy

g. tan mis son abuelas generosos padres como Mis

h. Mi más yo es mejor amigo hablador que

3. Complete with the missing words

a. Mi madre es más alta _____ mi padre — *My mother is taller than my father*

b. Mi madre es ______ habladora que yo — *My mother is less talkative than me*

c. Mi __________ es más bajo que ______ padre — *My grandfather is shorter than my father*

d. Mis primos son ______ perezosos que n____________ — *My cousins are lazier than us*

e. Mi perro _____ más ____________ que mi __________ — *My dog is noisier than my cat*

f. Mi tía es _____ guapa que ________ madre — *My aunt is less pretty than my mother*

g. Mi __________ es más _____________ que yo — *My brother is more stubborn than me*

h. Mis padres _______ más ____________ que mis tíos — *My parents are shorter than my uncles*

4. Word detectives: work out what the hidden sentences are and then translate them into English

a. M__ m__ __r__ e__ m__ __ b__j__ q__ __ m__ a__u__ __ __

b. Y__ s__ __ t__ __ t__ __ __o c__ __ __ m__ h__ __ __ __ __o

c. M__ t__ __ e__ m__ __ p__ __ __z__ __ __ q__ __ m__ t__o

d. M__ __ p__ __ __es s__ __ m__ __ al__ __ __ q__ __ y__

e. M__ h__ __ __ __ __o e__ t__ __ f__ __ __ __e c__ __ __ y__

f. M__ a__ __e__ __ e__ t__ __ h__ __l__ __ __ __ __ c__ __ __ m__ p__ __ __ __

5. Tangled translation into Spanish

a. ***My*** hermanos son ***as*** altos y ***good-looking*** como ***I***

b. Mis ***friends*** son ***more*** musculosos y ***stronger than*** yo

c. ***My*** padre es ***less*** terco y estricto ***than my mother***

d. Mis abuelos ***are*** tan generosos ***as my parents***

e. Mi ***mother*** es tan ***talkative*** como ***my grandomother***

f. Mi ***sister*** mayor es ***more hard-working*** que yo

g. Mi gato ***is*** menos ***strong*** que ***my dog***

h. ***My*** hermano mayor es ***more lazy*** que mi ***brother*** menor

6. Complete with suitable words

a. Mi madre es _______ alta _______ yo

b. _____ padre ______ más joven que mi tío

c. Mis padres son _______ altos como _________ abuelos

d. ______ hermanos _________ más deportistas que yo

e. Mi perro ____ más ruidoso ______ mi pato

f. Mis abuelos ________ tan cariñosos _______ mis padres

g. Mi novia es ________ guapa que _____ tortuga

h. Mi tío no __________ tan fuerte ______ mi padre

7. Word translation

a. Less

b. Stubborn

c. Young

d. More

e. Than

f. As

g. Old

h. Strong

8. Guided translation

a. Y__ s__ __ m__ __ __ __ a__ __ __ q __ __ é__

I am less tall than him

b. E__ __ __ __ s__ __ m__ __ f__ __ __ __ __ __ __ q __ __ y__

They (f) are stronger than me

c. M__ a__ __ __ __ __ __ e__ d__ __ __ __ __ __ __ __ __ h__ __ __ __ __ __ __

My grandfather is too talkative

d. M__ h__ __ __ __ __ __ __ e__ m__ __ j__ __ __ __ __ q __ __ y__

My brother is younger than me

9. English to Spanish translation

a. My sisters are taller than you

b. You guys (f) are stronger than us (f)

c. They (f) are as good-looking as us (f)

d. My brother is shorter than me

e. She is lazier than me

f. My friend Julia is more fun than me

2.5 ALL PERSONS OF SER + ADJECTIVE
(SAYING WHAT NATIONALITY ONE IS)

Masculine

SUBJECT PRONOUN		VERB		ADJECTIVE	
Yo	*I*	**Soy**	*I am*	**alemán** **inglés** **escocés** **español** **estadounidense** **francés** **galés** **mexicano**	*German* *English* *Scottish* *Spanish* *American (USA)* *French* *Welsh* *Mexican*
Tú	*You*	**Eres**	*you are*		
Él **Mi hermano** **Mi padre**	*He* *My brother* *My father*	**Es**	*he is*		
Nosotros **Mi padre y yo**	*We* *My father and I*	**Somos**	*we are*	**alemanes** **ingleses** **italianos** **escoceses** **españoles** **estadounidenses** **franceses** **galeses** **mexicanos**	
Vosotros	*You guys*	**Sois**	*you guys are*		
Ellos **Mis hermanos** **Mis padres**	*They* *My brothers/siblings* *My fathers/parents*	**Son**	*they are*		

Feminine

SUBJECT PRONOUN		VERB		ADJECTIVE
Yo	I	**Soy**	*I am*	**alemana** **escocesa** **española** **estadounidense** **inglesa** **francesa** **galesa** **mexicana**
Tú	*You*	**Eres**	*you are*	
Ella **Mi hermana** **Mi madre**	*She* *My sister* *My mother*	**Es**	*she is*	
Nosotras **Mi madre y yo**	*We* *My mother and I*	**Somos**	*we are*	**alemanas** **escocesas** **españolas** **estadounidenses** **francesas** **galesas** **inglesas** **italianas** **mexicanas**
Vosotras	*You ladies*	**Sois**	*you ladies are*	
Ellas **Mis hermanas**	*They* *My sisters*	**Son**	*they are*	

Author's note: In Spanish the subject pronoun is usually omitted, except in 3rd person (he/she), otherwise you don't know who you are speaking about!

- **Mi amigo es inglés** *My friend is English*

In this sentence, without mentioning **mi amigo**, we would not know who the English person is.

LANGUAGE AWARENESS: SER – NATIONALITY IN SPANISH

In Spanish, we use the verb ***ser*** to talk about nationality. This is because nationality is a fairly permanent thing, and like your personality or being tall or short, cannot quickly change.

Adjectives ending in '*o*'

If an adjective describing nationality ends in **-o**, it will change into **-a** to describe a female person, just like any of the other adjectives you have seen up to this point:

- Mi padre es **chileno** *(Chilean)*
- Mi tía es **chilena**

To speak about a group of people, as seen previously we just add **-s** to make the plural form:

- Mis padres **son colombianos** *(Colombian)*
- Mis tía son **colombianas**

Adjectives ending in a consonant

If nationality adjectives end in a consonant, then we just add **-a** to make the feminine form:

- Mi padre es **español**
- Mi tía es **española**
- Mi padre es **alemán**
- Mi tía es **alemana**

The rule for nationality adjectives ending in a consonant is that we add **-es** for the masculine plural form (for a group of guys or a mixed gender group), and **-as** for the feminine plural form (for a group of ladies):

- Mis padres son **españoles**
- Mis tías son **españolas**
- Mis padres son **alemanes**
- Mis tías son **alemanas**

Nationality adjectives: consonsants and accents!

If a nationality adjective ends in the **consonant *-án*** (*alemán*) or **-és** (*francés*) we add -a to make the feminine form (and **lose the accent**):

- Phillip es **alemán** — *Phillip is German*
- Gérald es **francés** — *Gérald is French*
- Claudia es **alemana** — *Claudia is German*
- Marie es **francesa** — *Marie is French*

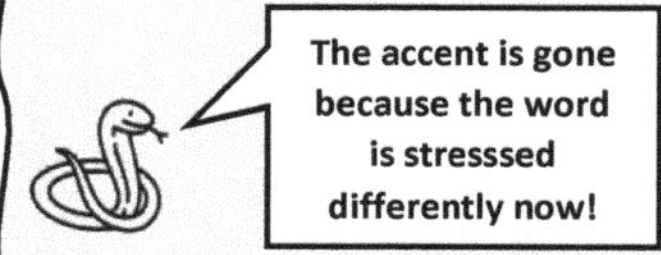

¡Qué coincidencia!

In Spanish, nationality adjectives do not have a capital letter!

- Soy inglés

- Soy Inglés

1. Match

español	*Mexican (masculine/singular)*
inglesa	*American (singular)*
franceses	*French (masculine/singular)*
inglés	*American (plural)*
francesa	*English (feminine/singular)*
francés	*French (masculine/plural)*
estadounidenses	*French (feminine/singular)*
estadounidense	*Spanish (masculine/singular)*
mexicano	*English (masculine/singular)*

2. Sentence Puzzle: arrange the words in the correct order and then translate them into English

a. alemán padre es Mi

b. Mi galés amigo es

c. inglés tío es Mi

d. padres ingleses son Mis

e. mexicana abuela Mi es

f. hermano yo somos y escoceses Mi

g. tías son Mis italianas

3. Complete and then listen to check

a. Mi madre es frances__

b. Mis padres son gales__ __

c. Nosotros somos aleman__ __

d. La señora Casares es español__

e. Mi padre es estadounidens__ y mi madre es ingles__

f. Mis abuelos son australian__ __

g. Mi primo Pedro es mexican__

h. Mis tíos son escoces__ __

4. Each Spanish sentence contains TWO mistakes: spot and correct them

a. Mi madre eres mexicano	*My mother is Mexican*
b. Mi tíos son alemanos	*My uncles are German*
c. Vosotras somos galeses	*You ladies are French*
d. Yo somos ingleses	*I am English*
e. Mis padres soy alemana	*My fathers are German*
f. Mi amiga Lisa eres mexicano	*My friend Lisa is Mexican*
g. Nosotros sois escocesas	*We are English*
h. Tú es mexicanos	*You are Mexican*

5. Listen and circle the form of the adjective you hear

a. Es **alemán/alemana**

b. Son **inglesas/ingleses**

c. Es **mexicano/mexicana**

d. Soy **italiano/italiana**

e. Son **francesas/franceses**

f. Soy **galés/galesa**

g. Somos **españoles/españolas**

h. ¿Sois **estadounidenses/ estadounidense?**

i. No somos **inglesas/ingleses**

j. Eres **mexicano/mexicana**

6. Complete with the missing letters

a. Mi madre es m__ __ __ __ __ __ __ *Mexican*

b. Mi madre es e__ __ __ __ __ __ __ *Spanish*

c. Vosotras sois i__ __ __ __ __ __ __ *English*

d. Mis primos son a __ __ __ __ __ __ __ __ __ *American*

e. Tú eres f__ __ __ __ __ __ *French (m)*

f. Mis hermanos y yo somos a__ __ __ __ __ __ __ *German*

g. Mis padres son c__ __ __ __ __ __ __ __ __ __ *Colombian*

h. Mis madres son i__ __ __ __ __ __ __ __ *Italian*

7. Dictation

a.

b.

c.

d.

e.

f.

g.

h.

i.

8. Word detectives: work out what the hidden sentences are and then translate them into English

a. M__ m__ __r__ e__ i__a__ __ a__ __

b. M__ __ a__u__l__ __ s__ __ m__x__ __ __ n__ __

c. V__ s__ __ __ a__ s__ __s i__ a__ __ __ n__ s

d. M__ __ t__ o__ s__ __ f__a__ c__ __ __ __

e. M__ h__ __ __ __ __o y y__ s__ __ __ __ c__l__ __ b__ __ __ __ s

f. M__ a__ __ __a e__ i__g__ __ s__

g. M__ a __ __ __ o Ian e__ g __ __ __ __

9. English to Spanish translation

a. My grandparents are Welsh

b. My friends (f) are Spanish

c. My dad is Italian

d. My brothers and I are French

e. My aunts are Chilean

f. My parents are English

g. My aunt is German

2.6 ALL PERSONS OF SER DE + PROPER NOUN *(SAYING WHERE ONE IS FROM)*

Yo	*I*	**Soy de** *I am from*	**Alemania** ***América** **Estados Unidos** **Chile** **Colombia** **España** **Escocia** **Francia** **Gales** **Grecia** **Inglaterra** **Italia** **México** **Rusia**	*Germany* *America (all of it)* *United States* *Spain* *Scotland* *Wales* *Greece* *England*
Tú	*You*	**Eres de** *You are from*		
Él / Ella **Mi hermano** **Mi madre**	*He/She* *My brother* *My mother*	**Es de** *He/she is from*		
Nosotros **Mi padre y yo**	*We* *My father and I*	**Somos de** *We are from*		
Vosotros **Vosotras**	*You guys* *You ladies*	**Sois de** *You guys/ladies are from*		
Ellos **Ellas** **Mis hermanos** ****Mis padres**	*They (guys)* *They (ladies)* *My siblings* *My parents*	**Son de** *They are from*		

Author's note: *If you say *América* in Spanish you are referring to the entire American continent (from Patagonia to our good friends in Canada!). *Estados Unidos* is the USA.
**You could also say "mis madres" if you were raised in a family with two mothers :)

1. Match English and Spanish

Yo soy de Escocia	*They are from Germany*
Nosotros somos de Escocia	*She is from Italy*
Vosotras sois de Escocia	*We are from Spain*
Ellas son de los Estados Unidos	*They are from Spain*
Tú eres de los Estados Unidos	*You guys are from Germany*
Vosotros sois de Alemania	*You ladies are from Scotland*
Ellos son de Alemania	*We are from Scotland*
Ella es de Italia	*They are from the USA*
Nosotras somos de Italia	*You are from the USA*
Ellas son de España	*I am from Scotland*
Nosotros somos de España	*We are from Italy*

LANGUAGE AWARENESS

COUNTRIES & NATIONALITIES

Like in English, you can also say where you are from by saying what your nationality is.

Be careful! **Nationalities** are always written in **lower case**. **Countries** are written with a **capital letter**, like in English.

- Soy **de España** *I am from* ***Spain***
- Soy **española** *I am* ***Spanish (f)***

SER + *DE* + COUNTRY

To say where you are from in Spanish, we use the verb ***ser*** (to be).

Soy de... ***I am from / I am of...***

In Spanish ***de*** can mean "from" or "of". When used with countries, in the above structure, it always means "from".

- Soy **de** Alemania *I am* ***from*** *Germany*
- Somos **de** Italia *We are* ***from*** *Italy*

2. Each Spanish sentence contains two mistakes: spot and correct

a. Mi amigos sois de España	*My friends are from Spain*
b. Mis tíos somos de América	*My uncles are from Germany*
c. Vosotras eres de Inglesa	*You ladies are from England*
d. Mi padres sois de España	*My parents are from Spain*
e. Mis abuelos eres de Gales	*My grandparents are from Chile*
f. Mi tía María son de Italia	*My aunt María is from Russia*
g. Nosotros sois de Francia	*We are from Scotland*
h. Tú es de México	*You are from Germany*

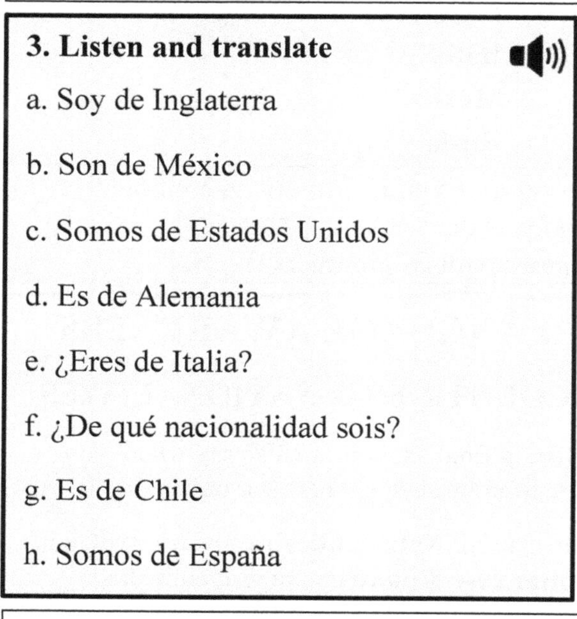

3. Listen and translate

a. Soy de Inglaterra

b. Son de México

c. Somos de Estados Unidos

d. Es de Alemania

e. ¿Eres de Italia?

f. ¿De qué nacionalidad sois?

g. Es de Chile

h. Somos de España

4. Tangled translation: translate into Spanish

a. ***My*** padres ***are*** de ***England***

b. Mis ***grandparents*** son ***from France***

c. Vosotros ***are*** de ***Spain***

d. Mis ***sisters*** son ***from Germany***

e. ***I am*** de ***Russia***

f. Nosotros ***are from*** Italia

g. ***My*** tío ***is*** de Chile

h. ***My*** amigo es ***from France***

5. Guided translation

a. Y__ s__ __ d__ E__ __ __ __ __ __

I am from Spain

b. M__ a__ __ __ __ __ e__ d__ F__ __ __ __ __ __ __

My friend is from France

c. M__ __ p__ __ __ __ __ __ s__ __ d__ G__ __ __ __ __ __

My parents are from Greece

d. M__ a__ __ __ __ __ __ e__ d__ G__ __ __ __ __

My grandfather is from Wales

e. M__ h__ __ __ __ __ __ __ e__ d__ I__ __ __ __ __ __ __ __ __ __

My brother is from England

f. M__ __ a__ __ __ __ __ __ __ s__ __ d__ E__ __ __ __ __ __ __

My friends are from Scotland

6. English to Spanish translation

a. My sisters are from England. They are English.

b. My brother is from France. He is French.

c. I am from Spain. I am Spanish.

d. You are from Wales. You are Welsh.

e. They (f) are from France. They are (f) French.

2.7 QUESTION WORD + SER + POSSESSIVE + NOUN
(ASKING QUESTIONS USING SER)

¿De dónde *Where*	**eres?**	*are you from?*
	es tu padre?	*is your father from?*
	es tu madre?	*is your mother from?*
	sois?	*are you guys from?*
	son tus abuelos?	*are your grandparents from?*
¿De qué nacionalidad *Which nationality*	**eres?**	*are you?*
	es tu padre/madre?	*is your father/mother?*
	sois?	*are you guys?*
	son tus amigos?	*are your friends?*
¿Cómo *What...*	**eres?**	*are you like?*
	es tu padre?	*is your father like?*
	es tu madre?	*is your mother like?*
	sois?	*are you guys like?*
	son tus amigos?	*are your friends like?*

LANGUAGE AWARENESS
QUESTION WORDS

Question words are used to make questions. In English "what?", "when?", "why?", "how?" and "why?" are all **question words**.

In Spanish, **question words** always have an accent. These are some of the most common **question words**:

- **¿Cómo?** *How?*
- **¿Cuándo?** *When?*
- **¿De dónde?** *Where... from?*
- **¿De qué nacionalidad?** *Which nationality?*
- **¿Dónde?** *Where?*
- **¿Por qué?** *Why?*

¿Cómo eres?
What are you like?

¿Cómo estás?
How are you?

¿Cómo + ser? and ***¿Cómo + estar?*** Have very different meanings.

You use the verb ***ser*** in order to ask about someone's **physical appearance** (tall/short/big/small etc.) and also someone's **character qualities** (smart/funny/curious etc.)

- **¿Cómo es?** *What is he/she like?*

You use the verb ***estar*** to ask about how someone is **feeling** (happy/sad/tired etc.)

- **¿Cómo está?** *How is he/she? (feeling)*

1. Match

¿De qué nacionalidad sois?	*Where are you from?*
¿De dónde sois?	*Where are they from?*
¿Cómo son tus amigos?	*What are you like?*
¿Cómo son ellos?	*Which nationality are you?*
¿De qué nacionalidad son tus padres?	*Which nationality are you guys?*
¿Cómo eres?	*What are they like?*
¿Cómo es él?	*Where are you guys from?*
¿De dónde son ellos?	*What are your friends like?*
¿De dónde eres?	*Where are your friends from?*
¿De dónde son tus amigos?	*Which nationality are your parents?*
¿De qué nacionalidad eres?	*What is he like?*

2. Translate into Spanish

a. You are
b. I am
c. She is
d. We are
e. They are
f. You guys are
g. Which nationality?
h. Where from?
i. What…like?
j. She is Spanish
k. I am English
l. We are from England
m. Where are you from?
n. Which nationality are you?
o. Which nationality are you guys?

3. Listen and complete the table following the same pattern in the example

	Question Word	Verb	Translation
e.g.	*¿De dónde*	*eres?*	*Where are you from?*
a.			
b.			
c.			
d.			
e.			
f.			

4. Match each question to its answer

¿De qué nacionalidad sois?	Somos de España
¿De dónde sois?	Ellos son altos
¿Cómo son tus amigos?	Soy listo
¿Cómo son ellos?	Ellos son de Rusia
¿De qué nacionalidad son tus padres?	Él es inteligente
¿Cómo eres?	Soy de Gales
¿Cómo es él?	Somos franceses
¿De dónde son ellos?	Mis amigos son de México
¿De dónde eres?	Soy escocés
¿De dónde son tus amigos?	Mis amigos son simpáticos
¿De qué nacionalidad eres?	Mis padres son alemanes

5. Spot the mistake in each sentence and correct it

a. ¿De cómo eres?
Which nationality are you?

b. ¿Cómo eres de?
What are you like?

c. ¿De cómo eres?
Where are you from?

d. ¿Cómo nacionalidad son ellos?
Which nationality are they?

e. ¿De dónde nacionalidad es ella?
Which nationality is she?

f. ¿De dónde son ellas?
Where are you guys from?

g. ¿Cómo sois ellos?
What are they like?

h. ¿De qué nacionalidad eres ellos?
Which nationality are they?

6. Sentence Puzzle: arrange the words in correct order and translate them into English

a. ¿eres Cómo?

b. ¿nacionalidad qué De eres?

c. ¿dónde eres De?

d. ¿qué De nacionalidad sois vosotros?

e. ¿son ellos Cómo?

f. ¿ellos nacionalidad De qué son?

g. ¿es Cómo él?

h. ¿Cómo ellos son?

7. Guided translation

a. ¿D__ d__ __ __ __ e__ __ __ t__?
Where are you from?

b. ¿D__ q__ __ n__ __ __ __ __ __ __ __
__ __ __ __ s__ __ e__ __ __ __?
Which nationality are they?

c. ¿D__ d__ __ __ __ s__ __ el __ __ __?
Where are they (f) from?

d. ¿C__ __ __ e__ __ __ t__?
What are you like?

e. ¿C__ __ __ s__ __ e__ __ __ __?
What are they (f) like?

f. ¿D__ q__ __ n__ __ __ __ __ __ __ __
__ __ __ __ s__ __ __ vosot__ __ __?
Which nationality are you guys?

g. ¿D__ d__ __ __ __ e__ t__ t__ __?
Where is your uncle from?

8. English to Spanish translation

a. My sisters are from England. They are English.

b. My brother is from France. He is French.

c. I am from Spain. I am Spanish.

d. They (f) are from France. They (f) are French.

e. My uncle is from Italy. He is Italian.

A 

ORAL PING PONG

SER

ENGLISH 1	SPANISH 1	ENGLISH 2	SPANISH 2
My sister is tall, muscular and strong but annoying.	Mi hermana es alta, musculosa y fuerte pero pesada.	My father is short, good-looking and fun but quite lazy.	
My older brother is fifteen years old and is good-looking, but he is a little bit lazy.	Mi hermano mayor tiene quince años y es guapo, pero es un poco perezoso.	My best friend Paco is Mexican. He is as fun as me.	
My parents are quite hard-working and fun, but my siblings and I are very lazy.	Mis padres son bastante trabajadores y divertidos, pero mis hermanos y yo somos muy perezosos.	My grandparents are very affectionate and more talkative than my parents.	
You are more boring than my best friend Ana.	(Tú) eres más aburrido/aburrida que mi amiga Ana.	My older sister is sportier than my brother.	
My grandmother is more talkative than my grandfather.	Mi abuela es más habladora que mi abuelo.	I have a friend that is Italian. He is very shy but very intelligent and fun.	
My sisters are calmer than me, but I am more hard-working.	Mis hermanas son más tranquilas que yo, pero yo soy más trabajador/ trabajadora.	My girl friends are less noisy than me.	
My brother and I are English, but my parents are Spanish.	Mi hermano y yo somos ingleses, pero mis padres son españoles.	My uncle is Spanish. He is more serious than my father.	
I have friends that are Italian and French. I am Scottish.	Tengo amigos que son italianos y franceses. Yo soy escocés/escocesa.	My brothers and I are French, but my mum is English and my dad is Colombian.	

INSTRUCTIONS - You are **PARTNER A.** Work in pairs. Each of you has two sets of sentences - one set has already been translated for you. You will ask your partner to translate these. The other set of sentences have not been translated. Your partner will ask you to translate these.
HOW TO PLAY - Partner A starts by reading out his/her/their first sentence in English. Partner B must translate. Partner A must check the answer and award the following points: **3 points** = perfect, **2 points** = 1 mistake, **1 point** = mistakes but the verb is accurate. If they cannot translate correctly, Partner A will read out the sentence so that Partner B can learn what the correct translation is.
Then Partner B reads out his/her/their first sentence, and so on.
OBJECTIVE - Try to win more points than your partner by translating correctly as many sentences as possible.

ORAL PING PONG

SER

ENGLISH 1	SPANISH 1	ENGLISH 2	SPANISH 2
My sister is tall, muscular and strong but annoying.		My father is short, good-looking and fun but quite lazy.	Mi padre es bajo, guapo y divertido, pero bastante perezoso.
My older brother is fifteen years old and is good-looking, but he is a little bit lazy.		My best friend Paco is Mexican. He is as fun as me.	Mi mejor amigo Paco es mexicano. Él es tan divertido como yo.
My parents are quite hard-working and fun, but my siblings and I are very lazy.		My grandparents are very affectionate and more talkative than my parents.	Mis abuelos son muy cariñosos y más habladores que mis padres.
You are more boring than my best friend Ana.		My older sister is sportier than my brother.	Mi hermana mayor es más deportista que mi hermano.
My grandmother is more talkative than my grandfather.		I have a friend that is Italian. He is very shy but very intelligent and fun.	Tengo un amigo que es italiano. Él es muy tímido, pero muy inteligente y divertido.
My sisters are calmer than me, but I am more hard-working.		My girl friends are less noisy than me.	Mis amigas son menos ruidosas que yo.
My brother and I are English, but my parents are Spanish.		My uncle is Spanish. He is more serious than my father.	Mi tío es español. Él es más serio que mi padre.
I have friends that are Italian and French. I am Scottish.		My brothers and I are French, but my mum is English and my dad is Colombian.	Mis hermanos y yo somos franceses, pero mi madre es inglesa y mi padre colombiano.

INSTRUCTIONS - You are **PARTNER B.** Work in pairs. Each of you has two sets of sentences - one set has already been translated for you. You will ask your partner to translate these. The other set of sentences have not been translated. Your partner will ask you to translate these.

HOW TO PLAY - Partner A starts by reading out his/her/their first sentence in English. Partner B must translate. Partner A must check the answer and award the following points: **3 points** = perfect, **2 points** = 1 mistake, **1 point** = mistakes but the verb is accurate. If they cannot translate correctly, Partner A will read out the sentence so that Partner B can learn what the correct translation is.

Then Partner B reads out his/her/their first sentence, and so on.

OBJECTIVE - Try to win more points than your partner by translating correctly as many sentences as possible.

No Snakes No Ladders

SALIDA	1 I am from Spain, I am Spanish	2 We are from England	3 Where are you from?	4 Which nationality is your father?	5 What are you like?	6 What is your sister like?	7 My sister is more fun than my mum
15 My snake is French. She is 2 years old	14 I have a friend that is Russian	13 My older brothers are quite muscular	12 My friends are Colombian	11 I am 12 years old and I am from Spain	10 My father is less lazy than my sister	9 My uncle is more talkative than my dad	8 My best friend is Italian
16 My brother has a friend that is annoying	17 My sister is less lazy than my brother	18 My French friends are fun	19 I have a Spanish dog	20 We are from Germany. We are German	21 My mum is more talkative than my dad	22 I have six Russian friends	23 My sister has an Italian friend
LLEGADA	30 My sister is lazier than my brother	29 My parents are quite intelligent	28 My sister has a Mexican bird	27 Where you guys from?	26 Which nationality is your friend Ana ?	25 My siblings and I are French and English	24 My aunt is less serious than my sister

No Snakes No Ladders

SER

SALIDA	1 Soy de España. Soy español/ española	2 (Nosotros/ as) somos de Inglaterra	3 ¿De dónde eres?	4 ¿De qué nacionalidad es tu padre?	5 ¿Cómo eres?	6 ¿Cómo es tu hermana?	7 Mi hermana es más divertida que mi madre
15 Mi serpiente es francesa. Tiene dos años	14 Tengo un /una amigo/a que es ruso/a	13 Mis hermanos mayores son bastante musculosos	12 Mis amigos son colombianos	11 Tengo doce años y soy de España	10 Mi padre es menos perezoso que mi hermana	9 Mi tío es más hablador que mi padre	8 Mi mejor amigo es italiano
16 Mi hermano tiene un amigo que es pesado	17 Mi hermana es menos perezosa que mi hermano	18 Mis amigos franceses son divertidos	19 Tengo un perro español	20 Somos de Alemania. Somos alemanes/as	21 Mi madre es más habladora que mi padre	22 Tengo seis amigos/as rusos/as	23 Mi hermana tiene un/a amigo/a italiano/a
LLEGADA	30 Mi hermana es más perezosa que mi hermano	29 Mis padres son bastante inteligentes	28 Mi hermana tiene un pájaro mexicano	27 ¿De dónde sois?	26 ¿De qué nacionalidad es tu amiga Ana?	25 Mis hermanos y yo somos franceses e ingleses	24 Mi tía es menos seria que mi hermana

PYRAMID TRANSLATION

Unit 2 - Ser

Translate each part of the pyramid out loud with your partner, then write it into the spaces provided below.

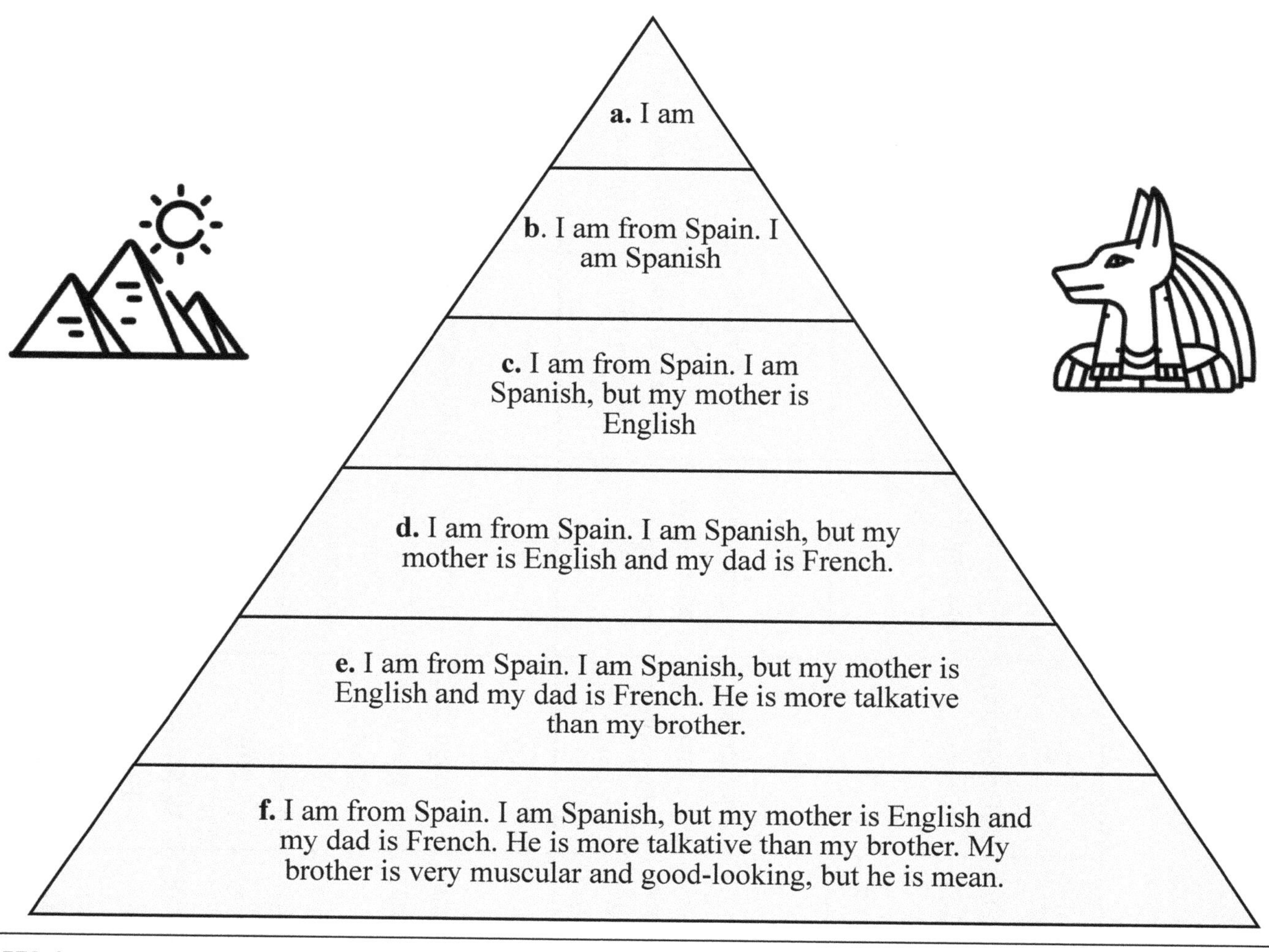

Write your translation here

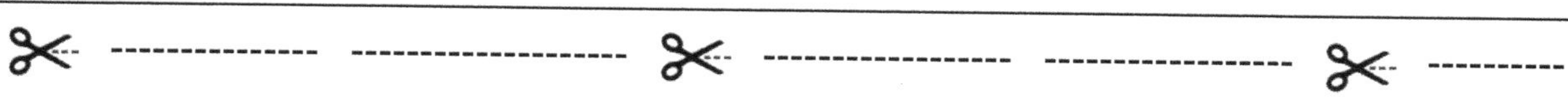

SOLUTION: *Soy de España. Soy español/a, pero mi madre es inglesa y mi padre es francés. Él es más hablador que mi hermano. Mi hermano es muy musculoso y guapo, pero es antipático.*

UNIT 3 – ESTAR

Yo	**Estoy**
Tú	**Estás**
Él / Ella	**Está**
Nosotros / as	**Estamos**
Vosotros / as	**Estáis**
Ellos / as	**Están**

3.1 HOY + ESTAR + FIRST THREE PERSONS OF ESTAR + ADJECTIVE
(ASKING AND SAYING HOW ONE FEELS)

FEELINGS/MOOD - SINGULAR				
First person – I – masculine & feminine				
Me llamo Felipe.	**Hoy** *Today*	**estoy** *I am feeling*	**aburrido** *bored* **cansado** *tired* **contento** *happy* **emocionado** *moved* **enfadado** *angry*	**enfermo** *ill* **malhumorado** *in a bad mood* **nervioso** *nervous* **preocupado** *worried* **tranquilo** *calm* **triste** *sad*
Me llamo María.			**aburrida** **cansada** **contenta** **emocionada** **enfadada**	**enferma** **malhumorada** **nerviosa** **preocupada** **tranquila** **triste**

Second person – you – masculine & feminine		
Hola Felipe,	**¿cómo estás hoy?** *how are you today?*	**¿Estás aburrido?** *Are you feeling bored?* **¿Estás contento?** *Are you feeling happy?*
Hola María,		**¿Estás aburrida?** *Are you feeling bored?* **¿Estás contenta?** *Are you feeling happy?*

Third person – he/she– masculine & feminine			
Felipe	**está** *is feeling*	**aburrido** bored **cansado** tired	**enfermo** ill **preocupado** *worried*
María	**está** *is feeling*	**aburrida** *bored* **cansada** *tired*	**enferma** ill **preocupada** *worried*

LANGUAGE AWARENESS

ESTAR – *TO BE*

As we explained in the previous unit, there are two Spanish verbs to express the idea of "to be", these are ***ser*** and ***estar***. This unit will look into how and when we use the verb ***estar***.

One of the main uses of ***estar*** in Spanish is to express how you or other people are **feeling,** in terms of **mood** and also **state** of **health/sickness**. On these occasions, ***estar*** can be translated as "to be feeling".

- ¿Cómo **estás** hoy? — *How **are you feeling** today?*
- **Estoy** contento pero cansado — *I **am feeling** happy but tired*
- Mi amiga **está** cansada y aburrida — *My friend **is feeling** tired and bored*

¡Estoy contento!

Estar is likely to refer to a temporary state when we are referring to things like **emotions**, **feelings** and **health**. However, the most important thing is that it is a **state/feeling/emotion** that we are describing and **not** that it can be given a **permanent** or **temporary** label.

1. Faulty translation: fix the English

a. Está enfermo — *I am ill*

b. Está triste — *I am sad*

c. Estás preocupado — *You are ill*

d. Está contento — *He is angry*

e. Estoy malhumorado — *I am bored*

f. Está enfadada — *She is happy*

g. Estoy aburrido — *I am tired*

2. Listen and write the words

a. quiloTran _ _ _ _ _ _ _ _ _

b. tentCoon _ _ _ _ _ _ _ _

c. adhuaMoromal _ _ _ _ _ _ _ _ _ _ _

d. faEndada _ _ _ _ _ _ _ _

e. fErenmo _ _ _ _ _ _ _

f. sandoCa _ _ _ _ _ _ _

g. cioEnmooad _ _ _ _ _ _ _ _ _ _

3. Split words

ste	rma	tento
nada	sado	vioso
uila	ada	pado

a. Estoy can______________

b. Está con______________

c. Estás emocio___________

d. ¿Estás enfe___________?

e. Estoy ner______________

f. Está preocu____________

g. ¿Estás tri____________?

h. Estoy enfad___________

i. Está tranq_____________

4. Complete with the missing word

enferma	contento	emocionada	preocupado	triste
enfadada	cómo	estoy	aburrida	cansada

a. ________________ cansado — *I am tired (m)*

b. ¿________________ estás? — *How are you feeling?*

c. Mi padre está muy _________ — *My father is very worried*

d. Mi madre está __________hoy — *My mother is tired today*

e. ¿Estás __________________? — *Are you happy? (m)*

f. Estoy muy ______________ — *I am very ill (f)*

g. Hoy está muy ____________ — *Today she is very angry*

h. ¿Por qué estás así de _______? — *Why are you so sad?*

i. No estoy _______________ — *I am not moved (f)*

j. Mi novia está ____________ — *My girlfriend is bored*

5. Spot the spelling mistake and rewrite the whole sentence correctly

e.g. Estoy canzado — ***<u>Estoy cansado</u>***

a. Está emozionado ______________________

b. ¿Estás contanto? ______________________

c. No estoy enphermo ______________________

d. Está tristo ______________________

e. ¿Estás abburido? ______________________

f. Estoy preoccupado ______________________

g. Está enfado ______________________

6. Listen, complete and translate:

a. Estoy cansad__

b. Estoy enferm__

c. Mi __adre está enfadad__

d. Felipe está enfadad__

e. Estoy emocionad__

f. Ana está preocupad__

g. Est__ __ aburrido

h. Estoy aburrid__

7. Missing letter challenge: complete the words and translate them into English

a. Hoy est_y cansa_o

b. ¿Está_ tris_e?

c. No est_ enfer_o

d. Es_á malhumora_o

e. Esto_ muy emo_ionado

f. Hoy e_toy muy nerv_osa

g. Est_ en_adada

h. ¿Est_s abur_ida?

i. ¿Có_o est_ tu padre ho_?

j. No _stoy tran_uilo

8. Find the Spanish translation and write it next to the English prompts

t	r	a	n	q	u	i	l	o	n	o	r	r	e	p	r	t	d	e	á	o	t	a	g
a	u	b	m	a	h	e	n	f	a	d	a	d	o	a	d	a	n	t	b	s	r	e	r
n	r	o	a	g	o	l	n	i	n	g	u	n	o	s	i	f	s	b	u	a	p	e	o
q	y	s	r	b	r	o	c	f	u	e	t	s	e	r	v	e	m	c	y	l	i	l	t
u	a	o	u	h	u	l	a	c	a	n	s	a	d	o	a	i	j	o	r	i	n	e	n
e	r	i	t	g	f	r	d	o	t	r	i	s	t	e	n	o	s	c	n	r	g	t	e
a	o	v	a	s	i	b	r	y	e	s	m	e	s	a	o	c	s	o	d	o	ü	r	t
s	n	r	e	m	e	a	t	i	l	n	t	a	e	x	c	s	c	ó	m	o	i	u	n
a	d	e	r	i	t	n	o	c	d	p	o	c	o	t	r	n	a	a	m	e	n	e	o
r	a	n	c	m	a	l	h	u	m	o	r	a	d	o	v	e	b	u	r	r	o	f	c

a. Calm

b. Angry

c. I am

d. Nervous

e. Ill

f. Bored

g. Sad

h. Is

i. How

j. Tired

k. Happy

l. In a bad mood

9. Translate into Spanish

a. Today I am tired

b. How is your sister today?

c. He is very worried

d. She is very worried today

e. How is your mum today?

f. My mum is ill today

g. My friend (f) is in a bad mood today

h. My friend (m) is happy today

i. I am happy today

j. My sister is in a bad mood

k. I am bored

l. My friend (f) is ill

m. Are you moved?

n. My mum is moved

o. My dad is nervous

p. My dad is worried

3.2 LOCATIVE OR TIME ADVERBIAL + ESTAR (PLURAL PERSONS) + ADJECTIVE
(SAYING HOW ONE FEELS)

		Masculine plural	
En la clase de matemáticas *In the maths lesson* **Esta mañana** *This morning* **Esta tarde** *This afternoon/evening* **Hoy** *Today* **Nunca** *Never* **Por la mañana** *In the morning* **Por la tarde** *In the afternoon/evening*	**(nosotros) estamos** *we are feeling* **(vosotros) estáis** *you guys are feeling* **(ellos) están** *they are feeling*	**aburridos** *bored* **cansados** *tired* **contentos** *happy* **emocionados** *moved* **enfadados** *angry*	**enfermos** *ill* **malhumorados** *in a bad mood* **nerviosos** *nervous* **preocupados** *worried* **tranquilos** *calm*
		Feminine plural	
	(nosotras) estamos *we are feeling* **(vosotras) estáis** *you guys are feeling* **(ellas) están** *they are feeling*	**aburridas** *bored* **cansadas** *tired* **contentas** *happy* **emocionadas** *moved* **enfadadas** *angry*	**enfermas** *ill* **malhumoradas** *in a bad mood* **nerviosas** *nervous* **preocupadas** *worried* **tranquilas** *calm*

1. Break the flow

a. Nuncaestoyaburrido.Siempreestoycontento.

b. Siempreestántranquilos.Nuncaestánnerviosos.

c. Mispadresestánsiemprepreocupados.

d. Hoymiprofesoradematemáticasestáenfadada.

e. Estatardemihermanoestáenfermo.

f. Sonmuyactivos.Nuncaestáncansados.

2. One of two

a. Mis padres están **nerviosos/nerviosas**

b. Nosotras estamos muy **aburridos/aburridas**

c. Vosotros estáis **enfermos/enfermas**

d. Mis hermanos están **nerviosos/nerviosas**

e. Mario y Nina están **enfadados/enfadadas**

f. Mis profesoras están muy **cansados/cansadas**

3. Spot and correct the mistakes. There is at least one in each sentence

a. Mi madre estás nerviosa

b. Mis padres están preocupado

c. Mi mejor amigo está emocionada

d. Mi profesor de francés siempre estoy malhumorada

e. Mi profesora de música siempre está contento

f. Mis padres siempre están enfadadas

g. Mis hermanos estamos tranquilos hoy

h. Nosotros nunca estamos tranquilo

i. Mi madre estoy emocionado

j. Mi abuela estáis triste

k. Mi tío están enfadados

4. Listen, complete the words and then decide if the sentence is positive (P) or negative (N)

a. Estoy muy n__rv__os__

b. Estoy un poco __b__rrid__

c. Estoy muy c__nt__nt__

d. Estoy bastante tr__st__

e. Estoy muy tr__nqu__l__ y r__laj__d__

f. Estoy m__lh__morad__

g. Estoy __nf__dad__

h. Estoy muy b__ __n

5. Fill in the blanks with the correct conjugation of the verb *estar*

a. Hoy yo __ __ __ __ __ muy contento

b. Mi padre __ __ __ __ enfadado

c. Mi hermano __ __ __ __ aburrido

d. Nosotros __ __ __ __ __ __ __ nerviosos

e. Mis gatos __ __ __ __ __ malhumorados

f. Mi novia __ __ __ __ muy cansada

6. Complete with the missing words, choosing from the option in the table below

a. Estamos muy ______________ *We are very tired*

b. Están un poco ______________ *They are a bit bored*

c. Hoy estoy __________ *I am sad*

d. Mi madre está ____________ *My mother is ill*

e. ¿__________ estás hoy? *How are you today?*

f. ___________ estamos malhumoradas *We (f) are in a bad mood*

g. Mi hermana ________ nerviosa *My sister is nervous*

h. ____________ muy estresados *They are very stressed*

i. Nosotras _______ tranquilas *We are calm*

j. ¿Cómo ___________ hoy? *How are you guys today?*

estáis	aburridos
nosotras	estamos
están	enferma
cómo	está
cansados	triste

7. Translate into English

a. Esta tarde estoy muy cansado

b. Hoy mi madre está enferma

c. Esta mañana mi hermano está muy emocionado

d. Mis padres hoy están muy preocupados

e. Por la mañana mi hermano está siempre enfadado

f. Hoy mi profe de matemáticas está tranquilo

g. La profe de ciencias está siempre malhumorada

h. En las clases de español estoy siempre contenta

i. Esta mañana mi amiga Luisa está nerviosa

j. Nosotros nunca estamos enfadados

8. Tangled translation: into Spanish

a. Mi madre ***is*** muy ***tired***

b. Mi padre está ***very worried***

c. ***My parents*** están un poco nerviosos

d. Mis hermanas ***are quite*** tristes

e. Nosotras estamos ***very nervous today***

f. María ***and*** Pedro ***are*** muy ***angry*** hoy

g. ¿Cómo ***are*** vosotros?

h. Yo estoy ***very calm***

i. ***My*** vecinos ***are*** siempre ***in a bad mood***

9. Guided translation

a. H__ __ e__ __ __ c__ __ __ __ __ __ __

She is happy today

b. E__ __ __ __ c__ __ __ __ __ __ __

They (f) are tired

c. E__ __ __ __ __ __ t__ __ __ __ __ __ __ __ __

We are calm

d. E__ __ __ __ n__ __ __ __ __ __ __

I am nervous

e. E__ __ __ __ __ __ e__ __ __ __ __ __ __

We (f) are ill

10. Translate into Spanish

a. My mother is very worried

b. My father is quite happy today

c. My French teacher is always in a bad mood

d. I am never angry

e. Today we are all very calm

f. My brother is always sad

g. My parents are very nervous today

h. My sisters are very nervous this evening

3.3 DETERMINER + NOUN + ESTAR (3rd PERSON) + ADJECTIVE
(DESCRIBING THE STATE OF THINGS)

Masculine				
El armario	*the wardrobe/cupboard*		**apagado**	*turned off*
El cajón	*the drawer*		**dañado**	*damaged*
El móvil	*the mobile phone*		**desordenado**	*untidy*
El ordenador	*the computer*		**encendido**	*turned on*
El plato	*the plate*		**limpio**	*clean*
El suelo	*the floor*	**está** *is*	**lleno**	*full*
El vaso	*the glass*		**manchado**	*stained*
El vestido	*the dress*		**ordenado**	*tidy*
			usado	*worn/used*
Mi coche	*my car*		**roto**	*broken*
Mi escritorio	*my desk*		**sucio**	*dirty*
Mi pantalón	*my trousers*		**vacío**	*empty*
Feminine				
La cocina	*the kitchen*		**apagada**	
La falda	*the skirt*		**dañada**	
La mochila	*the schoolbag*		**desordenada**	
La silla	*the chair*		**encendida**	
La taza	*the cup*		**limpia**	
La televisión	*the television*	**está** *is*	**llena**	
La ventana	*the window*		**manchada**	
			ordenada	
Mi camiseta	*my t-shirt*		**sucia**	
Mi cartera	*my wallet*		**usada**	
Mi habitación	*my room*		**rota**	
			vacía	

El cajón	*the drawer*	**está** *is*	**lleno de** *full of*	**calcetines** **cosas** **dinero**	*socks* *things* *money*
La botella	*the bottle*		**llena de** *full of*	**agua** **limonada** **zumo**	*water* *lemonade* *juice*

Author's note: to say that something is "not broken" you would say: *"la televisión no está rota"*. To say that the television "works" you would say: *"la televisión funciona"*.

LANGUAGE AWARENESS

Estar is also used to talk about the "state/condition" of things. Common examples are:

- **La habitación está sucia** *The room is dirty*

In this case, you are not describing the room itself, in terms of whether it is big or small, but the condition/state of it. Seeing as the state can change (if you clean the room, for example), this is **sometimes** referred to as a **temporary** usage.

The most accurate way of learning it, is to think of it as really describing the *condition* or *physical state* of the place or item. The same applies to ***estar*** for *emotions* and *mental states:*

- **Estoy contento/triste** *I am happy/sad.*

1. Match up

Camiseta	*Mobile phone*
Pantalón	*Glass*
Coche	*Computer*
Móvil	*T-shirt*
Taza	*Floor*
Vaso	*Trousers*
Ordenador	*Cup*
Suelo	*Desk*
Ventana	*Car*
Escritorio	*Window*

2. Faulty translation: fix the English translation

a. Tu camiseta está usada — *Your t-shirt is stained*

b. El vaso está vacío — *The glass is dirty*

c. Mi móvil está dañado — *My mobile phone is turned off*

d. Tu taza está llena — *Your cup is broken*

e. Mi coche está roto — *My car is switched off*

f. La ventana está sucia — *The window is clean*

g. Mi vaso está limpio — *My glass is full*

h. Mi móvil está apagado — *My computer is switched off*

i. Mi pantalón está usado — *My trousers are worn*

3. Break the flow

a. Latazaestárota

b. Elvasoestállenodeagua

c. Tufaldaestásuciayrota

d. Mimóvilestáapagado

e. Tuvestidoestáusado

f. Elarmarioestállenoderopa

g. Mitazaestállenadecafé

h. Mivasoestávacío

4. Gapped translation: complete the translation

a. Mi coche está roto — *My car is* ____________________

b. Mi ordenador está encendido — *My computer is* ______________

c. La taza está muy sucia — *The cup is very* ______________

d. Mi vaso ya está lleno — *My glass is already* ___________

e. Este pantalón está usado — *These trousers are* ___________

f. Esta camiseta está manchada — *This t-shirt is* ____________

g. La cocina está muy limpia — *The kitchen is very* ___________

h. Mi móvil está apagado — *My mobile phone is* ___________

5. Choose the correct spelling

	1	2	3
Broken	rotto	roto	rroto
Full	lleno	leno	llieno
Dirty	succio	sucio	suzio
Worn	usado	ussado	usaddo
Switched off	appagado	apagado	apadago
Empty	vacío	vacio	vacuo
Stained	manchaddo	mancahdo	manchado

6. Broken words

a. Apa__________ — *Switched off*

b. Encen__________ — *Switched on*

c. U____________ — *Worn*

d. Va___________ — *Empty*

e. Orde__________ — *Tidy*

f. Manc__________ — *Stained*

g. Lim___________ — *Clean*

7. Dicto-translation: listen, transcribe and translate into English

Español	English
a.	
b.	
c.	
d.	
e.	
f.	
g.	
h.	

8. Tangled translation: into Spanish

a. Mi ***t-shirt*** está stained

b. ***The*** taza está ***dirty***

c. Mi ***trousers*** está ***worn and*** sucio

d. Mi ***mobile phone*** está roto

e. ***My*** escritorio está ***full of papel***

f. Mi armario está ***empty***

g. La ***kitchen*** está ***very*** sucia

h. Mi ordenador ***is switched off***

9. Guided translation

a. U__ m________ r_________ *A broken mobile*

b. U___ c__________ s________ *A dirty kitchen*

c. U__ o__________ u____________ *A used computer*

d. U__ c___________ l____________ *A clean t-shirt*

e. U__ a__________ ll________ *A full wardrobe*

f. U__ t______ v_________ *An empty cup*

g. U__ v______ ll_________ *An empty glass*

10. Listen and spot the mistakes

a. Mi móvil está rota

b. Mi ordenador es apagado

c. La taza está sucio

d. Mi armario está llena de ropa

e. Mi pantalón están sucio

f. Mis gafas están dañados

g. Mi habitación está desordenado

h. Mi vaso es vacío

11. Translate into Spanish

a. My dress is stained

b. The kitchen is dirty and untidy

c. My room is clean and tidy

d. My car is broken

e. Your skirt is dirty and worn

f. My mobile phone is damaged

g. My computer is turned off now

h. This cup is broken

3.4 PROPER NOUN + ESTAR + LOCATIVE ADVERB + PREPOSITIONAL PHRASE/LOCATIVE ADVERBIAL

(SAYING IN WHICH PART OF A COUNTRY OR CONTINENT A PLACE IS LOCATED)

LOCATION: Country & City geography level						
Argentina **Barcelona** **Cádiz** **Extremadura**	**Ibiza** **La Coruña** **Madrid** **Valencia**	**está en** *is located in*	**el centro** **el norte** **el este** **el sur** **el oeste** **el noroeste** **el noreste** **el suroeste** **el sureste**	*the centre* *the north* *the east* *the south* *the west* *the northwest* *the northeast* *the southwest* *the southeast*	**de** *of*	**España**
Colombia **Cuba** **Ecuador**	**Perú** **México** **Uruguay**					**Latinoamérica**

LANGUAGE AWARENESS: *ESTAR* for location – Part 1

One of the main uses of ***estar*** is to describe **location**. When you are saying where a country or city is situated/located on the map, using the cardinal points (north, east, etc) you always use ***estar***.

• Uruguay **está** en el sur de Latinoamérica — *Uruguay is (situated/located) in the south of Latin America*

You also use ***estar*** for location in relation to other places/things (near/far/next to/etc.)

• Madrid **está** lejos de Barcelona — *Madrid is far from Barcelona*

In this unit you will get a feel for the geography of Spain and Latin America.

1. Match

...está en el centro de	*...is in the southeast of*
...está en el norte de	*...is in the northeast of*
...está en el este de	*...is in the centre of*
...está en el sur de	*...is in the southwest of*
...está en el oeste de	*...is in the east of*
...está en el noroeste de	*...is in the north of*
...está en el noreste de	*...is in the south of*
...está en el suroeste de	*...is in the in the northwest of*
...está en el sureste de	*...is in the west of*

2. Mystery countries: fill in the gaps

a. E __ __ __ __ __

b. A __ __ __ __ __ __ __ __

c. C __ __ __

d. M __ __ __ __ __

e. U __ __ __ __ __ __

f. P __ __ __

g. E __ __ __ __ __ __

h. C __ __ __ __ __ __ __

3. Break the flow

a. ArgentinaestáenelsurdeLatinoamérica

b. MéxicoestáenelnortedeLatinoamérica

c. EcuadorestáenelcentrodeLatinoamérica

d. MadridestáenelcentrodeEspaña

e. BarcelonaestáenelnorestedeEspaña

f. CádizestáenelsurdeEspaña

4. Geography Quiz: fill in the grids, using your own knowledge of geography / Google Maps

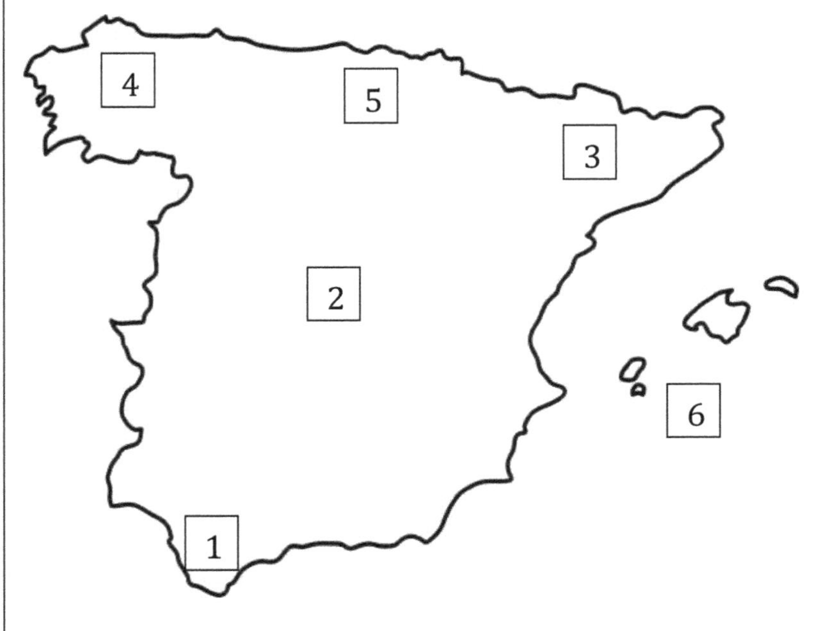

	Spain
	Barcelona
	Bilbao
	Cádiz
	Ibiza
	La Coruña
	Madrid

	Latin America
	Bogotá (Colombia)
	Buenos Aires (Argentina)
	La Habana (Cuba)
	La Paz (Bolivia)
	Lima (Perú)
	México D.F. (México)
	Montevideo (Uruguay)
	Quito (Ecuador)
	Santiago de Chile (Chile)

3.5 DETERMINER + SINGULAR & PLURAL NOUN + LOCATIVE PREPOSITION + DEFINITE ARTICLE + NOUN
(SAYING WHERE BUILDINGS ARE LOCATED IN RELATION TO OTHERS)

LOCATION: MY AREA					
		a cinco minutos *5 minutes away*		**Masculine places**	
Mi casa *My house*	**está** *is located*	**al lado** *next*	**del** *to/from the*	**castillo**	*castle*
Mi colegio *My school*		**cerca** *near*		**centro de la ciudad**	*city centre*
La casa de mi amigo *My friend's house*		**delante** *in front (of)*		**centro comercial**	*shopping centre*
		dentro *inside*		**cine**	*cinema*
		enfrente *opposite*		**estadio**	*stadium*
		lejos *far*		**gimnasio**	*gym*
		detrás *behind*		**museo**	*museum*
		a la derecha *on the right*		**parque**	*park*
		a la izquierda *on the left*		**polideportivo**	*sports centre*
				restaurante	*restaurant*
				supermercado	*supermarket*
				Feminine places	
Las tiendas *The shops*	**están** *are located*		**de la** *to/from the*	**biblioteca**	*library*
				calle peatonal	*pedestrian street*
				comisaría	*police station*
				piscina	*pool*
				playa	*beach*
				tienda de ropa	*clothes shop*
				tienda de música	*music shop*
				carnicería	*the butcher's*
				panadería	*the bakery*

LANGUAGE AWARENESS: *ESTAR* FOR LOCATION – Part 2

Does *de* mean "to" or "from"?

The English translation of ***de***, on its own, is usually **"from"**. However, in the context above, ***"del"*** and ***"de la"*** can translate into English as either **preposition** + **"to"** or **preposition** + **"from"** depending on what is required by the English sentence.

e.g. **Mi casa está cerca del castillo** — *My house is **near to** the castle*

Mi casa está lejos del parque — *My house is **far from** the park*

Masculine places: DE + EL = DEL

In the sentence "far from the castle" the ***de*** *(from)* + ***el*** *(the)* becomes ***del***

e.g. **Mi casa está lejos del castillo** — *My house is far from the castle*

Feminine places: DE + LA

In the sentence "near to the beach" the ***de*** *(to)* + ***la*** *(the)* **stay as they are.**

e.g. **Mi casa está cerca de la playa** — *My house is near to the beach*

1. Match

El estadio	*The police station*
La biblioteca	*My school*
El parque	*The restaurant*
El restaurante	*The park*
La comisaría	*The shops*
La playa	*My house*
Mi colegio	*The stadium*
Mi casa	*The library*
Las tiendas	*The beach*

2. Translate into English

a. La casa de mi amigo está cerca del estadio

b. La biblioteca está enfrente de la casa de Antonio

c. La tienda de ropa está dentro del centro comercial

d. La comisaría está lejos del hospital

e. La piscina está al lado del gimnasio

f. La calle peatonal está a la izquierda del supermercado

g. El castillo está cerca de la biblioteca

h. La playa está delante del restaurante italiano

i. El cine está enfrente de la estación de autobuses

3. *Verdadero* (true) o *falso* (false). Write V for *verdadero* or F for *falso* next to each statement below, based on the map:

<table>
<tr><td colspan="3">Club de golf</td><td colspan="4">Parque</td></tr>
<tr><td>Carnicería
Butcher's</td><td>La casa de Antonio</td><td>Biblioteca</td><td>Tienda de música</td><td>Panadería</td><td>Supermercado</td><td>Tienda de ropa</td></tr>
<tr><td colspan="7">Calle Paco de Lucía</td></tr>
<tr><td>La casa de B. Alba</td><td>Gimnasio</td><td>Bar</td><td>Restaurante indio</td><td>Restaurante chino</td><td>Cine</td><td>Un 24 horas
a convenience store</td></tr>
<tr><td>Mercadona</td><td>Piscina</td><td>Restaurante italiano</td><td colspan="2">Jardín</td><td colspan="2">Aparcamiento</td></tr>
</table>

a. La casa de Antonio está enfrente del gimnasio

b. La piscina está al lado de Mercadona

c. El restaurante indio está a la derecha del restaurante chino

d. El 24 horas está delante del aparcamiento

e. La panadería está entre el supermercado y la tienda de música

f. El cine está lejos de la tienda de música, pero cerca de la casa de B. Alba

g. El supermercado está al lado del cine

h. El bar está enfrente de la biblioteca

i. La carnicería está detrás del aparcamiento

4. Faulty translation: fix the English translation

a. Mi casa está al lado del parque	*My house is near the park*
b. La comisaría está cerca de la calle peatonal	*The police station is far from the pedestrian street*
c. La piscina está enfrente del jardín	*The swimming pool is behind the garden*
d. La casa está lejos de las tiendas	*The house is near the shops*
e. La comisaria está al lado del supermercado	*The police station is opposite the supermarket*
f. El gimnasio está cerca del restaurante	*The gym is far from the restaurant*
g. Las tiendas están detrás del aparcamiento	*The shops are in front of the parking*
h. El bar está lejos de la estación de trenes	*The bar is next to the train station*
i. La panadería está delante de la carnicería	*The bakery is behind the butcher's*

5. Listen and break the flow: draw a line between each word 

a. Lacomisaríaestáenfrentedelapiscina

b. Lacasademiamigoestácercadelparque

c. Lastiendasestánlejosdemicolegio

d. Micasaestáacincominutosdelcentro

e. Migimnasioestádelantedelapiscina

f. Elaparcamientoestáalladodelatienda

g. LacasadeAntonioestádetrásdelparque

h. Elrestauranteestádentrodelcentrocomercial

i. Eljardínestádelantedelacasa

6. Tangled translation: translate into Spanish

a. Mi ***house*** está ***near*** de la ***beach***

b. La ***police station*** está ***opposite*** del ***park***

c. Mi casa ***is located*** a ***five*** minutos de la ***pedestrian street***

d. La casa ***of my friend*** está al lado del ***stadium***

e. Las ***shops*** están ***inside*** del ***shopping centre***

f. ***My school*** está ***near*** del ***restaurant*** italiano

g. La ***shop*** de ropa está ***next to*** la ***pool***

h. ***The house*** de mi amigo ***is*** cerca ***from the park***

7. Gapped translation: complete the translation

a. La ____________ está __________ de la estación

The police station is opposite the train station

b. La casa _____ Antonio está detrás _______ restaurante

Antonio's house is behind the restaurant

c. El jardín está ___________ _______ colegio

The garden is in front of the school

d. Las tiendas _________ ________ del gimnasio

The shops are far from the gym

e. El restaurante está _______ ______ mi casa

The restaurant is near my house

f. La _______ de música está ___ _______ ___ la biblioteca

The music shop is next to the library

g. La piscina está ________ _____ gimnasio

The swimming pool is inside the gym

h. Mi casa está _________ del centro de la ____________

My house is near the city centre

8. Listen, fill in the gaps and translate into English

a. Mi casa está _____ de la estación

b. La piscina está ______ de mi casa

c. Mi casa está _________ del cine

d. El gimnasio está _______ de mi colegio

e. Mi casa está _____ del centro de la ciudad

f. La tienda de música está _______ del centro comercial

g. La casa de Antonio está al _____ de mi casa

h. El bar está ________ del cine

i. La biblioteca está _______ del museo

9. Complete with the missing words

a. El gimnasio e __ __ __ cerca d__ mi casa

b. Mi casa está al l__ __ __ de l__ piscina

c. El restaurante está d__ __ __ __ __ __del p__ __ __ __ __

d. L__ __ tiendas e__ __ __ __ dentro del centro comercial

e. La casa d__ Antonio está e__ __ __ __ __ __ __ __ del colegio

¿El agua está mojada o seca?

Las aventuras de Teruel, el tiburón filósofo

10. Translate into Spanish

a. My house is far from the city centre

b. The shops are near my school

c. The library is opposite the bus station

d. The restaurant is to the right of my house

e. The park is behind the stadium

f. The car park is in front of the gym

g. The gym is inside the shopping centre

h. The pharmacy is near Paco's house

i. The music shop is next to the hospital

3.6 DETERMINER + NOUN + ESTAR + LOCATIVE PREPOSITION + DEFINITE ARTICLE + NOUN

(SAYING WHERE THINGS ARE LOCATED IN THE HOUSE)

El despertador	*The alarm clock*		**a la derecha** *on the right*		**Masculine nouns**	
El espejo	*The mirror*		**a la izquierda** *on the left*		**armario**	*wardrobe*
El gato	*The cat*		**al lado** *beside*		**espejo**	*mirror*
El libro	*The book*	**está** *is located*	**cerca** *near*	**del** *(of) the*	**estante**	*shelf*
El ordenador	*The computer*		**debajo** *under*		**escritorio**	*desk*
El sillón	*The armchair*		**delante** *in front of*		**frigo**	*fridge*
La camiseta	*The t-shirt*				**horno**	*oven*
La puerta	*The door*				**suelo**	*floor*
La mesita de noche	*The bedside table*					
			dentro *inside*		**Feminine nouns**	
Las cortinas	*The curtains*		**detras** *behind*		**cama**	*bed*
Los calcetines	*The socks*	**están** *are located*	**encima / en** *on*	**de la** *(of) the*	**mesa**	*table*
Los libros	*The books*		**enfrente** *opposite*		**silla**	*chair*
Los ratones	*The mice*		**lejos** *far*		**puerta**	*door*
					televisión	*TV*
					ventana	*window*

LANGUAGE AWARENESS:

See the box on Page 73 for a reminder about DE / DEL / DE LA

1. Break the flow

a. Ellibroestáenelescritorio

b. Elgatoestáencimadelacama

c. Elespejoestáaladerechadelarmario

d. Elordenadorestáencimadelescritorio

e. Lacamaestáaladerechadelarmario

f. Lascortinasestándelantedelaventana

2. Missing letter challenge: complete the words

a. __l ga__o e__tá enci__a d__ l__ cam__

b. E__ lib__o es__á __n e__ es__ante

c. L__ ca__iseta est__ e__cima d__ __a si__la

d. __as co__tinas está__ __erca __e __a venta__a

e. E__ s__ll__n est__ al l__d__ de l__ p__ __rt__

f. Lo __ ratones es__á__ d__b__jo d__ l__ cam__

3. Match

Debajo	*Next to*
Encima	*Below*
Dentro	*On the left*
Lejos	*Inside*
Al lado	*On the right*
A la izquierda	*On*
Enfrente	*Behind*
A la derecha	*Near*
Cerca	*Far*
Detrás	*Opposite*

4. One of two

	1	2
Debajo	*Under*	*On*
Encima	*On*	*Far*
Dentro	*Outside*	*Inside*
Lejos	*Far*	*Near*
Detrás	*Behind*	*Under*
Al lado	*Near*	*Next to*
A la izquierda	*To the right*	*To the left*
A la derecha	*Next to*	*To the right*
Cerca	*Far*	*Near*
Enfrente	*In front of*	*Opposite*

5. Translate into English

a. La camiseta está dentro del armario

b. La cama está detrás de la puerta

c. La cocina está a la izquierda

d. Los calcetines están encima del armario

e. Los dormitorios están cerca del cuarto de baño

f. Los vaqueros están en la cama

g. La televisión está enfrente del sofá

h. La ducha está al lado del cuarto de baño

i. La cama está al lado de la mesita de noche

j. El armario está detrás de la puerta

6. Listen and complete: true or false? 

a. El _____ está debajo de la cama

b. La televisión está enfrente de la _______

c. El _________ está a la izquierda

d. La mesita de noche está ______ de la cama

e. El _______ está cerca de la puerta

f. La puerta está _______ del sillón

g. El gato está _______ del armario

h. La ________ está a la izquierda de la tele

i. La televisión está ________ de la cama

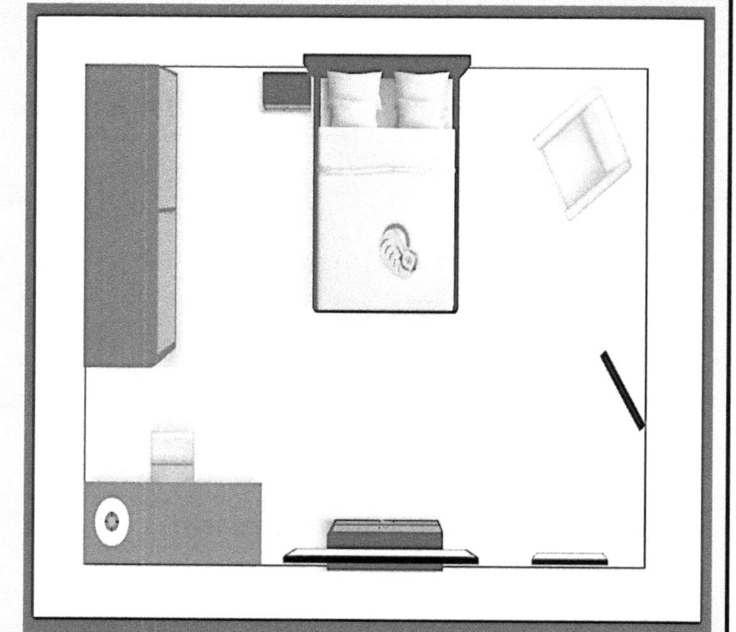

7. Complete with *del* or *de la*

a. El armario está al lado _______ cama

b. El escritorio está cerca ______ armario

c. El gato está encima ______ televisión

d. Mi ropa está dentro ________ armario

e. Las cortinas están detrás ______ escritorio

f. La puerta está a la izquierda _______ ventana

g. La camisa está encima _______ puerta

h. Los zapatos están debajo ________ silla

8. Listen and complete: likely or unlikely?

a. El sillón está _______ del ordenador

b. La puerta está _______ de las cortinas

c. El escritorio está ______ de la lámpara

d. Los zapatos están ______ del escritorio

e. La televisión está _______ de la cama

f. El armario está ________ del escritorio

g. El gato está ________ de la puerta

h. La cama está a la ________ del espejo

9. Faulty translation: fix the Spanish translation

a. *The armchair is near the bed*	El sillón está al lado de la cama
b. *The wardrobe is behind the door*	El armario está cerca de la puerta
c. *The desk is in front of the bed*	El escritorio está enfrente de la cama
d. *The cat is on the desk*	El gato está debajo del escritorio
e. *The television is on the right of the door*	La televisión está detrás de la puerta
f. *The curtains are opposite the television*	Las cortinas están detrás de la televisión
g. *The jeans are near the wardrobe*	Los vaqueros están dentro del armario
h. *The clothes are under the bed*	La ropa está en la cama

10. Complete

a. A__ l______ d___ e__________	*Next to the mirror*
b. D_______ d__ l__ p_________	*Behind the door*
c. D________ d__ l__ c_________	*Under the bed*
d. E________ d___ e___________	*On the desk*
e. E_________ d__ l__ t_________	*Opposite the TV*
f. D_______ d__ l___ c__________	*Behind the curtains*
g. D_______ d___ a___________	*Inside the wardrobe*
h. D________ d__ l__ p________	*In front of the door*
i. D________ d___ e____________	*Under the desk*

11. Translate into Spanish

a. The wardrobe is next to the door

b. The TV is opposite the bed

c. The cat is on the desk

d. The bed is to the right of the door

e. The window is behind the curtains

f. The curtains are in front of the bed

g. The dog is under the desk

h. The shorts are inside the wardrobe

i. The armchair is next to the window

3.7 ESTAR – BRINGING IT ALL TOGETHER

LANGUAGE AWARENESS

The three uses of *ESTAR*

Estar has **three main functions** which you have seen over the course of this unit. By learning these three, you can more easily identify when to use ***estar***, as opposed to ***ser*** (because if it's not ***estar*** then it has to be... ***ser***)

LOCATION: general and relative

- **Madrid está en España** — *Madrid is in Spain*
- **El gato está debajo de la mesa** — *The cat is under the table*

STATE: of repair/cleanliness

- **Mi televisión está rota** — *My television is broken*
- **Hoy el suelo está limpio** — *Today the floor is clean*

MOOD: How someone is feeling

- **Hoy estoy muy contento** — *Today I am feeling really happy*
- **Hoy mi amigo está enfermo** — *Today my friend is sick*

L
S
M

A good rule of thumb is: if you can start the sentence with **"today"** or **"at the moment"**, you are describing the current **state** or **mood**, so ***estar*** is likely to apply. However, always remember that you are describing, first and foremost: **Location/State/Mood.** This is more important than the idea of being **temporary** or **permanent**. For example, even if someone is **always** sad because their car is **permanently** dirty, it is still:

- **Siempre está triste porque su coche siempre está sucio** — *He is always sad because his car is always dirty*

1. Match

Cansado	*Stained*
Estropeado	*Tired*
Roto	*Ill*
Feliz	*Broken*
Triste	*Damaged*
Sucio	*Sad*
Limpio	*Full*
Emocionado	*Empty*
Lleno	*Happy*
Vacío	*Dirty*
Dañado	*Moved*
Enfermo	*Clean*
Manchado	*Broken down*

2. Complete with the correct present form of *ESTAR* and translate into English

a. Hoy (yo) _____________ muy triste

b. Ahora (él) _____________ enfadado

c. Mis camisetas _____________ manchadas

d. Mi coche _____________ estropeado

e. Esta mañana ellas _____________ muy felices

f. ¿Cómo ____________ (vosotros)?

g. Mi hijo _____________ muy emocionado

h. (Tú) ____________ muy nervioso hoy

i. Mi apartamento _____________ vacío

j. Mis vaqueros _____________ usados

k. Mis zapatillas de deportes _____________ rotas

3. Tangled translation: translate into Spanish

a. Mis vaqueros ***are*** manchados

b. El ***wardrobe is*** en mi habitación

c. Nosotros ***are*** en la sala de estar

d. La iglesia ***is*** en la calle ***pedestrian next*** del cine

e. La ***bed*** está ***opposite*** la ***television***

f. La silla está ***behind the*** escritorio

g. La ***swimming pool*** está ***in front of the*** colegio

h. La ***window is*** detrás de las ***curtains***

4. Listen and translate into English

a.	h.
b.	i.
c.	j.
d.	k.
e.	l.
f.	m.
g.	n.

5. Gapped translation: complete the translation

a. El jardín está ___________ de la ___________	*The garden is in front of the house*
b. El banco está al _________ de ___ biblioteca	*The bank is next to the library*
c. _________ muy _________ hoy	*I am very angry today*
d. La ________ está ________ del centro comercial	*The shop is inside the shopping centre*
e. Mis vaqueros __________ usados y ___________	*My jeans are worn and stained*
f. ¿Cómo ________ vosotros?	*How are you guys?*
g. Mi hermano _________ está ___________ hoy	*My younger brother is ill today*
h. Esta ________ está ____________	*This cup is dirty*

6. Translate the following phrases into Spanish

a. Next to the wardrobe	d. On the table	g. On the right of the door
b. Opposite the bed	e. In the northeast	h. Near my house
c. Behind the house	f. In the southwest	i. In front of the building

7. Translate the following sentences into Spanish

a. The shirt is dirty	g. I am very tired this morning
b. My house is near my school	h. How are you?
c. Paco's car is in front of the house	i. My father is angry today
d. Barcelona is in the north of Spain	j. Where is my green t-shirt?
e. My mobile phone is damaged	k. The cup is dirty
f. My parents are ill	l. My brother is sad today

3.8 SER & ESTAR: PART 1 – *WHERE I AM FROM VS LOCATION*

SER: where I am from			ESTAR: location			
Yo soy *I am* **Mi madre es** *My mother is* **Nosotros somos** *We are (masculine)* **Nosotras somos** *We are (feminine)* **Mis padres son** *My parents are*	**de** *from*	**España.** *Spain.* **Inglaterra.** *England.* **Madrid.**	**Madrid** **Mi casa** *My house* **Mi ciudad** *My city*	**está** *it is located*	**en** *in*	**España** *Spain* **el norte** *the north* **el sur** *the south* **el este** *the east* **el oeste** *the west*
						el centro *the centre* **la playa** *the beach* **las afueras** *the outskirts*

1. Choose the correct option: *es* or *está*? Then listen to check 

a. Mi madre **es/está** de Madrid, que **es/está** en el centro de España.

b. Mi amigo **es/está** de Inglaterra. Su casa **es/está** en el sur.

c. Mi abuelo **es/está** de Colombia. Colombia **es/está** en Sudamérica.

d. Mi padre **es/está** de México. México **es/está** lejos de España.

e. Mi ciudad **es/está** en el este de Inglaterra.

f. Mi casa **es/está** en las afueras de mi ciudad. Mi casa **es/está** muy bonita.

g. Mi ciudad **es/está** en España, **es/está** Madrid.

h. Mi ciudad **es/está** Barcelona y **es/está** en el norte de España.

2. Complete with *estar* or *ser* as appropriate

a. Mi madre __________ de Madrid

b. Madrid __________ en España, en el centro

c. Nosotros __________ de Londres

d. Londres __________ en Inglaterra

e. Mis padres __________ de Bogotá

f. Bogotá __________ en Colombia

g. Mi hermano __________ en España

h. Nosotros __________ en México

i. Mis padres __________ en Italia

j. Mis padres __________ de Roma

k. Roma __________ en Italia

l. Nosotras __________ en Inglaterra

m. Yo _____ de España, pero _____ en Inglaterra

3. Gapped translation: complete the translation

a. Nosotras _______ de _______. Madrid ______ en el centro de ________.

We are from Madrid. Madrid is in the centre of Spain.

b. ____ abuelos _____ de Roma, en _______. Roma _____ la capital de ________.

My grandparents are from Rome, in Italy. Rome is the capital of Italy.

c. Mi madre ____ de Londres. Londres ______ en ________.

My mum is from London. London is in England.

d. Mis _______ _______ en México, pero _____ de ________.

My parents are in Mexico, but they are from Spain.

4. Tangled translation: into Spanish

a. Mi ***mother*** es ***from England***

b. ***I am*** en ***Spain,*** pero ***I am*** de Colombia

c. ***My*** padres ***are*** en Roma

d. Mis ***friends are*** de Rusia

e. Nosotros ***are*** en Inglaterra

f. Mis ***parents are in*** Nueva York

g. Nueva York ***is*** en Estados Unidos

h. Nosotras ***are*** de Segovia, en el ***north*** de ***Spain***

5. Correct the mistakes

a. Soy de Argentina, pero soy en Ibiza.

b. Mi casa es en las afueras de mi ciudad.

c. Mi ciudad es en el centro de España. Es Madrid.

d. Nosotras estamos de Italia, pero ahora estamos en Sevilla.

e. Mi padre es en mi casa ahora.

f. Mis padres están de Roma, en Italia.

g. Mi abuelo está de España.

h. Mis amigos son en la playa.

6. Translate into Spanish

a. I am in Spain

b. I am in England

c. We (f) are from Peru

d. I am from Spain

e. We (f) are on the beach

f. My house is in the centre

g. My city is in the west of England

h. My sister is in Rome

i. My city is the capital of England

j. Scotland is in the north

7. Listen, fill in the gaps and then translate the sentences into English

a. Nosotras ________ de Inglaterra, pero _________ en Barcelona de vacaciones.

b. Mi casa ______ en el centro de Valencia. Valencia ______ una ciudad en el este de España.

c. Mi ciudad _______ en el este de Inglaterra.

d. Londres ______ la capital de Inglaterra.

e. Mis padres ______ de Rusia, pero ______ en México.

f. Mi abuelo ______ de Estados Unidos, pero _____ en España.

g. Mi madre ______ de España.

3.8 SER & ESTAR: PART 2 – NOUN PHRASE+ ES + ADJECTIVE + CONJUNCTION + TIME MARKER + ESTA' + ADJECTIVE

(COMPARING PHYSICAL DESCRIPTIONS & STATES)

SER: physical description			ESTAR: state or condition			
Mi ciudad *My city* **Mi casa** *My house* **Mi habitación** *My bedroom* **La casa de mi amigo** *My friend's house*	**es** *(it) is*	**bonita** *pretty* **fea** *ugly* **grande** *big* **moderna** **pequeña** *small* **vieja** *old*	**pero** *but* **y** *and*	**ahora** *now* **últimamente** *lately*	**está** *(it) is*	**desordenada** *untidy* **ordenada** *tidy* **llena de hormigas** *full of ants* **limpia** *clean* **sucia** *dirty*
Mi colegio *My school* **Mi piso** *My flat*		**bonito** **feo** **grande** **moderno** **pequeño** **viejo**				**desordenado** *untidy* **ordenado** *tidy* **lleno de hormigas** *full of ants* **limpio** *clean* **sucio** *dirty*

1. ¿Es o Está?

a. Mi colegio ______ sucio

b. Mi habitación ______ demasiado pequeña

c. Mi piso ____ moderno y _____ en el centro

d. Mi colegio _____ viejo pero bonito

e. La casa de mi amigo ____ ordenada

f. Últimamente mi habitación _____ desordenada

g. Mi colegio _____ lleno de hormigas

h. Mi casa _____ grande y vieja

i. Mi piso _____ demasiado pequeño

j. Mi habitación ____ limpia hoy

2. Translate into English

a. Mi casa es demasiado pequeña, pero está en el centro de Madrid.

b. Mi habitación está más desordenada que la habitación de mi hermano.

c. Mi colegio es muy viejo y grande. Últimamente está muy sucio.

d. Mi habitación está llena de hormigas.

e. La casa de mi amigo está en las afueras, pero es muy bonita y grande.

f. Mi colegio está en el centro de mi ciudad.

g. Mi habitación es demasiado pequeña, pero la habitación de mi hermano es muy grande.

h. Mi casa está limpia siempre.

i. Últimamente mi habitación está muy desordenada.

3. Gapped translation: complete the translation

a. Mi ___________ __________ desordenada _________ *My room is untidy always*

b. ______ casa ______ grande, pero __________ *My house is big but modern*

c. Mi ______ ______ bonita, pero _______ _______ sucia *My house is pretty but now is dirty*

d. _____ colegio _______ en las _________ de la ________ ... *My school is in the outskirts of the city*

e. ...pero ______ muy bueno *...but it is very good*

f. __________ mi colegio _______ lleno de ____________ *Lately my school is full of ants*

g. Mi _______ _______ fea, pero siempre ________ limpia *My house is ugly, but it is always clean*

h. La casa ____ ______ _______ ______ en el centro... *My friend's house is in the centre...*

i. ...pero ______ _______ *...but it is old*

4. Sentence Puzzle

a. casa Mi está en centro y bonita es el

b. colegio pero viejo es limpio Mi está

c. casa pero amigo La es en las de está afueras mi moderna

d. habitación grande desordenada pero es está Mi

e. casa es Mi moderna últimamente sucia está pero

f. habitación grande hormigas llena es está pero Mi de

5. Tangled translation: translate into Spanish

a. Mi ***house is*** en el ***centre*** y ***is*** bonita

b. ***My school is big,*** pero últimamente ***is dirty***

c. Mi ***room is*** grande, pero ***is full*** de ***ants***

d. La ***house*** de ***my friend is*** moderna, pero ***is*** en ***the outskirts***

e. Mi habitación ***is*** demasiado ***small*** y ***lately is*** desordenada

f. Mi ***school is*** moderno, pero últimamente ***is dirty***

g. Mi ***room is*** grande y ***is tidy***

6. Listen and correct the mistakes

a. Mi casa está grande, pero hoy es sucia

b. Mi habitación está muy grande, pero es desordenada

c. La casa de mi amigo está en el centro de la ciudad, pero está pequeña

d. Mi habitación está muy pequeña y es llena de hormigas

e. Mi colegio está grande, pero últimamente está muy sucio

f. La habitación de mi amigo está bonita, pero últimamente es desordenada

7. Translate into Spanish

a. My house is very modern and big, but it is in the outskirts

b. My school is old but lately is very dirty

c. Lately my room is full of ants, but it is big

d. My house is quite pretty but it is old

e. My friend's house is in the centre of the city, but it is old

f. My school is small, but it is always clean

g. My house is very modern, but it is not in the centre

h. My school is pretty and it is always clean

i. My bedroom is too small, but it is very tidy

3.8 SER & ESTAR: PART 3 – NOUN PHRASE + ES + ADJECTIVE + CONJUNCTION + TIME MARKER + ESTÁ + ADJECTIVE

(COMPARING ONE'S PERSONALITY USUALLY WITH ONE'S CURRENT MOOD)

<table>
<tr><th colspan="4">SER: character descriptions</th><th colspan="4">ESTAR: mood</th></tr>
<tr><td rowspan="2">Mi mejor amigo
My best friend (m)
Mi novio
My boyfriend
Mi padre
My father
Mi primo
My cousin (m)</td><td rowspan="3">es
is</td><td rowspan="2">alegre
fuerte
gracioso
listo
paciente
perezoso
simpático
trabajador</td><td rowspan="2">cheerful
strong
funny
clever
patient
lazy
nice
hard-working</td><td rowspan="3">pero

y</td><td rowspan="3">hoy
today

ahora
now</td><td rowspan="3">está
he / she is feeling</td><td>contento
happy
deprimido
depressed
enfermo
ill</td></tr>
<tr><td>de buen humor
in a good mood
de mal humor
in a bad mood
triste sad</td></tr>
<tr><td>Mi mejor amiga
My best friend (f)
Mi madre
My mother
Mi novia
My girlfriend
Mi prima
My cousin (f)</td><td colspan="2">alegre
fuerte
graciosa
lista
paciente
perezosa
simpática
trabajadora</td><td>contenta
deprimida
enferma</td></tr>
</table>

LANGUAGE AWARENESS
Using *SER* and *ESTAR* in the same sentence

Knowing when to use *ser* or *estar* is really important!

You can use them together to compare **what a person is like** (in general) with **how they are feeling** (today/now).

- **Normalmente, mi padre es una persona alegre, pero hoy está triste**

Normally, my father ***is a happy person*** *but today* ***he is feeling sad***

If you describe someone's **character** (what they are like as a person), you must use *ser*.

To say how they are **feeling** or talk about their **mood** you use ***estar.***

Some adjectives work with both ***SER*** and ***ESTAR***. This is because you could have a cheerful **character** (*e.g. Soy una persona alegre*) or just be in a cheerful **mood** (*e.g. Hoy estoy alegre*)

Adjectives that work best with *ESTAR*

Some adjectives that refer specifically to **moods**, **health conditions**, nearly always go with ***estar.***

- **Mi amigo está triste**

  My friend is feeling sad

- **Hoy mi padre está un poco enfermo**

  Today my dad is a bit unwell

All the adjectives in the *Estar* section above can only be used with *estar*

1. ¿Es o Está?

a. Mi mejor amiga _____ fuerte

b. Mi prima normalmente ______ alegre…

c …pero hoy _____ triste

d. Mi madre ______ de buen humor hoy

e. Mi padre normalmente _____ paciente y listo

f. Mi novio normalmente _____ simpático

g. Mi prima _____ trabajadora…

h. …pero hoy _____ enferma

i. Mi padre ______ perezoso normalmente

j. Mi hermano ______ de mal humor hoy

k. Ahora mi prima ______ contenta

l. Mi mejor amigo ______ alegre normalmente…

m. …pero hoy _______ deprimido

2. Correct the mistake or mistakes in each sentence. Review not only usage of *ES* or *ESTÁ*, but also adjective agreement!

a. Mi madre es fuerta, pero hoy está enfermo

b. Mi padre es alegre, pero hoy es de mal humor

c. Mi novia está perezoso y hoy está triste

d. Mi mejor amiga es triste hoy, pero normalmente está de buen humor

e. Mi padre es deprimido hoy, pero normalmente es alegro

f. Normalmente mi novio es alegre, pero hoy es enferma

g. Mi mejor amiga es trabajadora, pero hoy está enfermo

h. Mi padre es fuerte y simpática, pero hoy es de mal humor

3. Listen, complete and translate into English

a. Hoy mi hermana está _________

b. Mi madre es trabajadora, ____ hoy está enferma

c. Mi ________ está enfermo

d. Mi novia ______ deprimida

e. Normalmente soy alegre, pero hoy _____ triste

f. Hoy estoy de ______ humor

g. Mi madre está __________ ahora

h. Hoy mi padre está de ______ humor

4. Tangled translation: into Spanish

a. Mi madre ***is hard-working,*** pero hoy ***is ill***

b. Mi ***father is*** simpático y ***cheerful,*** pero hoy ***is*** triste

c. Mi primo ***is*** fuerte y ***hard-working*** but ***now*** is deprimido

d. Mi prima ***is*** lista y ***funny,*** pero hoy ***is*** enferma

e. ***Normally my*** padre ***is*** paciente***, but*** hoy ***is in a bad mood***

f. Mi madre ***is in a bad mood*** hoy, pero ***normally is*** simpática y ***cheerful***

5. Translate into Spanish

a. Normally, my mum is very nice, but today she is in a bad mood

b. My boyfriend is lazy and today he is ill

c. My dad is strong and clever and today he is sad

d. My girlfriend is not lazy, but today she is ill

e. My father is very clever and is not lazy

f. My mum is in a bad mood, but normally she is cheerful

g. My cousin (f) is sad today, but normally she is nice

h. My boyfriend is ill today

ORAL PING PONG

ESTAR

ENGLISH 1	SPANISH 1	ENGLISH 2	SPANISH 2
Today I am bored but happy. My sister is in a bad mood.	**Hoy estoy aburrido/a pero contento/a. Mi hermana está malhumorada.**	**I am sad because my skirt is dirty.**	
My mother is quite angry and worried.	**Mi madre está bastante enfadada y preocupada.**	**Today my cat is calm because the television is turned on.**	
My parents are not nervous today, they are worried.	**Mis padres no están nerviosos hoy, están preocupados.**	**Are you tired today?**	
My brothers are tired and cold. They are ill.	**Mis hermanos están cansados y tienen frío. Están enfermos.**	**My dad is worried and in a bad mood because the car is broken.**	
The computer is broken, that's why (*por eso*) is turned off.	**El ordenador está roto, por eso está apagado.**	**The kitchen is very clean today, that's why (*por eso*) I am happy.**	
My bedroom is untidy, that's why (*por eso*) my mother is angry.	**Mi habitación está desordenada, por eso mi madre está enfadada.**	**My grandmother is happy when the television is turned off.**	
The drawer is full of pens, but they are broken. I am sad.	**El cajón está lleno de bolígrafos, pero están rotos. Estoy triste.**	**Colombia is in Latin America, but Madrid is in the centre of Spain.**	
I am happy because I am in Ibiza. Ibiza is in the east of Spain.	**Estoy contento porque estoy en Ibiza. Ibiza está en el este de España.**	**Are you in Spain?**	

INSTRUCTIONS - You are **PARTNER A.** Work in pairs. Each of you has two sets of sentences - one set has already been translated for you. You will ask your partner to translate these. The other set of sentences have not been translated. Your partner will ask you to translate these.
HOW TO PLAY - Partner A starts by reading out his/her/their first sentence in English. Partner B must translate. Partner A must check the answer and award the following points: **3 points** = perfect, **2 points** = 1 mistake, **1 point** = mistakes but the verb is accurate. If they cannot translate correctly, Partner A will read out the sentence so that Partner B can learn what the correct translation is.
Then Partner B reads out his/her/their first sentence, and so on.
OBJECTIVE - Try to win more points than your partner by translating correctly as many sentences as possible.

B

ORAL PING PONG

ESTAR

ENGLISH 1	SPANISH 1	ENGLISH 2	SPANISH 2
Today I am bored but happy. My sister is in a bad mood.		**I am sad because my skirt is dirty.**	**Estoy triste porque mi falda está sucia.**
My mother is quite angry and worried.		**Today my cat is calm because the television is turned on.**	**Hoy mi gato está tranquilo porque la televisión está encendida.**
My parents are not nervous today, they are worried.		**Are you tired today?**	**¿Estás cansado/a hoy?**
My brothers are tired and cold. They are ill.		**My dad is worried and in a bad mood because the car is broken.**	**Mi padre está preocupado y malhumorado porque el coche está roto.**
The computer is broken, that's why (*por eso*) is turned off.		**The kitchen is very clean today, that's why (*por eso*) I am happy.**	**La cocina está muy limpia hoy, por eso estoy contento/a.**
My bedroom is untidy, that's why (*por eso*) my mother is angry.		**My grandmother is happy when the television is turned off.**	**Mi abuela está contenta cuando la televisión está apagada.**
The drawer is full of pens, but they are broken. I am sad.		**Colombia is in Latin America, but Madrid is in the centre of Spain.**	**Colombia está en Latinoamérica, pero Madrid está en el centro de España.**
I am happy because I am in Ibiza. Ibiza is in the east of Spain.		**Are you in Spain?**	**¿Estás en España?**

INSTRUCTIONS - You are **PARTNER B.** Work in pairs. Each of you has two sets of sentences - one set has already been translated for you. You will ask your partner to translate these. The other set of sentences have not been translated. Your partner will ask you to translate these.
HOW TO PLAY - Partner A starts by reading out his/her/their first sentence in English. Partner B must translate. Partner A must check the answer and award the following points: **3 points** = perfect, **2 points** = 1 mistake, **1 point** = mistakes but the verb is accurate. If they cannot translate correctly, Partner A will read out the sentence so that Partner B can learn what the correct translation is.
Then Partner B reads out his/her/their first sentence, and so on.
OBJECTIVE - Try to win more points than your partner by translating correctly as many sentences as possible.

ESTAR

No Snakes No Ladders

SALIDA	1 The cup is full of water	2 I am happy because I am near the park	3 My school is behind the museum	4 The shops are in the main street	5 My room is untidy	6 The t-shirt is on the bed	7 The cat is under the table
15 The cat is on the television	14 My sister is happy because she is near the shops	13 Are you worried?	12 My mum is happy because the car is clean	11 The shoes are under the bed	10 Barcelona is in the northeast of Spain	9 The armchair is in front of the television	8 The television is turned off
16 The window is opposite the door	17 The trousers are dirty	18 The computer is broken	19 My house is near the beach	20 The books are near the bed	21 The mirror is on the right of the door	22 We are tired and hot	23 My cat is on the table
LLEGADA	30 The sports centre is near the pool	29 The bottle is full of water	28 We are happy	27 The beach is behind the restaurant	26 The castle is near the library	25 We are in a bad mood	24 The shops are behind the parking

No Snakes No Ladders

ESTAR

SALIDA	1 La taza está llena de agua	2 Estoy contento/a porque estoy cerca del parque	3 Mi colegio está detrás del museo	4 Las tiendas están en la calle peatonal	5 Mi habitación está desordenada	6 La camiseta está encima de la cama	7 El gato está debajo de la mesa
15 El gato está encima de la televisión	14 Mi hermana está contenta porque está cerca de las tiendas	13 ¿Estás preocupado /a?	12 Mi madre está contenta porque el coche está limpio	11 Los zapatos están debajo de la cama	10 Barcelona está en el noreste de España	9 El sillón está delante de la televisión	8 La televisión está apagada
16 La ventana está enfrente de la puerta	17 Los pantalones están sucios	18 El ordenador está roto	19 Mi casa está cerca de la playa	20 Los libros están cerca de la cama	21 El espejo está a la derecha de la puerta	22 Estamos cansados y tenemos calor	23 Mi gato está encima de la mesa
LLEGADA	30 El polideportivo está cerca de la piscina	29 La botella está llena de agua	28 Estamos contentos /as	27 La playa está detrás del restaurante	26 El castillo está cerca de la biblioteca	25 Estamos malhumoraos /as	24 Las tiendas están detrás del aparcamiento

PYRAMID TRANSLATION

ESTAR

Translate each part of the pyramid out loud with your partner, then write it into the spaces provided below.

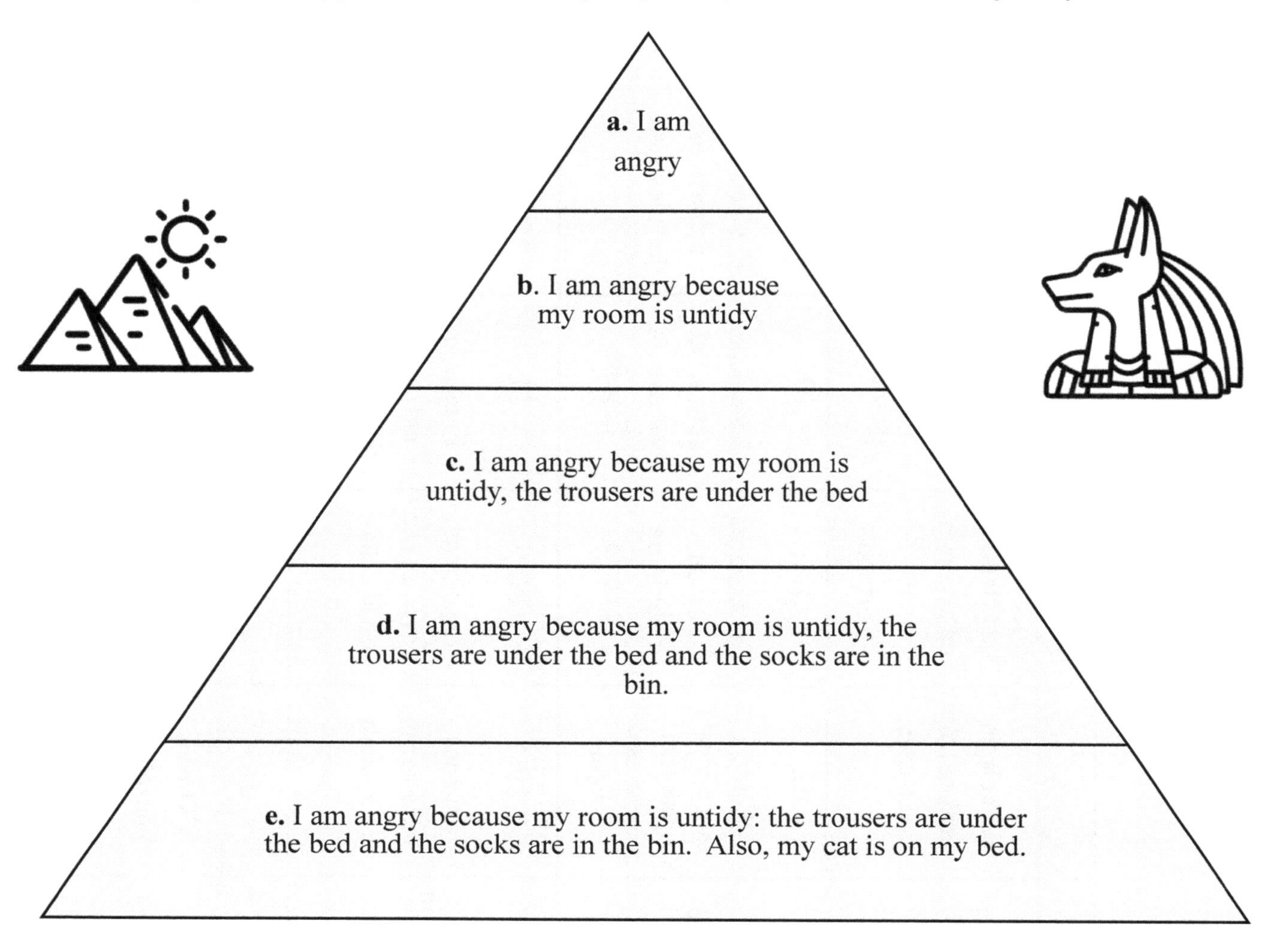

Write your translation here

SOLUTION: Estoy enfadado/a porque mi habitación está desordenada: los pantalones están debajo de la cama y los calcetines están en la papelera. También, mi gato está encima de mi cama.

UNIT 4 – IR

Yo	Voy
Tú	Vas
Él / Ella	Va
Nosotros / as	Vamos
Vosotros / as	Vais
Ellos / as	Van

4.1 VOY + PREPOSITION + PLACE + FREQUENCY ADVERB
(SAYING WHERE I GO AND HOW OFTEN)

NEGATIVE					
(Yo) *I*	**(no)** *don't*	**voy** *go*	**a** *to*	**casa de Paco** *Paco's house* **Barcelona** **Madrid** **ninguna parte** *nowhere*	**a menudo** *often* **casi nunca** *hardly ever* **todos los días** *every day* **todos los fines de semana** *every weekend*
			al *to the*	**centro comercial** *shopping centre* **centro de la ciudad** *city centre* **cine** *cinema*	
			a la *to the*	**fiesta** *party* **iglesia** *church* **piscina** *swimming pool*	
(Yo) *I*	**(nunca)** *never*	**voy** *go*	**a casa de mi amigo** **al cine** **a la playa**		

POSITIVE						
(Yo) *I*	**voy** *go*	**a** *to*	**casa de María** *María's house* **Barcelona** **Madrid**			**a menudo** *often* **a veces** *sometimes* **de vez en cuando** *from time to time* **raramente** *rarely* **(casi) todos los días** *(nearly) every day* **(casi) todos los fines de semana** *(nearly) every weekend* **una vez al mes** *once a month* **una vez a la semana** *once a week*
		al *to the*	**colegio** *school* **estadio** *stadium* **gimnasio** *gym* **parque** *park* **supermercado** *supermarket*			
			restaurante	**chino** *Chinese* **indio** *Indian* **italiano** *Italian*		
		a la *to the*	**playa** *beach*		**todos** *every*	**los lunes** *Monday* **los martes** *Tuesday* **los miércoles** *Wednesday* **los jueves** *Thursday* **los viernes** *Friday* **los sábados** *Saturday* **los domingos** *Sunday*
			tienda de *(...) shop*	**deporte** *sport* **música** *music* **ropa** *clothes*		

LANGUAGE AWARENESS
DEFINITE ARTICLES: *EL* & *LA*

In English there is only one definite article, **"the"**. This is because English nouns are not assigned a gender. However, Spanish nouns are **all** either **masculine** or **feminine** – this is known as their "gender". ***El*** and ***la*** are **definite articles**. They both translate as **"the"** in English.

Masculine – **El colegio** *The school*

Feminine – **La playa** *The beach*

A + LA = A LA

A means **'to'** in English. The feminine form follows the same pattern as the English:

• Yo voy **a la** playa *I go* ***to the*** *beach*

A + EL = AL

In Spanish when ***a*** comes into contact with ***el*** it mutates into ***al***.

• Yo voy ***a + el*** cine >>>>>> Yo voy **al** cine

I go ***to the*** *cinema*

You must always say ***al*** when saying that you go to places that are masculine.

NEGATIVES: *NUNCA*

Nunca means never, and it can be used in **two ways** to form a sentence.

The easier way

•Yo **nunca** voy a la playa

I never go to the beach

This structure is slightly easier because it is the same word order as the English.

The less easy way

•Yo **no** voy a la playa **nunca**

I don't go *to the beach* ***"never"***

This structure has a **double negative.** This is usually avoided in English, but works well in Spanish!

Voy a la playa y al parque, pero nunca voy al cine

1. Match

Fiesta	*Swimming pool*
Iglesia	*Party*
Nunca	*From time to time*
Piscina	*Church*
Playa	*Shop*
De vez en cuando	*Beach*
Tienda	*Often*
Estadio	*Never*
Casa	*Stadium*
A menudo	*Rarely*
Raramente	*House*

2. Listen and complete with *a*, *al* or *a la*

a. Voy _____ piscina a menudo

b. Nunca voy _______ cine

c. Voy ______ restaurante indio a menudo

d. Voy ______ casa de Paco todos los días

e. Nunca voy ______ parque

f. No voy ______ iglesia a menudo

g. Casi nunca voy ______ tienda de deporte

h. Voy ______ Barcelona una vez al mes

i. Voy ______ fiesta de mi prima

j. Voy ______ iglesia todos los domingos

k. Voy ______ estadio los sábados

3. Faulty translation: fix the English translation

a. Voy a la iglesia a menudo	*I rarely go to church*
b. Nunca voy al cine	*I never go to the stadium*
c. Voy a la tienda de deporte raramente	*I rarely go to the clothes shop*
d. Nunca voy a Barcelona	*I often go to Barcelona*
e. Voy a casa de Marta a menudo	*I go to Marta's house from time to time*
f. Voy al parque todos los domingos	*I go to the park every Saturday*
g. Voy a la playa de vez en cuando	*I often go to the beach*

4. Complete with the missing letters

a. Vo__ a la t__enda de deport__

b. N__nca v__y al par__ue

c. __oy a casa d__ Marta a menu__o

d. Voy a la pla__a de ve__ en cuand__

e. Voy a la igle__ia todo__ los domin__os

f. Nun__a voy a la fie__ta

g. Voy a__ centro comercial to__os los s__bados

h. Voy al gimnas__o una ve__ a la se__ana

i. V__y a Barcel__n__ una v__z al m__s

5. Broken words

a. V____ a la igl______ a men______

b. Nun____ voy al par_____

c. V___ a ca___ de Marta to___ los ____bados

d. ____nca voy a la pla____

e. Voy a l__ pisc____ una v____ a la sem____

f. Voy al restau_____ indio rara______

g. Nun____ voy al gimn_____

h. Voy al cen____ ______rcial todos los d____

i. Voy a la tien____ de depo_____ raramente

6. Tangled Translation: translate into Spanish

a. ***I go to the*** centro comercial ***nearly*** todos los fines de semana

b. Voy ***to the*** piscina por la tarde ***every day***

c. Voy ***to the*** playa ***every*** los sábados

d. ***I go to the*** tienda de ropa ***every weekend***

e. Voy ***to the*** iglesia todos los ***Sundays***

f. ***I go to the*** fiesta de mi ***cousin***

7. Translate into English

a. Voy a Barcelona a menudo

b. Nunca voy a casa de Miguel

c. Voy al parque todos los días

d. Voy a la tienda de ropa a menudo

e. Nunca voy a Madrid

f. Voy al colegio todos los días

g. Nunca voy a la piscina

8. Listen and translate into English

a. I go…

b. I never go…

c. I go…

d. I never go…

e. I go…

f. I go…

g. I never go…

h. I go…

9. Choose the correct option

a. Voy **a/a la/al** Madrid todos los fines de semana

b. Nunca voy **a/a la/al** gimnasio

c. Voy **a/a la/al** casa de Marta a veces

d. Mi hermano va **a/al/a la** Barcelona a menudo

e. Voy **a/al/a la** fiesta de Pedro

f. Voy **a/al/a la** piscina una vez a la semana

g. Nunca voy **a/al/a la** casa de Miguel

h. Siempre voy **a/al/a la** centro comercial

i. Voy **a/al/a la** restaurante indio todos los días

10. Complete with *a*, *a la* or *al* as appropriate

a. Voy _____ playa de vez en cuando

b. Nunca voy _____ centro comercial

c. El fin de semana voy ______ piscina

d. Después del colegio, siempre voy ______ parque

e. Raramente voy ______ casa de Miguel

f. Voy _______ tienda de deporte todos los domingos

g. Nunca vamos _______ casa de Pedro

h. Voy _____ Barcelona una vez al mes

i. Mi hermano va ____ gimnasio una vez a la semana

11. Complete with an appropriate noun without repeating the same word twice

a. Voy al __________ a menudo

b. Paco y yo vamos a la _________ raramente

c. María va a _________ todos los días

d. Miguel y yo nunca vamos al ___________

e. Mi familia va a la _________ todos los días

f. ¿Con qué frecuencia vas al ___________?

g. Raramente voy al _____________

h. Mi hermano va a ________ de Pedro casi todos los días

12.Translate into Spanish

a. I go to the park every weekend

b. I go to Marta's house from time to time

c. I never go to the Italian restaurant

d. I go the shopping centre once a week

e. I go to the beach sometimes with my friends

f. I go to the gym once a month

g. I go to the swimming pool every Monday

h. I rarely go to the stadium with my father

13. Complete with an appropriate word

a. Voy a ___ piscina de vez en _________

b. Voy ____ parque todos ____ días

c. Vamos a ______ de Miguel a menudo

d. Voy___ centro comercial ___ menudo

e. Mi hermano va ___ gimnasio todos ____ días

f. Voy ___ la playa de _____ en cuando

g. Voy _____ cine una vez a la ________

h. Voy a ____ playa todos ____ domingos

4.2 FULL PRESENT CONJUGATION OF IR + PLACES + FREQUENCY ADVERB

(SAYING HOW OFTEN AND WHEN I GO TO PLACES)

<table>
<tr><th colspan="6">NEGATIVE</th></tr>
<tr><td rowspan="3">(Yo)
I

(Tú
You

(Él/Ella
He/She

(Nosotros/Nosotras)
We

(Vosotros/Vosotras)
You guys/You ladies

(Ellos/Ellas)
They</td><td rowspan="3">No
Don't /
Doesn't</td><td rowspan="3">voy
go

vas
go

va
goes

vamos
go

vais
go

van
go</td><td>a
to</td><td>casa de Lola Lola's house
Barcelona
ninguna parte nowhere</td><td rowspan="3">a menudo
often

casi nunca
hardly ever

todos los días
every day

todos los fines de semana
every weekend</td></tr>
<tr><td>al
to the</td><td>centro comercial
centro de la ciudad city centre
cine cinema</td></tr>
<tr><td>a la
to the</td><td>fiesta party
iglesia church
piscina pool</td></tr>
<tr><td colspan="2">Nunca
Never</td><td colspan="2">voy/vas/va etc
go</td><td>a
al
a la</td><td>casa de mi amigo my friend's house
casa de su amigo his/her friend's house
cine
playa</td></tr>
</table>

<table>
<tr><th colspan="6">POSITIVE</th></tr>
<tr><td rowspan="5">Yo
I

Tú
You

Él/Ella
He/She

Nosotros/Nosotras
We

Vosotros/Vosotras
You guys/You ladies

Ellos/Ellas
They</td><td rowspan="5">voy
go

vas
go

va
goes

vamos
go

vais
go

van
go</td><td>a
to</td><td colspan="2">casa de María
Barcelona
Madrid</td><td rowspan="3" colspan="2">a veces
sometimes
de vez en cuando
from time to time
por la tarde
in the afternoon
raramente
rarely
(casi) todos los fines de semana
(nearly) every weekend
una vez al mes
once a month
una vez a la semana
once a week</td></tr>
<tr><td rowspan="2">al
to the</td><td colspan="2">colegio school
estadio stadium
gimnasio gym
parque park
supermercado</td></tr>
<tr><td>restaurante</td><td>chino
indio
italiano</td></tr>
<tr><td rowspan="2">a la
to the</td><td colspan="2">playa beach</td><td rowspan="2">todos</td><td rowspan="2">los lunes
los martes
los miércoles
los jueves
los viernes
los fines de semana</td></tr>
<tr><td>tienda de
(...) shop</td><td>deporte
sport
música
music
ropa
clothes</td></tr>
</table>

LANGUAGE AWARENESS

ADVERBS OF FREQUENCY

Some **adverbs of frequency** can go at the **start** or at the **end** of a sentence:

- **Yo voy a la playa a menudo**
  I go to the beach often
- **A menudo yo voy a la playa**
  I often go to the beach

Sometimes the adverbs work better at the **end** of the sentence:

- **Yo voy a la playa todos los fines de semana**
  I go to the beach every weekend

Mi perro va al parque muy a menudo

Usually, the placement is very similar to English.
If it sounds good in English, it will ***usually** sound good in Spanish too!

*Terms and conditions may apply

POSSESSIVES – *El perro de Dylan*

Spanish word order to explain possession is different from English. To say "Dylan's dog" we actually need to say "the dog of Dylan"

- **El perro de Dylan**
  Dylan's dog
  Literally: *The dog of Dylan*

Hola, soy Lily. Voy al parque casi todos los fines de semana

The same applies when saying what kind of shop you're going to!

- **La tienda de música**
  The music shop
  Literally: *The shop of music*

1. Match

Vamos	*I go*
Voy	*You go*
Va	*He/She goes*
Van	*We go*
Vais	*You guys go*
Vas	*They go*

2. Select the correct form of *IR*

a. Hoy nosotros **van/vais/vamos** al cine

b. Ellos **vamos/van/vais** a la piscina a menudo

c. Yo nunca **vas/voy/va** al centro comercial

d. Ella **vas/va/van** a la playa raramente

e. ¿Adónde **vas/va/vais** tú?

f. ¿Adónde **vamos/vais/van** vosotros?

g. Vosotros **voy/vais/va** al cine todos los fines de semana

h. Ellos **vas/vais/van** al gimnasio por las tardes

3. Break the flow

a. Vamosalaiglesiatodoslossábados

b. Nuncavoyalcineconmispadres

c. Vamosalcentrocomercialdevezencuando

d. Voyalatiendadedeporteamenudo

e. ¿Adóndevaiselfindesemana?

f. Mihermanomenorvaalestadiotodoslosdomingos

g. ¿Adóndevastúhoy?

4. Complete with the missing letters

a. Nun__ __ vam__ __ al ci__ __

b. V__ __ a la igle__ __ __ de ve__ en cuan__ __

c. M__ m__dr__ v__ al sup__ __me __cado a m__ n__ do

d. M__ s h__rma__ __ __ va__ al e__tad__ __ tod__ __ lo__ d__ __ __ __ __ __ __ __

e. ¿Adón__ __ va__ el fi__ de sema__ __ ?

f. ¿A__ __nde va__ __ ho__?

g. No v__y a ning__ __ __ par__ __

5. Partial dictation

a. Casi nunca ________ a la iglesia

b. Mi hermana ______ al gimnasio a veces

c. Mis padres ______ al centro los fines de semana

d. ¿______ al parque todos los días?

e. ¿______ al cine a veces?

f. Mis amigos nunca ______ a la iglesia

6. Sentence Puzzle

a. a vamos la playa Nunca	*We never go to the beach*
b. a piscina todos Van los días la	*They go to the swimming pool every day*
c. ¿fin Adónde semana vas el de?	*Where do you go at the weekend?*
d. yo Paco y vamos a al gimnasio menudo	*Paco and I go to the gym often*
e. padres centro al van comercial Mis raramente	*My parents go to the shopping centre rarely*
f. ¿sábados al Vais estadio todos los?	*Do you guys go to the stadium every Saturday?*

7. Spot the error

a. Voy al playa

b. Voy al iglesia

c. Voy a la gimnasio

d. Vamos a la parque

e. Va a la colegio

f. Vamos al casa de Marina

g. Va a la centro comercial

h. Van al piscina

i. Voy al fiesta

j. Van a la restaurante indio

8. One of two

		1	2
a.	**Vamos a la playa**	*They go to the beach*	*We go to the beach*
b.	**Voy al gimnasio a menudo**	*We go to the gym often*	*I go to the gym often*
c.	**¿Con quién vas?**	*Who are you going with?*	*Who are you guys going with?*
d.	**Va allí de vez en cuando**	*He goes there from time to time*	*They go there from time to time*
e.	**Nunca va a la iglesia**	*We never go to the church*	*He never goes to church*
f.	**Van a la fiesta**	*They are going to the party*	*You guys are going to the party*
g.	**No vamos todos los sábados**	*We don't go every Saturday*	*We never go every Saturday*
h.	**Voy de vez en cuando**	*I go from time to time*	*I go every day*
i.	**¿Adónde vais?**	*Where are you guys going?*	*Where are you going?*
j.	**Nunca vamos a Madrid**	*They never go to Madrid*	*We never go to Madrid*

9. Complete with a suitable word

a. Nunca voy a la p__________

b. Vamos a c________ de Marta todos los días

c. Mi madre v_______ al centro comercial

d. Hoy Paco y María v________ a la playa

e. Mi padre va al estadio t_________ los sábados

f. ¿Con q_____ vas al parque?

g. Mi hermano v__ al gimnasio a menudo

h. Voy a la tienda de deporte de vez en c________

i. Mis padres van al centro de la c__________

10. Listen and translate into English

a. My mother…

b. My father…

c. My brother and I…

d. My friend…

e. Are you going…

f. We…

g. Are you guys going…

11. Faulty translation: fix the Spanish translation

a. *They go to the beach every day*	Vamos a la playa todos los días
b. *They never go to the church*	Nunca van al centro comercial
c. *She goes to the gym rarely*	Voy al gimnasio raramente
d. *Enrique and I go to the stadium from time to time*	Enrique y yo vamos al estadio a menudo
e. *Where are you guys going today?*	¿Adónde vas hoy?
f. *You go there from time to time*	Va allí de vez en cuando
g. *Who do you go to the party with?*	¿Con quién va a la fiesta?
h. *My brothers never go to Alicia's house*	Mis amigos siempre van a casa de Alicia

12. Tangled translation: translate into Spanish

a. ***I go to the*** estadio a menudo

b. Alejandro y yo vamos ***to the party*** de Marta

c. ¿Con ***whom*** vas ***to the swimming pool***?

d. Mis hermanos ***go to the*** gimnasio ***every day***

e. ¿***Where*** vais?

f. ***They go to the*** centro de la ciudad raramente

g. Mi hermano ***goes to the*** cinema todos los ***Sundays***

h. ¿***Do you guys go*** a la ***beach*** todos los días?

i. Nunca **we *go to the*** parque

13. Spot and correct the errors

a. Voy a estadio todos los sabados

b. Nunca voy al piscina

c. Mi madre va a centro commercial a menudo

d. Marta vas al parque ahora

e. Mis hermanos no vais a la fiesta

f. ¿Adonde van tus padres?

g. Nosotros no van a ninguna parte

h. Mis hermanos vas al cine raramente

14. Complete with *voy, vas, va, vamos, vais* or *van* as suitable

a. (Nosotros) ______ al cine todos los domingos

b. Ella nunca ______ a la playa

c. Mi hermano ______ al gimnasio todos los días

d. Alicia y yo no _______ a la fiesta

e. Mis hermanas ______ al centro comercial

f. Mi madre ______ a la panadería todos los días

g. Él _____ al parque todos los días

h. ¿Adónde _____ hoy tú y tu madre?

i. Marta _____ al parque temático una vez al mes

j. (Tú) ¿Con quién _____ a la piscina hoy?

k. Mi novia y yo _______ a casa de Mario hoy

l. Nosotros nunca _______ a la iglesia

15. Guided translation

a. M__ p______ v___ a___ c______ a m________	*My parents go to the cinema often*
b. H____ v____ _ l_ f_______ d__ Pedro	*Today I am going to Pedro's party*
c. N_____ v________ a__ e___________	*We never go to the stadium*
d. V____ a__ g________ t________ l_____ d______	*They go to the gym every day*
e. V_ a__ c______ c__________ t______ l___ d______	*He goes to the shopping centre every day*
f. ¿A______ v___ h___?	*Where are you going today?*
g. M__ h_________ y y__ v______ a l__ p___________…	*My brother and I go to the pool…*
h. …d___ v___ e__ c_______	*…from time to time*
i. ¿_____ a l__ f________ d__ Marta?	*Are you going to Marta's party?*
j. V___ a l__ p_______ r____________	*They rarely go to the beach*
k. ¿A_______ v__ t__ h__________?	*Where is your sister going?*

4.3 TIME MARKER + PRESENT OF IR (FULL CONJUGATION) + PLACES. PRESENT OF IR +PARA + INFINITIVE + NOUN PHRASE

(SAYING WHERE I GO ON DIFFERENT DAYS AND WHAT I GO THERE FOR)

Time marker	Present of ir		Preposition	Place	
Esta mañana *This morning* **Esta tarde** *This afternoon / evening* **Los miércoles** *On Wednesdays* **Los viernes** *On Fridays* **Los fines de semana** *On weekends* **Todos los días** *Everyday*	***voy** **vas** **va** **vamos** **vais** **van**	*I go/am going* *you go* *he/she goes* *we go* *you guys go* *they go*	**a** *to*	**Barcelona** **Granada** **Madrid** **casa de Paco**	 *Paco's house*
			al *to the*	**centro de la ciudad** **centro comercial** **cine** **estadio** **gimnasio** **parque** **polideportivo** **supermercado**	*city centre* *shopping centre* *cinema* *stadium* *gym* *park* *sports centre* *supermarket*
			a la *to the*	**piscina** **tienda de deporte / ropa / música**	*swimming pool*

Ir	Para	Infinitive	Noun phrase
Voy **Vas** **Va** **Vamos** **Vais** **Van**	**para** *in order to*	**comprar** *(to) buy*	**un CD** **una camiseta** *a t-shirt* **un vestido** *a dress* **unas zapatillas de deporte** *trainers*
		dar un paseo	*(to) go for a walk*
		hacer *(to) do*	**las compras** *the shopping* **footing** *jogging* **turismo** *sightseeing* **pesas** *weights* **natación** *swimming*
		ir de tiendas	*(to) go shopping*
		jugar *(to) play*	**al baloncesto** *basketball* **al fútbol** *football* **a la PlayStation** *the PlayStation*
		mirar escaparates	*(to) go window shopping*
		montar en bici	*(to) go for a bike ride*
		tocar la guitarra	*(to) play the guitar*
		ver *(to) watch*	**el partido del Barcelona** *the Barcelona match* **un concierto** *a concert* **una comedia** *a comedy* **una película de acción** *an action film*
		visitar a *(to) visit*	**mis abuelos** *my grandparents* **mis tíos** *my uncle and aunt*

***Author's note:** depending on the context/situation, you can translate ***voy* (*vas*, *va*, etc.)** either as *"I go"* or *"I am going"*. See the next page for more information about this.

LANGUAGE AWARENESS: WHAT IS AN INFINITIVE?

An infinitive is a verb as we find it in the dictionary, before **conjugating** it. In English, infinitives have **"to"** in front of them. However, in Spanish infinitives end in **-ar/-er/-ir.**

This is why we talk about -ar verbs, -er verbs or -ir verbs:

- **Comprar** = *to buy*
- **Ver** = *to watch*
- ***Ir***=*to go*

THE VERB *IR* – I GO or I AM GOING?

Ir means "to go" in Spanish and it can be translated in **two** different ways in English:

- **Normalmente voy al parque** — ***I normally go*** *to the park* **(describing a routine)**

We may also translate it as "I am going" when we are implying a future action of going.

- **Mañana voy al cine** — *Tomorrow **I am going** to the cinema* **(future action)**

¿IR o HACER?

In English, we use the verb "to go" to talk about some sports and activities we do. For example, I go swimming/hiking/running. However, in Spanish, we use the verb ***hacer*** ("to do"):

- **Voy al polideportivo para hacer natación**
  *I am going to the sports centre in order **to go swimming (to do swimming)***

USE OF *PARA* – IN ORDER TO

Para generally means "for", but when used with an infinitive it means "in order to" and we use it to express the purpose of doing something. We use ***para*** after the verb ***ir*** to indicate the purpose of the action of "going" somewhere.

- Voy al parque **para** jugar al fútbol — *I go to the park (in order to) play football*
- Voy al cine **para** ver una película — *I am going to the cinema (in order to) watch a film*

In English, we can just translate the sentence as "I go to the park to play football", so it may be difficult to spot when to use ***para*** before an infinitive in Spanish. As a general rule, if we can say "in order to" in English, and the sentence makes sense, we will need ***para*** in front of the infinitive in Spanish!

1. Complete with the correct verb

a. Voy a la tienda de ropa para _________ una camiseta

b. Vamos al estadio para ________ un partido del Barcelona

c. Van al cine para _______ una película de acción

d. Vais al parque para ________ en bici

e. Mis hermanos van al gimnasio para _______ pesas

f. Voy a Madrid para ________ a mis abuelos

g. Mi hermana va al parque para _______ footing

h. Paco y yo vamos al centro de la ciudad para _____ un paseo

2. Complete with a noun, then listen and check if you were right. Correct any that were different.

a. Comprar un v______________

b. Ver una p________________

c. Hacer la c________________

d. Ir al g__________________

e. Visitar a mis a_____________

f. Hacer t_________________

g. Jugar al b________________

h. Montar en b_______________

3. Sentence Puzzle

a. acción al Voy cine ver para película una de — *I am going to the cinema to watch an action movie*

b. en al parque Vamos para bici montar — *We go to the park to ride a bike*

c. turismo Va para a Barcelona hacer — *He goes to Barcelona to go sightseeing*

d. primo Van a mi Madrid a visitar para — *They go to Madrid to visit my cousin*

e. ¿vais Adónde semana de este fin? — *Where are you guys going this weekend?*

f. vestido ropa Va la a tienda para de comprar un — *She is going to the clothes shop to buy a dress*

g. baloncesto al al Vamos polideportivo para jugar — *We go to the leisure centre to play basketball*

4. Break the flow

a. Vamosalatiendadedeporteparacomprarzapatillas

b. Vanalgimnasioparahacerpesas

c. ¿Adóndevaisestefindesemana?

d. Vaalcineparaverunapelícularomántica

e. MispadresvanaBarcelonaparahacerturismo

f. Mishermanosvanalparqueparamontarenbici

g. Voyalpolideportivoparahacernatación

h. VamosacasademiamigoPacoparatocarlaguitarra

i. Vanalcentrocomercialparamirarescaparates

j. ¿Paraquévaisalsupermercadohoy?

5. Match

Montar en bici	*To buy a dress*
Ir de tiendas	*To go window shopping*
Hacer turismo	*To play basketball*
Mirar escaparates	*To go swimming*
Jugar al baloncesto	*To go for a walk*
Ver un partido	*To watch a film*
Hacer natación	*To play the guitar*
Ver una película	*To go sightseeing*
Tocar la guitarra	*To go shopping*
Dar un paseo	*To watch a match*
Comprar un vestido	*To go for a bike ride*

6. Gapped sentences

a. Mis hermanos ___ al polideportivo para ________ natación

My brothers go to the sports centre in order to go swimming

b. ___ al centro comercial para ______ escaparates

I go to the shopping centre in order to go window shopping

c. ____ a Madrid para ________ a sus abuelos

They go to Madrid in order to visit their grandparents

d. _______ al supermercado para _________ bebidas

We go to the supermarket in order to buy some drinks

e. ____ a Barcelona para _______ turismo

She goes to Barcelona in order to go sightseeing

f. _______ a casa de Pablo para ______ a los videojuegos

We go to Pablo's in order to play videogames

g. Mi amigo _________ al gimnasio para _________ pesas

My friend goes to the gym in order to do weights

h. Mis amigos y yo _________ al parque para __________ al fútbol

My friends and I go to the park in order to play football

7. Listen and translate into English

a. I go to…

b. My sister…

c. We go to…

d. I go to…

e. They go to…

f. I go to…

g. Are you going…

h. We are going to…

8. Guided translation

a. H______ v________ a____ c________ c___________ p_________ m___________ e___________ *Today I am going to the shopping centre to go window shopping*

b. E______ m__________ m ____ a_______ v_____ a______ g___________ p____ h_______ p__________ *This morning my friend is going to the gym in order to do weights*

c. E ________ t_________ m_____ a__________ y y_____ v_________ a___ p____________ p______ j_______ a_ b_____________ *This evening my friends and I are going to the park in order to play basketball*

d. H_______ v________ a____ c________ p____ v_______ u__ c_________ *Today I am going to the cinema in order to watch a comedy*

e. E______ t________ m____ a________ v_____ a___ c________ p_____ v_____ u____ p_______ d__ a_________ *This evening my friends are going to the cinema to watch an action film*

f. H________ m____ p________ v_______ a__ g__________ p____ h_____ n____________ *Today my parents are going to the gym in order to go swimming*

4.4 EN + NOUN + PRESENT OF IR + FREQUENCY ADVERB + A + NOUN
(SAYING HOW OFTEN ONE TRAVELS TO FOREIGN COUNTRIES WHEN ON HOLIDAY AT DIFFERENT TIMES IN THE YEAR)

En *In*	**invierno** *winter* **primavera** *spring* **verano** *summer* **otoño** *autumn* **Navidad** *Christmas* **enero** *January* **febrero** **marzo** **abril** **mayo** **junio** **julio** **agosto** **septiembre** **octubre** **noviembre** **diciembre**	**a menudo** *often* **a veces** *sometimes* **de vez en cuando** *from time to time* **nunca** *never* **por lo general** *generally* **raramente** *rarely* **(casi) siempre** *(nearly) always*	**voy** *I go* **vas** *you go* **va** *he/she goes* **vamos** *we go* **vais** *you guys go* **van** *they go*	**de vacaciones** *on holidays* **de viaje** *on a trip*	**a** *to*	**Alemania** *Germany* **Canadá** **China** **Escocia** *Scotland* **Francia** **España** *Spain* **Gales** *Wales* **Grecia** *Greece* **Inglaterra** *England* **Irlanda** **Italia** **Japón** **México** **Portugal** **Rusia**
No voy a ninguna parte *I don't go anywhere*						

1. Match

Por lo general	*Often*
Raramente	*Sometimes*
Casi siempre	*In the winter*
En verano	*In the spring*
En otoño	*In the autumn*
De vez en cuando	*Always*
Siempre	*At Christmas*
En primavera	*From time to time*
A veces	*Generally*
A menudo	*In the summer*
En invierno	*Rarely*
En Navidad	*Nearly always*

2. Translate into English

a. En invierno

b. En otoño

c. A menudo

d. En Navidad

e. En verano

f. Por lo general

g. En primavera

h. A veces

i. De vez en cuando

j. En enero

k. Siempre

l. Nunca

3. Broken words

a. (Nosotros) En Nav_____ siem____ va____ de vaca_______ a Fr_________.

b. (Ellas) En prima_____ a men_____ va____ de _____ciones a Ja_______, en Asia.

c. (Yo) En ago____, por lo general, vo____ de vac______nes a México.

d. En ver_______ mis padres siem_____ va_____ de vac_________ a Italia.

e. ¿(Vosotros) Nun______ va___ de ______ciones a Escocia?

f. (Ella) En diciem_____ siemp_____ va a Inglat________ para visit_____ a sus padres.

g. En jul____, Mario v___ a men_______ a España par___ visi_____ a su famil___.

h. En ago______ nun____ vo___ a Alema_____. Por lo gene_____, ___y a Grec___ o a Esp______.

4. Break the flow

a. EnveranoporlogeneralvoyaItaliaoaGrecia

b. EnagostonuncavoyaMéxico

c. EninviernoenNavidadsiemprevoyaEspaña

d. EnprimaveradevezencuandovoyaEstadosUnidos

e. EneneroporlogeneralvoydevacacionesaAustria

f. Enotoñonovoydevacacionesaningunaparte

g. EnmarzosiemprevoyaIrlandaparavisitaramimadre

5. Anagrams

a. uRisa

b. lAeanami

c. ónJap

d. aiGerc

e. haCin

f. aspEña

g. nlIagrrtea

h. aEocsci

6. Gapped translation: please complete

a. On holidays	D__ vacaciones
b. To Greece	__ Grecia
c. In the winter	E__ invierno
d. From time to time	De v__ __ en cuando
e. In December	En dicie __ __ __ __
f. I always go	Siempre v__ __
g. To England	A Inglat __ __ __ __
h. We always go	Siempre v__ __ __ __
i. Often	A m__ __ __ __ __
j. To Japan	__ Japón
k. Generally	Por l__ general

7. Listen and spot the missing words

a. De vez cuando vamos de vacaciones a Inglaterra

b. En agosto siempre vamos Alemania

c. Diciembre, por lo general, voy a Italia

d. Mis padres siempre de vacaciones a Francia

e. En Navidad siempre vamos a España para visitar mis abuelos

f. En primavera, veces vamos a Portugal

g. Vez en cuando en julio, vamos de vacaciones a Grecia

h. En verano, por lo general, no vamos ninguna parte

i. En invierno, mi familia nunca de vacaciones a ninguna parte

8. Tangled translation: translate into Spanish

a. En ***spring***, por lo general ***I go*** de vacaciones ***to*** Alemania

b. ***In*** verano ***never*** vamos ***to*** Italia. ***Generally***, ***we go*** a Grecia

c. En ***Christmas*** mis ***parents*** raramente ***go*** de vacaciones a ***Japan***

d. En ***summer***, mi ***friend*** Paco siempre ***goes on holiday*** a Tailandia. De vez en cuando ***goes*** a China

e. En ***January***, mis padres y ***I often*** vamos a Escocia. Mi hermano ***goes to*** Irlanda.

f. En abril, por lo general, ***we go*** a Gales para visitar a ***my grandparents***.

g. En verano ***we generally go*** a ***Spain*** o Portugal. En otoño, ***never*** vamos a ***nowhere***.

h. ¿Adónde ***do you go generally*** en Navidad?

9. Broken translation

a. *Generally*	Por lo gen__ __ __ __
b. *Often*	A men__ __ __
c. *In the summer*	En ver__ __ __
d. *We go*	Vam__ __
e. *In January*	En en__ __ __
f. *Nowhere*	A ning__ __ __ pa__ __ __
g. *At Christmas*	En Nav__ __ __ __
h. *On holiday*	De vac__ __ __ __ __ __ __

10. Translate into Spanish

a. Often I go

b. Generally we go

c. I never go

d. At Christmas they go

e. Sometimes we go

f. From time to time she goes

g. Once a month they go to Scotland

11. Staircase translation – Translate each sentence from memory

a.	In the winter	I go				
b.	In the spring	we go	to France			
c.	In the autumn	they never go	on holiday	anywhere		
d.	In the summer,	generally,	my family	goes	to Wales	
e.	In August	my friends and I	go	on holiday	to Girona	in Spain

a. ______________________________

b. ______________________________

c. ______________________________

d. ______________________________

e. ______________________________

4.5 PRESENT OF IR + A + PLACE + A/EN + MEANS OF TRANSPORT

(SAYING WHERE AND HOW ONE GOES TO DIFFERENT PLACES IN TOWN)

		a la *to the*	**fiesta**	*party*	**a** *on*	**caballo** *horseback*
			oficina	*office*		**pie** *foot*
			piscina	*swimming pool*		
	Voy *I go*		**playa**	*beach*	**en** *by*	**autobús** *bus*
			zona peatonal	*pedestrian zone*		**autocar** *coach*
	Vas *You go*		**plaza mayor**	*main square*		**avión** *plane*
		al *to the*	**cine**	*cinema*		**barco** *boat*
(No) *No*	**Va** *He/she goes*		**colegio**	*school*		**bici** *bike*
			gimnasio	*gym*		**coche** *car*
(Nunca) *Never*	**Vamos** *We go*		**polideportivo**	*sports centre*		**ferry**
			paseo marítimo	*seafront*		**helicóptero**
	Vais *You guys go*		**centro de la ciudad**	*city centre*		**metro** *tube*
			campo	*countryside*		**motocicleta** *motorbike*
	Van *They go*		**extranjero**	*abroad*		**tren** *train*
		a *to*	**Alicante**	**Cádiz**		
			Barcelona	**Casa de Cañetes**		
			Madrid	**Pinoso**		
			Alemania	**Polonia**		
			España	**Groenlandia**		
			Grecia	**Suecia**		

LANGUAGE AWARENESS: MEANS OF TRANSPORT

When we talk about means of transport, in Spanish, we use the prepositions ***en*** and ***a*** while in English we use **"by"** or **"on"**.

- **Voy al centro en coche** *I go to the centre* **by** *car* Literally: *I go to the centre* **in** *car*
- **Voy a la playa a pie** *I go to the beach* **on** *foot* Literally: *I go to the beach* **to** *foot*

Only ***a pie*** and ***a caballo*** take the proposition ***a***. The vast majority of means of transport go with ***en***.

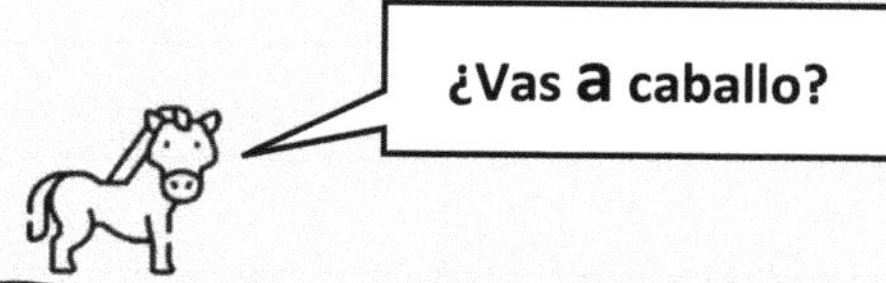

1. Match

En avión	*To the party*
En barco	*By train*
A pie	*To the sports centre*
En ferry	*By boat*
A caballo	*On horseback*
A Alemania	*By ferry*
Al polideportivo	*On foot*
En tren	*By bus*
En autobús	*To the pedestrian zone*
A la zona peatonal	*To Germany*
A la fiesta	*By plane*

2. Complete the table

English	Español
	En barco
	A caballo
By bus	
By train	
	Al polideportivo
	En avión
To the party	
To Germany	
	En autocar

3. Listen and complete the sentences

a. Casi nunca ______ al __________ en __________

b. Por lo general, _______ al __________ en _______

c. Siempre _______ a la _______ en _________

d. Nunca _______ al _________ en __________

e. Normalmente mis padres _______ a ______

f. ____________, mi padre _______ a Cádiz en ____

g. Siempre ________ al __________ en _________

h. Él nunca ________ a ninguna _______ en _______

4. Listen, complete and translate 

a. Voy al colegio a p__ __

b. Vamos a Al__m__n__a en tren

c. Van a la f__ __st__ en taxi

d. Va al gimnasio en b__c__

e. ¿Adónde va__s?

f. Vamos a Francia en b__rc__

g. Van al c__mp__ a caballo

5. Broken words

a. Nun__ __ vam__ __ a__ cole__ __ __ a pi__	*We never go to school on foot*
b. Siemp__ __ v__ a l__ ofici__ __ en a__ __ __ bús	*He always goes to the office by bus*
c. D__ ve__ e__ cuan__ __ …	*From time to time…*
d. … va__ a Espa__ __ e__ avi__ __	*…they go to Spain by plane*
e. Po__ l__ gener__ __, va__ e__ co__ __ __	*Generally, they go by car*
f. Mi__ pad__ __ __ siem__ __ __ v__ __...	*My parents always go…*
g. …__ ca__ __ d__ mi__ abue__ __ __ a pi__	*…to my grandparents' house on foot*
h. M__ h__rm__n__ v__ a__ gimn__ __ __ __ e__ bi__ __	*My brother goes to the gym by bike*
i. Vo__ a__ cam__ __ a cab__ __ __ __	*I go to the countryside on horseback*

6. Faulty translation: fix the English translation

a. Voy al colegio en bici	*I go to school on foot*
b. Vamos a Alemania en coche	*We go to Scotland by car*
c. Van al cine en taxi	*She goes to the cinema by taxi*
d. Nunca vamos al centro de la ciudad en autobús	*We rarely go to the town centre by bus*
e. Siempre vamos a la playa en taxi	*We never go to the beach by plane*
f. Mi padre va a la oficina en tren	*My mother goes to the office by bus*
g. Ella siempre va al colegio a pie	*I always go to school on foot*
h. ¿Cómo vas al gimnasio? ¿En coche?	*How do you go to the gym? By coach?*

7. Sentence Puzzle

a. vamos Nunca colegio al bici en

b. padres van Mis siempre a la en oficina coche

c. a Mi al centro hermano va comercial pie

d. a caballo De vamos vez cuando al en campo

e. Por van lo general la autobús playa a en

f. vamos Siempre Barcelona a tren en

g. ¿Cómo gimnasio al vas? ¿A o en bici pie?

h. piscina Nunca en voy a autobús la

8. Listen and write the ONE missing word in each sentence

a. Mi padre nunca a la oficina en autobús

b. Siempre voy al colegio pie

c. A veces vamos la playa en autobús

d. De vez cuando voy al campo a caballo

e. Por lo general vamos al extranjero avión

f. Mis padres van al campo coche

g. Mi hermano nunca va al colegio bici

h. Paco y yo siempre al estadio en metro

9. Translate into English

a. Por lo general vamos al campo en coche

b. Mi madre va a la oficina a pie

c. Nunca voy al colegio en metro

d. De vez en cuando vamos al club de polo a caballo

e. A veces voy a Madrid en autocar

f. De vez en cuando vamos a la playa en autobús

g. Raramente van al gimnasio en coche. Por lo general van a pie.

h. ¿Y vosotros? ¿Cómo vais al colegio? ¿A pie o en bici?

10. Translate the following phrases into Spanish

a. My parents

b. We always go

c. In general

d. From time to time

e. I never go

f. By bike

g. To the beach

h. On foot

i. To the party

j. By coach

k. By car

l. Abroad

m. He goes

n. By motorbike

o. By bus

p. To the countryside

q. She often goes

r. They never go

11. Guided translation

a. M__ p______ n______ v__ a M_______e_ c______ *My parents never go to Madrid by car*

b. S______ v___ a_ g_________ a p_____ *I always go to the gym on foot*

c. D_ v___ e_ c_____ v_____ a_ c_______ e_ b___ *From time to time we go to school by bike*

d. A v____ v_ a_ p______ a c_________ *Sometimes she goes to the park on horseback*

e. P__ l_ g________, v______ a I_______ e_ t_____ *Generally, we go to Italy by train*

f. E_ i________ v___ a_ c_________ e__ a________ *In the winter I go to school by bus*

12. Translate the following sentences into Spanish

a. I never go to England by coach. I always go by plane.

b. We never go to the beach by coach.

c. We generally go by train.

d. She never goes to school on foot. Generally, she goes by car.

e. From time to time we go to the gym by bus.

f. We never go by helicopter.

g. Sometimes my parents go to the town centre by bus, but generally they go by car.

h. How do you go to the office usually? By car, by bus, by bike or on foot?

4.6 PRESENT OF IR + PLACE+ CON/SIN + POSSESSIVE ADJECTIVE+NOUN

(SAYING WHERE ONE GOES WITH ONE'S FRIENDS OR FAMILY)

<table>
<tr><td rowspan="5">**(No)** *No*

(Nunca) *Never*</td><td rowspan="5">**Voy** *I go*

Vas *You go*

Va *He/she goes*

Vamos *We go*

Vais *You guys go*

Van *They go*</td><td rowspan="2">**a la** *to the*</td><td rowspan="2">**fiesta** *party*
piscina *pool*
playa *beach*
zona peatonal *pedestrian zone*
plaza mayor *main square*</td><td rowspan="5">**con** *with*

sin *without*</td><td colspan="2">**Masculine**</td></tr>
<tr><td>**mi(s)** *my*
tu(s) *your*
su(s) *his/her*
nuestro(s) *our*
vuestro(s) *your*
su(s) *their*</td><td>**amigo(s)** *friend(s)*
compañero(s) de clase *school pal(s)*
hermano(s) *brother(s)/siblings*
novio *boyfriend*
padre(s) *father/parents/fathers*
primo(s) *cousin(s)*
tío *uncle*
tíos *uncles / uncle & aunt*</td></tr>
<tr><td rowspan="2">**al** *to the*</td><td rowspan="2">**cine** *cinema*
colegio *school*
gimnasio *gym*
polideportivo *sports centre*</td><td colspan="2">**Feminine**</td></tr>
<tr><td rowspan="2">**mi(s)** *my*
tu(s) *your*
su(s) *his/her*
nuestra(s) *our*
vuestra(s) *your*
su(s) *their*</td><td rowspan="2">**amiga(s)** *friend(s)*
compañera(s) de clase *school pal(s)*
hermana(s) *sister(s)*
novia *girlfriend*
madre *mother*
prima(s) *cousin(s)*
tía *aunt*
tías *aunts*</td></tr>
<tr><td>**a** *to*</td><td>**Alicante**
Barcelona
Madrid
Alemania
España
Grecia</td></tr>
</table>

LANGUAGE AWARENESS: POSSESSIVE ADJECTIVES – Part 1

Possessive adjectives are the words we use to express possession.

Mi *My*	• Voy al cine con **mi** hermano	*I go to the cinema with **my** brother*
Tu *Your*	• Vas al cine con **tu** novio	*You go to the cinema with **your** boyfriend*
Su *His/her/their*	• Mi amigo va al cine con **su** madre	*My friend goes to the cinema with **his** mother*
Nuestro *Our*	• Vamos al cine con **nuestro** padre	*We go to the cinema with **our** father*
Vuestro *Your*	• Vais al cine con **vuestro** padre	*You guys go to the cinema with **your** father*

NUMBER AGREEMENTS – PLURAL *MIS/TUS/SUS*

In Spanish, we need to modify **possessive adjectives** to make them agree with the noun they refer to. There is only **number agreement** for ***mi/tu/su***. It doesn't matter if the noun they refer to is masculine or feminine. The only options are ***mi/mis***, ***tu/tus***, ***su/sus***.

Mis *My (plural)*

- Voy al cine con **mis** amigos — *I go to the cinema with **my** friends*

Tus *Your (plural)*

- **Tus** amigos van al cine — ***Your** friends go to the cinema*

Sus *His/her/their (plural)*

- **Sus** amigos van al cine — ***His/her/their** friends go to the cinema*

HIS/HER/THEIR

Seeing as in Spanish, we don't distinguish between "his/her/their", for all those three possessive adjectives, we use ***su(s)***, good news!

- **Su padre** = *his/her/their father*
- **Sus padres** = *his/her/their parents*

NUESTRO: GENDER & NUMBER AGREEMENTS

Unlike ***mi/tu/su***, which only changes to ***mis/tus/sus,*** in the case of referring to plural nouns, there are four forms of ***nuestro*** (our) and ***vuestro*** (your, for 'you guys').

- **Nuestro padre** — *Our father* (masculine singular)
- **Nuestra madre** — *Our mother* (feminine singular)
- **Nuestros amigos** — *Our friends* (masculine plural)
- **Nuestras amigas** — *Our friends* (feminine plural)

The masculine/feminine singular/plural mentioned above **refers to the noun** ***amigos*** or ***amigas***, **not** to the person speaking. For example, two boys speaking about their two girlfriends would say:

- Vamos al cine con **nuestras** novias — *We go to the cinema with **our** girlfriends*

VUESTRO

Vuestro (your, when talking about "you guys") works in exactly the same way as ***nuestro***:

- **Vuestro padre** — *Your father*
- **Vuestra madre** — *Your mother*
- **Vuestros amigos** — *Your friends (masculine/mixed)*
- **Vuestras amigas** — *Your friends (female)*

1. Match

Mi amigo	*Our brothers/siblings*
Mis amigos	*My boyfriend*
Vuestra madre	*My (male) friend*
Mi novia	*Your parents/fathers*
Su novio	*Our sister*
Mi novio	*My girlfriend*
Nuestra hermana	*My (male) friends*
Nuestros hermanos	*Your school pals*
Tus compañeros de clase	*Your mother (you guys)*
Vuestros padres	*Her/his/their boyfriend*

2. Complete the table

English	Español
My mother	
Our mother	
Your boyfriend	
His sister	
Their sisters	
My parents	
My school pals	
His school pals	
Your father (you guys)	

3. One of three

a. Voy al cine con **tus/mis/sus** amigos

I go to the cinema with my friends

b. Va a la piscina sin **sus/mis/tus** hermanas

She goes to the swimming pool without her sisters

c. Vamos al parque con **nuestros/vuestros/sus** primos

We go to the park with our cousins

d. Van a Madrid con **sus/mis/tus padres**

They go to Madrid with their parents

e. No vamos a ninguna parte sin **vuestro/su/nuestro** abuelo

We don't go anywhere without our grandfather

f. ¿Vais a Italia con **sus/vuestros/tus** padres?

Are you guys going to Italy with your parents?

g. Vamos a Madrid sin **nuestro/nuestra/nuestros** hermano

We go to Madrid without our brother

h. ¿Vas a la fiesta **de/con/sin** tu novia?

Are you going to the party without your girlfriend?

4. Listen, complete and translate into English

a. Vamos a la ______________ con ____________ padre.

b. Va a la ________ con ____ novia

c. No voy a ____________ parte sin mi mejor amigo

d. Mis padres _______ al cine con ______ tíos

e. Mi hermana siempre va a la _______ ___ ______ con mi madre

f. ¿Vas a Inglaterra sola o con _____ familia?

g. _____ a Madrid con ______padres

h. No va a _______ parte solo

i. _____ de vacaciones a Barcelona, que ______ en España

j. ______ a Barcelona con _____ novios

5. Correct the mistakes. HINT: they refer either to the use of *ir* or the possessive adjectives

a. Voy al cine con mi padres

b. Nunca vamos al estadio sin nuestra padre

c. Siempre va a la discoteca con su hermanos

d. De vez en cuando voy a Madrid con mi tíos

e. Nunca vamo al parque con nuestro padres

f. ¿Vais al colegio con vuestro madre hoy?

g. Van de vacaciones con su abuelos

h. ¿Vas al centro comercial con tus padre?

6. One of three. Listen and choose the correct option – then translate

a. Voy al cine con **tus/mis/sus** amigos

b. Va a la piscina sin **sus/mis/tus** hermanas

c. Vamos al parque con **nuestros/vuestros/sus** primos

d. Van a Madrid con **sus/mis/tus** padres

e. No vamos a ninguna parte sin **vuestro/su/nuestro** abuelo

f. ¿Vais a Italia con **sus/vuestros/tus** padres?

g. Vamos a Madrid con **nuestro/nuestra/nuestros** hermano

7. Gapped translation: complete the translation

a. Vam __ __ a la playa con nuest __ __ __ novias	*We go to the beach with our girlfriends*
b. V__ __ a la piscina con m__ __ hermanos	*I go to the swimming-pool with my brothers*
c. Paco v__ al gimnasio con s__ mejor amigo	*Paco goes to the gym with his best friend*
d. ¿Va __ __ a París con vues __ __ __ __ padres?	*Do you guys go to Paris with your parents?*
e. Hoy v__ __ a España con __ __ __ tíos	*Today they are going to Spain with their uncles*
f. V__ de vacaciones a Italia s__ __ s__ __ padres	*She goes on holidays without her parents*
g.¿V__ __ a Francia con t__ familia?	*Do you go to France with your family?*
h. Nunca v__ al estadio s__ __ s__ padre	*He never goes to the stadium without his father*

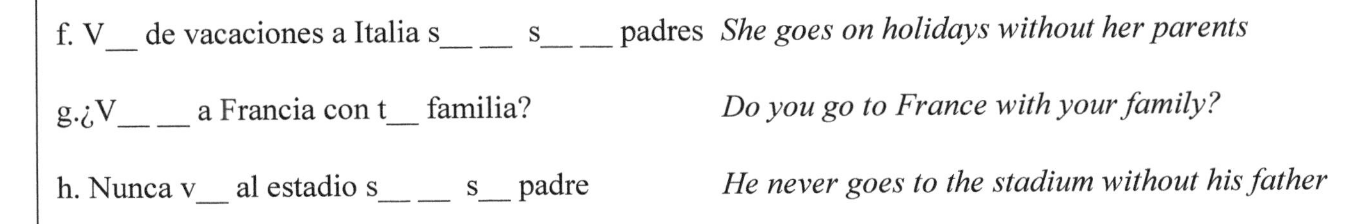

8. Sentence Puzzle

a. al Siempre vamos padres comercial con centro nuestros
We always go to the shopping centre with our parents

b. con Este enero sus van a novias Madrid
This January they are going to Madrid with their girlfriends

c. Por lo familia Navidad a mi general en voy con Italia
Generally, I go to Italy with my family at Christmas

d. De de mis vez en cuando voy vacaciones sin padres
From time to time I go on holidays without my parents

e. Marta a va no hermana ninguna sin parte su
Marta doesn't go anywhere without her sister

f. gimnasio al Hoy mi y hermano vamos yo
Today my brother and I are going to the gym

g. al Esta vamos tarde padres supermercado con nuestros hacer para compras las
This evening we are going to the supermarket with our parents in order to do the shopping

9. Translate into English

a. Por lo general, voy al gimnasio con mi familia.

b. Mi hermano siempre va al centro comercial con sus compañeros de clase. Sin su novia.

c. El sábado mis padres casi siempre van al restaurante indio con mis tíos.

d. Mi hermana nunca va a las fiestas sin su novio.

e. Nunca vamos de vacaciones sin nuestros padres.

f. Mis primos nunca van de vacaciones con sus padres.

g. Mi mejor amigo, Roberto, siempre va al colegio con su hermano menor y su novia, Inés.

h. ¿Con quién vais a España? ¿Con o sin vuestros padres?

10. Translate into Spanish

a. We go to Italy with our family

b. I never go on holiday with my parents

c. Generally, she goes to school with her boyfriend

d. Do you go to the gym with your brother?

e. Are you guys going to the party with your girlfriends?

f. We always go to the supermarket with our parents

g. They always go to Spain with their grandparents

4.7 NEGATIVES + PRESENT OF IR + PLACES

(MAKING NEGATIVE SENTENCES WITH THE VERB IR)

***No** *…don't/doesn't…* **Nunca** *…never…* **Ya no** *…no longer…*	**voy** *I … go* **vas** *you … go* ***va** *he/she … go(es)* **vamos** *we … go* **vais** *you guys … go* **van** *they … go*	**a ninguna parte** *nowhere*
***e.g. No va a…** *He/she doesn't go… /* **Nunca va a…** *He/she never goes…*		**a Barcelona** **a España** **a casa de Ana** *to Ana's house* **a la fiesta** *to the party* **a la piscina** **a la playa** *to the beach* **a la tienda** *to the shop* **al colegio** **al centro comercial** **al cine** **al gimnasio** **al parque**
Ni tú ni yo *Neither you nor I*	**vamos** *(we) go*	
Ni tú ni él *Neither you nor he* **Ni tú ni ella** *Neither you nor she*	**vais** *(you guys) go*	
Ni él ni ella *Neither he nor she* **Ni ella ni él** *Neither she nor he*	**va** *(he/she) goes*	
Nadie *Nobody*	**va** *(he/she) goes*	

No voy	**ni** *neither*	**a la playa**	**ni** *nor*	**al cine**
Nunca voy *I never go*	**al gimnasio**	**con nadie** *with anyone* **solo / sola** *alone*		

LANGUAGE AWARENESS
Using Negatives in Spanish

The easiest way to negate in Spanish is to use ***no*** before the verb.

- **No** voy al cine — *I **don't** go to the cinema*

To say that you don't do anything **any more**, or **no longer do** something you need to use *ya*

- **Ya no** voy al cine — *I **don't** go to the cinema **any more** / **I no longer** go to the cinema*

To talk about what two people don't do, you use ***ni* + *ni***

- **Ni** mi amigo **ni** yo vamos al cine — ***Neither** my friend **nor** I go to the cinema*

To say that you go somewhere alone, you need another double negative. ***Nadie*** literally means *"nobody"*

- Yo **no** voy al gimnasio con **nadie** — ***I don't** go to the gym with **anyone*** *(Lit. I don't go with **nobody**)*

SOLO

There are four forms of ***solo*** because it is a regular adjective:

- **Nunca** voy al cine **solo** — *I **never** go to the cinema **on my own*** ***(masculine singular)***
- **Nunca** voy al cine **sola** — *I **never** go to the cinema **on my own*** ***(feminine singular)***
- **Nunca** vamos al cine **solos** — *We **never** go to the cinema **on our own*** ***(masc./mixed plural)***
- **Nunca** vamos al cine **solas** — *We **never** go to the cinema **on our own*** ***(feminine plural)***

1. Match

Nadie	*Alone*
Ni tú ni yo	*With*
Ya no	*Never*
A ninguna parte	*Neither we nor them*
Ni nosotros ni ellos	*Neither he nor I*
Con	*Nowhere*
Nunca	*No longer*
Ni él ni yo	*Neither you nor I*
Solo	*Nobody*

2. Missing letter challenge

a. Nun__ __ voy al colegio sola

b. Hoy no voy a ning__ __ __ parte

c. N__ tú n__ yo vamos al centro comercial

d. Y__ no vamos al gimnasio

e. En mi familia, nadi__ va al estadio

f. Mis hermanos no van al parque solo__

g. Mis padres va__ al cine raramente

h. Nosotros vamo__ al restaurante chino a menudo

3. Listening, gapped translation

a. No voy a la fiesta con __ __ __ __ __ — *I don't go to the party with anyone*

b. Ni tú __ __ yo vamos al colegio hoy — *Neither you nor I are going to school today*

c. No vamos al gimnasio __ __ __ __ __ — *We don't go to the gym alone*

d. Hoy no vamos a __ __ __ __ __ __ __ parte — *We don't go anywhere*

e. __ __ __ __ __ voy al supermercado con mi madre — *I never go to the supermarket with my mother*

f. Vamos al centro comercial __ __ __ nuestros padres — *We go to the shopping centre with our parents*

4. Faulty translation: fix the English translation

a. No vamos a Inglaterra con nadie — *We don't go to England any longer*

b. Va a la fiesta sola — *They are going to the party alone*

c. No voy al colegio sin mi madre — *She doesn't go to school without her mother*

d. Ni nosotros ni él vamos al estadio — *Neither I nor he go to the gym*

e. No vamos al parque con nadie — *They don't go to the beach with anyone*

f. Nunca van a la piscina con sus padres — *He never goes to church with his parents*

5. Translate into English

a. Vamos

b. Con

c. Sola

d. Nadie

e. Nunca

f. Ni…ni

g. A ninguna parte

h. Van

i. Vamos

j. Iglesia

k. Va

l. Ya no

6. Sentence Puzzle

a. no Ya va gimnasio al su con hermano — *He doesn't go to the gym with his brother any longer*

b. Siempre las voy a solo fiestas, novia sin mi — *I always go to the parties alone, without my girlfriend*

c. yo ni Ni tú la a vamos playa con Enrique — *Neither you nor I go to the beach with Enrique*

d. tarde Esta va nadie parte a ninguna — *This afternoon nobody is going anywhere*

e. en Nadie estadio va mi familia al — *Nobody in my family goes to the stadium*

7. Tangled translation: translate into Spanish

a. Nunca ***we go*** a Barcelona ***with*** nuestros padres

b. No ***they go*** al estadio a menudo.

c. Por lo general, Alejandra ***goes*** al colegio ***alone***

d. Nosotras ***never go*** al parque ***alone***

e. Nadie en ***my family goes*** al ***gym***

f. Ya no voy al club de ***tennis*** con ***my friends***

g. Mis hermanos ***go to the sports centre alone***

h. ***Nobody*** en mi familia ***goes to church***

8. Listen and correct the errors

a. Nunca vamos al colegio sola

b. No voy al cine con nunca

c. Alejandra voy al gimnasio solo

d. Mi padre va nunca al mercado con mi madre

e. Ni mi hermano ni mi hermana va al gimnasio

f. Esta tarde no vamos a ningún parte

g. Mis hermanos siempre van al colegio sola

h. Ni tú y yo vamos a la tienda de música solo

9. Guided translation

a. *We never go* — N_ _ _ _ v_ _ _ _

b. *They always go* — S_ _ _ _ _ _ v_ _

c. *Nobody goes* — N_ _ _ _ v_

d. *She goes alone* — V_ s_ _ _

e. *We (f) don't go alone* — N_ v_ _ _ _ s_ _ _ _

f. *They don't go any more* — Y_ n_ v_ _

g. *I don't go anywhere* — N_ v_ _ a n_ _ _ _ _ _ p_ _ _ _

h. *We never go anywhere* — N_ _ _ _ v_ _ _ _ a n_ _ _ _ _ _ p_ _ _ _

4.8 TIME MARKER + PRESENT OF IR + A + INFINITIVE + NOUN OR PREPOSITIONAL PHRASE + CON + POSSESSIVE + NOUN

(SAYING WHAT ONE IS GOING TO DO WHERE, WHEN AND WITH WHOM)

Ahora *Now*	**voy** *I am going*		**comer un bocadillo** *(to) eat a sandwich*	
			comprar *(to) buy*	**zapatillas de deporte** *trainers* **una camiseta** *a t-shirt* **un vestido** *a dress*
Esta mañana *This morning*	**vas** *you are going*		**dar un paseo** *(to) go for a walk*	
			hacer los deberes *(to) do homework*	
Esta tarde *This afternoon / evening*	**va** *he/she is going*	**a** **to*	**ir** *(to) go*	**a casa de Marta** *to Marta's house* **al centro comercial** *to the shopping centre* **al colegio** *to school* **al supermercado** *to the supermarket*
Este fin de semana *This weekend*	**vamos** *we are going*		**jugar** *(to) play*	**a la PlayStation** *on the PlayStation* **al fútbol** *football*
	vais *you guys are going*		**montar en bici** *(to) ride a bike*	
			salir con mi familia *(to) go out with my family*	
Hoy *Today*			**tomar un café** *(to) have a coffee*	
Mañana *Tomorrow*	**van** *they are going*		**ver** *(to) watch*	**una serie en Netflix** *a series on Netflix* **una película de acción** *an action film*
			visitar a mis abuelos *(to) visit my grandparents*	

¿Con quién? *With whom?*				
con	**mi amigo/a**	*my friend*	**mis amigos**	*my friends*
	tu amigo	*your friend*	**tus amigos**	*your friends*
	su amigo	*his/her friend*	**sus amigos**	*his/her/their friends*
	nuestros amigos	*our friends*	**vuestros amigos**	*your (pl) friends*

LANGUAGE AWARENESS: THE IMMEDIATE FUTURE

The immediate future is the easiest way to talk about the future in Spanish. In English it is translated as "I am going to do something". It is a super handy and easy structure! It is formed following this pattern: **Present indicative of *IR* + *A* + *INFINITIVE VERB***

***"Voy a jugar"** literally translates to "I am going – **to** – **to** play". In English, this extra preposition is omitted.

DON'T FORGET THE *"A"*

Voy	<u>A</u>	Jugar
I am going	to	to play
Present tense of IR	Preposition "A"	Infinitive verb

When using this tense, just remember to include all three parts **(VOY)** + **(A)** + **(INFINITIVE)** and don't worry too much about the extra 'to'.

POSSESSIVE ADJECTIVES – Part 2

You can apply your knowledge of **possessives *mi/ tu/ su/ nuestro/ vuestro*** (and plurals) from Unit 4.6 (Pages 114-115), in order to say **with whom** someone is doing an activity.

- Voy a salir con **mis** amigos — *I am going to go out with **my** friends*
- Mis amigos van a salir con **tus** amigos — *My friends are going to go out with **your** friends*
- Mi hermano va a salir con **sus** amigos — *My brother is going to go out with **his** friends*
- Nosotros vamos a salir con **nuestras** amigas — *We are going to go out with **our** friends*
- Vosotros vais a salir con **vuestras** amigas — *You guys are going to go out with **your** friends*

Don't forget, the **possessives agree with the noun, not the speaker!**

"THE PERSONAL *A*"

VOY A VISITAR A MIS PRIMOS

When the person who is the "**recipient of the action**" is a person or animal, we need to add an extra ***a*** to the sentence. The person or animal, in this case is known as the "**direct object**", and the ***a*** is called "**the personal *a***":

Voy a visitar	**a**	**mis abuelos**
Immediate future	Personal *a*	Direct Object
Translation: I am going to visit my grandparents		

You will see this "personal ***a***" appear in other Spanish structures, such as the ones below. They always involve people (and sometimes animals)

- **Voy a ayudar a mis padres**
  I am going to help (to) my parents
- **Voy a pasear a mi perro Lily**
  I am going to walk my dog, Lily
- **Voy a escuchar a mis profesores**
  I am going to listen to my teachers

INFINITIVES – RECAP

Infinitives are verbs as you find them in the dictionary before they are conjugated. The immediate future is one of several structures where you add on the infinitive at the end:

- Voy a **hablar** — *I am going **to talk***

Another really useful infinitive structure is ***me gusta*** (I like):

- Me gusta **hablar** — *I like **to talk***

1. Match

Voy a	*Are you guys going to?*
Mi abuela va a	*I am going to*
Mis padres van a	*Are you going to?*
Vamos a	*My mother is going to*
Mi hermana va a	*We are going to*
¿Vas a?	*My brother is going to*
Mis amigos van a	*My sister is going to*
Mi madre va a	*My grandma is going to*
¿Vais a?	*My parents are going to*
Mi hermano va a	*My friends are going to*

2. Match

Voy a visitar a mis abuelos	*I am going to go for a walk*
Voy a comer un bocadillo	*Are you going to do the homework?*
Voy a dar un paseo	*I am going to visit my grandparents*
Vamos a ver una película	*Are you going to go out with your friends?*
¿Vas a hacer los deberes?	*I am going to eat a sandwich*
¿Vas a salir con tus amigos?	*We are going to watch a film*

3. Anagrams

a. amotnr ne cibi

b. ri la pesrueracmdo

c. rchae osl dbreees

d. ri a saca de rMaat

e. ri la necrto mocecrail

f. ard nu spaeo

g. prcorma nua amtacies

h. cpmorra nu tovseid

i. rev nua erise ed xfiNtel

j. cpmoarr nuas llasaztapi ed etedopr

k. rev nau lpeícula ed ónacci

l. tvisari a ism labosue

m. mreoc nu obaclldio

n. rmtoa nu éfac

o. ri la lcogeoi

4. Complete with a suitable verb

a. Hoy voy a ________ una camiseta nueva

b. Esta mañana vamos a ___________ al ajedrez

c. Este fin de semana vamos a _________ al cine

d. Esta tarde voy a _________ un bocadillo en el centro

e. Hoy vamos a ____________ en bici en el parque

f. Mañana mis amigos y yo vamos a ________ una película

g. Este domingo voy a _____________ a mi abuela

h. Esta mañana vamos a _____________ un paseo

i. Hoy mi padre y yo vamos a __________ un café

j. Voy a _________ los deberes esta tarde

5. Write the correct form of the verb *IR*

a. Mi hermano _______ a comprar una camiseta nueva en el centro comercial

b. Mis hermanos y yo _______ a visitar a nuestros abuelos en Colombia

c. Esta mañana mis padres _______ a dar un paseo en el parque que está en las afueras

d. Hoy mis amigas y yo ______ a jugar a la Play

e. Mi mejor amigo _______ a tomar un café

f. ¿________ a salir con tus amigos hoy?

g. ¿________ a visitar a vuestros abuelos?

h. Mis primos _______ a jugar al fútbol esta tarde en el parque con mi hermano y conmigo

6. Sentence Puzzle

a. salir a Voy tarde amigos esta con mis	*I am going to go out with my friends this evening*
b. a madre al Mi mañana va ir gimnasio	*My mother is going to go to the gym tomorrow*
c. Mi va abuelo a comprar verde camiseta una	*My grandfather is going to buy a green t-shirt*
d. hermana va ver a una Mi película acción de	*My sister is going to watch an action film*
e. Netflix Voy ver a serie una hoy en	*I am going to watch a series on Netflix today*
f. padres van comer a bocadillo un hoy Mis	*My parents are going to eat a sandwich today*

7. Gapped dictation: listen, complete and translate into English

a. Voy a __________ con mis amigos esta ________

b. Mi __________ va a ir al _________ con su ________

c. Mis ________ van __ _____ un paseo hoy

d. ¿_____ a ir ____ ______ hoy?

e. ¿_____ a _______ a la Play esta _____?

f. Este _________ vamos a ___________ a mis abuelos

g. Hoy _____ a ________ al cine con sus padres

8. Tangled translation: translate into Spanish

a. Voy ***to*** ver ***an action film***

b. Mi ***brother*** no ***going*** a ***to go*** al centro comercial ***this weekend***

c. Mis ***parents*** no van a ***to buy*** zapatillas de deporte

d. ***My*** abuelos ***are going*** a ***to go for a walk*** hoy

e. Voy a ***to watch a*** serie en Netflix ***this evening***

f. ***Tomorrow*** no voy a ***to go out with*** mis ***friends neither*** jugar al ***football***.

g. Ni ***my*** madre ***neither my*** hermana ***are going*** a comer un ***sandwich***

h. No ***I am going to*** a salir ***with mis friends*** hoy

i. Mi ***friend is not going to*** ir al colegio ***today*** porque ***is*** enfermo

9. Translate into Spanish

a. Tomorrow I am going to do my homework

b. My parents are going to watch a series on Netflix this weekend

c. My sister is going to go out with her friends to the shopping centre

d. Are you going to watch a film today?

e. My friends and I are going to buy trainers

f. My sister is going to play football and go to the supermarket

g. Neither my mum nor my dad are going to watch a film this morning

h. My friends are not going to play football this afternoon because they are ill

A

ORAL PING PONG

IR

ENGLISH 1	SPANISH 1	ENGLISH 2	SPANISH 2
I never go to the cinema nor to the shops with anyone.	Nunca voy al cine ni a las tiendas con nadie.	Neither he nor she go either to the shopping centre or the gym alone.	
My mum goes to the shopping centre every weekend.	Mi madre va al centro comercial todos los fines de semana.	Neither my mum nor my grandmother go to the playground nowadays.	
We (f) go to the gym often in order to do weights.	Nosotras vamos al gimnasio a menudo para hacer pesas.	This morning we (m) are going to buy a t-shirt in the shops.	
My friends go to the park in order to go for a bike ride every Saturday.	Mis amigos van al parque para montar en bici todos los sábados.	In July I often go on holiday to Spain, but I never go alone.	
Today my dad is going to Madrid in order to visit his parents.	Hoy mi padre va a Madrid para visitar a sus padres.	My parents go to the gym in order to do weights every Thursday.	
My family and I often go on holidays to Greece by plane.	Mi familia y yo vamos de vacaciones a menudo a Grecia en avión.	My friend and I go to the shopping centre in order to go window shopping.	
Tomorrow my brothers are going to watch a Netflix series with their friends.	Mañana mis hermanos van a ver una serie de Netflix con sus amigos.	I am going to ride a bike with my sister in the park today.	
We (m) are going to visit our grandparents in Italy by car.	Nosotros vamos a visitar a nuestros abuelos en Italia en coche.	Neither my mum nor my sister go to the gym at the weekends.	

INSTRUCTIONS - You are **PARTNER A.** Work in pairs. Each of you has two sets of sentences - one set has already been translated for you. You will ask your partner to translate these. The other set of sentences have not been translated. Your partner will ask you to translate these.
HOW TO PLAY - Partner A starts by reading out his/her/their first sentence in English. Partner B must translate. Partner A must check the answer and award the following points: **3 points** = perfect, **2 points** = 1 mistake, **1 point** = mistakes but the verb is accurate. If they cannot translate correctly, Partner A will read out the sentence so that Partner B can learn what the correct translation is.
Then Partner B reads out his/her/their first sentence, and so on.
OBJECTIVE - Try to win more points than your partner by translating correctly as many sentences as possible.

B

ORAL PING PONG

IR

ENGLISH 1	SPANISH 1	ENGLISH 2	SPANISH 2
I never go to the cinema nor to the shops with anyone.		Neither he nor she go either to the shopping centre or the gym alone.	Ni él ni ella van ni al centro comercial ni al gimnasio solos.
My mum goes to the shopping centre every weekend.		Neither my mum nor my grandmother go to the playground nowadays.	Ni mi madre ni mi abuela van al cine hoy en día.
We (f) go to the gym often in order to do weights.		This morning we (m) are going to buy a t-shirt in the shops.	Esta mañana nosotros vamos a comprar una camiseta en las tiendas.
My friends go to the park in order to go for a bike ride every Saturday.		In July I often go on holiday to Spain, but I never go alone.	En julio a menudo voy de vacaciones a España, pero nunca voy solo/a.
Today my dad is going to Madrid in order to visit his parents.		My parents go to the gym in order to do weights every Thursday.	Mis padres van al gimnasio para hacer pesas todos los jueves.
My family and I often go on holidays to Greece by plane.		My friend and I go to the shopping centre in order to go window shopping.	Mi amigo/a y yo vamos al centro comercial para mirar escaparates.
Tomorrow my brothers are going to watch a Netflix series with their friends.		I am going to ride a bike with my sister in the park today.	Voy a montar en bici con mi hermana en el parque hoy.
We (m) are going to visit our grandparents in Italy by car.		Neither my mum nor my sister go to the gym at the weekends.	Ni mi madre ni mi hermana van al gimnasio los fines de semana.

INSTRUCTIONS - You are **PARTNER B.** Work in pairs. Each of you has two sets of sentences - one set has already been translated for you. You will ask your partner to translate these. The other set of sentences have not been translated. Your partner will ask you to translate these.
HOW TO PLAY - Partner A starts by reading out his/her/their first sentence in English. Partner B must translate. Partner A must check the answer and award the following points: **3 points** = perfect, **2 points** = 1 mistake, **1 point** = mistakes but the verb is accurate. If they cannot translate correctly, Partner A will read out the sentence so that Partner B can learn what the correct translation is.
Then Partner B reads out his/her/their first sentence, and so on.
OBJECTIVE - Try to win more points than your partner by translating correctly as many sentences as possible.

No Snakes No Ladders

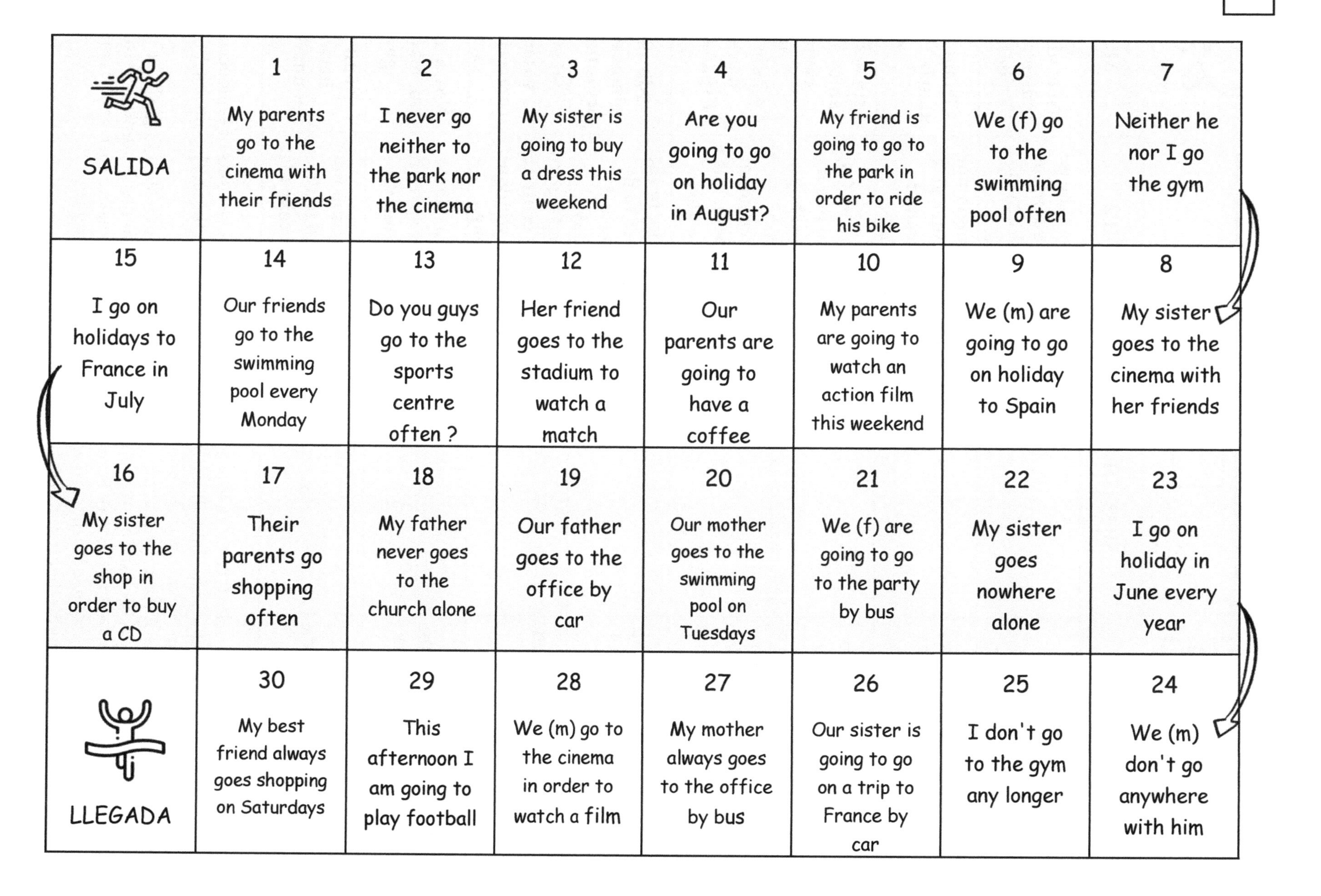

SALIDA	1 My parents go to the cinema with their friends	2 I never go neither to the park nor the cinema	3 My sister is going to buy a dress this weekend	4 Are you going to go on holiday in August?	5 My friend is going to go to the park in order to ride his bike	6 We (f) go to the swimming pool often	7 Neither he nor I go the gym
15 I go on holidays to France in July	14 Our friends go to the swimming pool every Monday	13 Do you guys go to the sports centre often ?	12 Her friend goes to the stadium to watch a match	11 Our parents are going to have a coffee	10 My parents are going to watch an action film this weekend	9 We (m) are going to go on holiday to Spain	8 My sister goes to the cinema with her friends
16 My sister goes to the shop in order to buy a CD	17 Their parents go shopping often	18 My father never goes to the church alone	19 Our father goes to the office by car	20 Our mother goes to the swimming pool on Tuesdays	21 We (f) are going to go to the party by bus	22 My sister goes nowhere alone	23 I go on holiday in June every year
LLEGADA	30 My best friend always goes shopping on Saturdays	29 This afternoon I am going to play football	28 We (m) go to the cinema in order to watch a film	27 My mother always goes to the office by bus	26 Our sister is going to go on a trip to France by car	25 I don't go to the gym any longer	24 We (m) don't go anywhere with him

IR

No Snakes No Ladders

SALIDA	1 Mis padres van al cine con sus amigos	2 Nunca voy ni al parque ni al cine	3 Mi hermana va a comprar un vestido este fin de semana	4 ¿Vas a ir de vacaciones en agosto?	5 Mi amigo va a ir al parque para montar en bici	6 Nosotras vamos a la piscina a menudo	7 Ni él ni yo vamos al gimnasio
15 Voy de vacaciones a Francia en julio	14 Nuestros amigos van a la piscina todos los lunes	13 ¿Vais al polideportivo a menudo?	12 Su amigo va al estadio para ver un partido	11 Nuestros padres van a tomar un café	10 Mis padres van a ver una película de acción este fin semana	9 Nosotros vamos a ir de vacaciones a España	8 Mi hermana va al cine con sus amigas
16 Mi hermana va a la tienda para comprar un CD	17 Sus padres van de tiendas a menudo	18 Mi padre nunca va a la iglesia solo	19 Nuestro padre va a la oficina en coche	20 Nuestra madre va a la piscina los martes	21 Nosotras vamos a ir a la fiesta en autobús	22 Mi hermana no va a ninguna parte sola	23 Voy de vacaciones en junio todos los años
LLEGADA	30 Mi mejor amigo siempre va de tiendas los sábados	29 Esta tarde voy a jugar al fútbol	28 Nosotros vamos al cine para ver una película	27 Mi madre siempre va a la oficina en autobús	26 Nuestra hermana va a ir de viaje a Francia en coche	25 Ya no voy al gimnasio	24 Nosotros no vamos a ninguna parte con él

PYRAMID TRANSLATION

IR

Translate each part of the pyramid out loud with your partner, then write it into the spaces provided below.

a. I go to the sports centre

b. I go to the sports centre every weekend with our friends

c. I go to the sports centre every weekend with our friends, but I never go neither to the swimming pool nor the gym.

d. I go to the sports centre every weekend with our friends, but I never go neither to the swimming pool nor the gym. Tomorrow my sister and I are going to watch an action film at home

e. I go to the sports centre every weekend with our friends, but I never go neither to the swimming pool nor the gym. Tomorrow my sister and I are going to watch an action film at home. My parents are going to have a coffee with their friends.

Write your translation here

SOLUTION: Voy al polideportivo todos los fines de semana con nuestros amigos, pero nunca voy ni a la piscina ni al gimnasio. Mañana mi hermana y yo vamos a ver una película de acción en casa. Mis padres van a tomar un café con sus amigos.

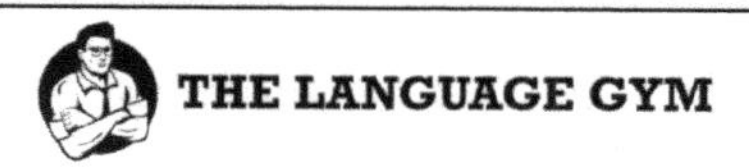

UNIT 5 – HACER

Yo	**Hago**
Tú	**Haces**
Él / Ella	**Hace**
Nosotros / as	**Hacemos**
Vosotros / as	**Hacéis**
Ellos / as	**Hacen**

5.1 TIME MARKER + HAGO + NOUN PHRASE

(SAYING WHAT ONE IS GOING TO DO IN THE NEAR FUTURE)

Time marker	English
A menudo	*Often*
Cuando salgo	*When I go out*
De vez en cuando	*From time to time*
En mi clase de…	*In my … class*
ciencias	*science*
español	*Spanish*
francés	*French*
Los lunes	*On Mondays*
Los martes	*On Tuesdays*
Los miércoles	*On Wednesdays*
Los jueves	*On Thursdays*
Los viernes	*On Fridays*
Los sábados	*On Saturdays*
Los domingos	*On Sundays*
Los fines de semana	*At the weekends*
Nunca	*Never*
Siempre	*Always*
Todos los días	*Every day*
Una vez a la semana	*Once a week*

Verb	Noun phrase	English
(yo) **hago** *I 'do'*	**deporte**	*sport*
	ejercicio físico	*physical exercise*
	las compras	*the shopping*
	las tareas domésticas	*house chores*
	los deberes	*homework*
(yo) no hago nada		*I don't do anything*
(yo) **hago** *I 'make'*	**mi/la cama**	*my/the bed*
	la comida	*food (lunch)*
	(nuevos) amigos	*(new) friends*
(yo) **hago** *I 'ask'*	**una pregunta**	*a question*
	preguntas	*questions*
(yo) **hago** *I 'pay'*	**una visita**	*a visit*

LANGUAGE AWARENESS

HACER: to do, to make, and more!

In Spanish, the verb ***hacer*** can generally be translated, as either **"to do"** or **"to make"**. However, when combined with certain words, it can also be translated as **"to ask** a question", "**to go**" or even **"to pay** a visit":

- Hago **los deberes** — *I **do** my homework*
- Hago **vela** — *I **go** sailing*
- Hago **la comida** — *I **make** food/lunch*
- Hago **una pregunta** — *I **ask** a question*
- Hago **una visita** — *I **pay** a visit*

¡Hola pez!

DOUBLE NEGATIVES

NO HAGO NADA

Remember how to use negatives in Spanish? In Spanish we sometimes negate twice! So, when we want to say, *I don't do anything*, we say:

No hago nada	*I don't do **anything***
Literally:	*I **don't** do **nothing***
Or: **Nunca hago nada**	*I never do **anything***
Literally:	*I **never** do **nothing***

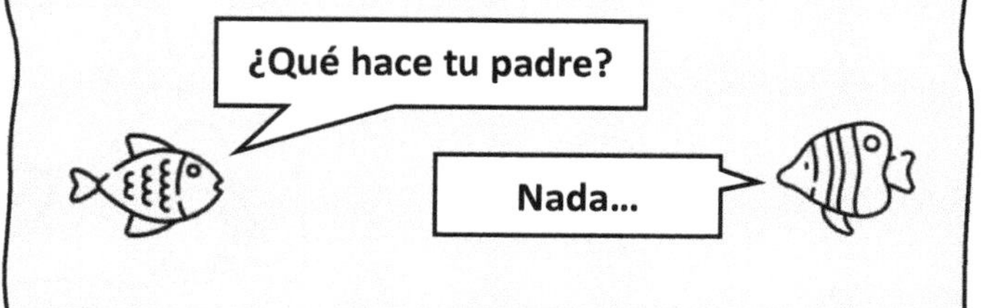

1. Match

Siempre hago amigos	*I ask a question*
Hago una visita	*I always make friends*
Hago una pregunta	*I do nothing*
No hago nada	*I do the house chores*
Nunca hago la cama	*I pay a visit*
Hago mis deberes	*I never do the shopping*
Hago la tareas domésticas	*I never make the bed*
Nunca hago las compras	*I make lunch*
Hago deporte todos los días	*I do sport every day*
Hago la comida	*I do my homework*

2. Broken words

a. No hago na __ __

b. Hago la com __ __ __

c. Hago las ta __ __ __ __ domésticas

d. Nunca hago ami __ __ __

e. Los sábados hago las comp __ __ __

f. Hago una preg __ __ __ __ al profesor

g. Hago una visi __ __ a un amigo

h. Nunca hago depo __ __ __

i. Nunca hago mis deb__ __ __ __

3. Listen and complete

a. Hago las __________ __________ a menudo

b. Casi nunca hago ___________

c. Siempre hago las ________ con mi _______

d. Nunca hago mis ____________

e. Siempre hago la ____________

f. Nunca hago ejercicio ___________

g. Hago la ____________ todos los días

h. Hago las ____________ domésticas

i. En clase hago muchas _________________

4. Complete with a suitable word, then listen and note down the differences

a. Hago la ____________ todos los días.

b. Nunca hago las ___________ domésticas.

c. Hago ___________ al profesor a menudo.

d. Hago una ___________ a mis abuelos todos los sábados.

e. El fin de semana no hago __________. Descanso.

f. Soy deportista. Hago mucho ___________ físico.

g. Siempre hago mis _____________ de francés.

h. Los domingos hago la _____________ con mi padre.

5. Anagrams

a. al maca	*the bed*	g. canun	*never*
b. gmisoa	*friends*	h. priesme	*always*
c. osl esdebre	*the homework*	i. nau agrupent	*a question*
d. ed zev ne daucon	*from time to time*	j. slo uevjse	*on Thursdays*
e. eportde	*deporte*	k. sla mrpcsoa	*the shopping*
f. adan	*nothing*	l. ols ásodsab	*on Saturdays*

6. Sentence Puzzle

a. hago Siempre cuando nuevos salgo amigos — *I always make new friends when I go out*

b. hago de Nunca deberes mis ciencias — *I never do my science homework*

c. sábados hago Los deberes mis — *On Saturdays, I do my homework*

d. días domésticas todos tareas Hago las los — *I do the house chores every day*

e. las Nunca compras hago — *I never go shopping*

f. los Siempre de hago fines la semana comida — *I always make lunch at the weekends*

g. cama Hago la todos días los — *I make my bed every day*

7. Break the flow

a. Siemprehagonuevosamigos

b. Nuncahagolosdeberes

c. Hagolacamatodoslosdías

d. Nohagonadalosfinesdesemana

e. Losjueveshagounavisitaamiabuelo

f. Hagodeporteraramente

g. Hagolastareasdomésticassiempre

h. Losvierneshagounavisitaamiabuela

8. Gapped translation: complete the translation

a. Hago _______ amigos — *I make new friends*

b. _______ hago deporte — *I never do sport*

c. Siempre hago las ________ — *I always go shopping*

d. Nunca hago mis _________ — *I never do my homework*

e. Siempre hago la ________ — *I always make my bed*

f. Hago ejercicio __________ — *I do physical exercise*

g. Los jueves hago ________ — *On Thursdays I do weights*

h. Raramente hago ________ — *I rarely do exercise*

9. Spot and correct the errors

a. Siempre hago nuevos amigo.

b. Nunca no hago la comida.

c. Los sábados siempre hago las tareas domestica.

d. Hago deporte de vez a cuando.

e. Hago las compras con mi madre todas los jueves.

f. En mi clases de matemáticas…

g. …siempre hagor muchos preguntas.

h. El domingo hago nada. Solo descanso.

10. Listen and translate into Spanish 

a. I make new friends

b. I do the house chores

c. I do sport

d. I make my bed

e. I do nothing

f. I make lunch

g. I do my homework

11. Complete with the words in the box

a. Todos los días hago mi __________ en mi dormitorio.

b. Cuando salgo los sábados, siempre hago nuevos __________.

c. Los jueves, por lo general, hago las ________ con mi madre.

d. En las clases de ciencias, siempre hago ____________ cuando no comprendo algo.

e. Para ayudar a mi madre, hago las ____________ domésticas casi todos los días.

f. Todos los días hago mi cama, y por la tarde hago la _____________ en la cocina.

g. En mis clases de español trabajo duro. Siempre hago los ____________.

h. Soy muy perezoso. Nunca hago __________ físico.

i. De vez en cuando hago una __________ a mi primo, que vive en Barcelona.

j. Soy muy deportista. Hago ___________, sobre todo natación, todos los días.

tareas	deberes	deporte	compras	ejercicio
preguntas	comida	amigos	visita	cama

12. Complete the translation

a. *New friends*

N__ __ __ __ __ a__ __ __ __ __

b. *A question*

U__ __ p__ __ __ __ __ __ __

c. *The shopping*

L__ __ c__ __ __ __ __ __

d. *Physical exercise*

E__ __ __ __ __ __ __ __ f__ __ __ __ __

e. *House chores*

L__ __ t__ __ __ __ __ d__ __ __ __ __ __ -
__ __ __

f. *Food (lunch)*

L__ c__ __ __ __ __

g. *Sport*

D__ __ __ __ __ __

h. *I don't do anything*

N__ h __ __ __ n__ __ __

13. Tangled translation: translate into Spanish

a. ***I always*** hago la ***food***

b. ***Never*** hago ***exercise*** físico

c. Nunca ***I make the*** cama

d. De vez en ***when*** hago las ***shopping***

e. ***Always*** hago las ***house chores***

f. En mis clases ***of*** inglés, siempre ***do*** los ***homework***

g. Nunca hago ***questions when*** no comprendo algo

14. Translate into Spanish

a. I make new friends

b. I do the house chores

c. I do my homework

d. I do sport

e. I make my bed

f. I make lunch

g. I do the shopping

h. I do physical exercise

i. I make (ask) questions

5.2 HAGO + NOUN + TIME MARKER + ME GUSTA + PORQUE + ES + ADJECTIVE
(SAYING WHAT LEISURE ACTIVITY YOU DO AND WHY YOU LIKE/DISLIKE IT)

Hago *I do*	**atletismo**	*athletics*	**a menudo**	*often*
	boxeo	*boxing*	**de vez en cuando**	*from time to time*
	buceo	*scuba diving/snorkelling*	**los lunes**	*on Mondays*
	ciclismo	*cycling*	**los martes**	*on Tuesdays*
	deporte	*sport*	**los miércoles**	*on Wednesdays*
	ejercicio físico	*physical exercise*	**los jueves**	*on Thursdays*
	equitación	*horse riding*	**los viernes**	*on Fridays*
No hago *I don't do*	**escalada**	*rock climbing*	**los sábados**	*on Saturdays*
	footing	*jogging*	**los domingos**	*on Sundays*
	nada	*I don't do anything*	**los fines de semana**	*at the weekends*
	natación	*swimming*	**nunca**	*never*
Nunca hago *I never do*	**pesas**	*weights*	**siempre**	*always*
	senderismo	*hiking*	**todos los días**	*every day*
	vela	*sailing*	**una vez a la semana**	*once a week*

Me encanta	*I love it*	**porque es** *because it is*	**aburrido**	*boring*
Me gusta mucho	*I like it a lot*		**agotador**	*exhausting/tiring*
Me gusta	*I like it*		**apasionante**	*exciting*
No me gusta	*I don't like it*		**difícil**	*difficult*
No me gusta nada	*I don't like it at all*		**divertido**	*fun*
			relajante	*relaxing*

LANGUAGE AWARENESS:
HACER DEPORTE – I DO or I GO?

In Spanish we use ***hacer*** *(to do)* to talk about the sports/activities we practise. ***Jugar*** *(to play)* is used with sports we "play", such as ball sports: football, rugby, golf etc.

For other sports, we use ***hacer.*** It can be translated with either an **"I do"** or an **"I go"** structure in English:

- **Hago atletismo** — *I **do** athletics*
  (Hacer + noun) — (I do + noun)
- **Hago natación** — *I **do/go** swimming*
  (Hacer + noun) — (I do/go + gerund)

HAGO VELA – I GO SAILING
Verb + NOUN / Verb + GERUND

As shown, the verb ***hacer*** can be translated using different verbs, but there is also an important structural difference to be aware of.

Not only does ***hago*** mutate from **"I do"** to **"I go"**, but the phrase structure also often changes from **"*hacer* + noun"** to **"to do/go + gerund"**.

- **Hago senderismo** — ***I do/go hiking***
  (Hacer + noun) — (To go + gerund)

1. Match

Hago senderismo	*I don't do anything*
Hago buceo	*I do boxing*
Hago boxeo	*I do swimming*
Hago atletismo	*I do sport*
Hago deporte	*I do hiking*
Hago vela	*I do jogging*
Hago pesas	*I do scuba diving*
Hago footing	*I do sailing*
Hago natación	*I do weights*
Hago equitación	*I do athletics*
No hago nada	*I do horse riding*

2. Faulty translation: fix the English translation

a. A veces hago vela — *I always do weights*

b. Hago footing — *I do hiking*

c. No hago natación — *I don't do anything*

d. Hago equitación — *I do jogging*

e. Nunca hago pesas — *I never do climbing*

f. Hago senderismo raramente — *I rarely do sailing*

g. Nunca hago atletismo — *I always do athletics*

h. Hago deporte — *I do scuba diving*

3. Break the flow

a. Hagosenderismoyequitaciónamenudo

b. Nuncahagovelanibuceo

c. Hagoboxeotresvecesalasemana

d. Nohagonada

e. Hagopesasyescaladatodoslosdías

f. Hagofootingyyogatodoslosdomingos

g. Hagodeporteraramente

h. Nuncahagodeporte

4. Cross out all the phrases which do not refer to sports

a. Hago la cama

b. Hago la comida

c. Hago footing

d. Hago las compras

e. Hago buceo

f. Hago natación

g. Hago las tareas domésticas

h. Hago los deberes

5. Likely or unlikely? Rewrite any unlikely statement into a plausible one

a. Me gusta porque es aburrido

b. No me gusta mucho porque es apasionante

c. Me gusta porque es relajante

d. Me gusta porque es muy divertido

e. No me gusta porque es muy agotador y difícil

f. Me gusta mucho porque es apasionante

g. No me gusta nada porque es divertido

6. Translate into English

a. Agotador

b. Apasionante

c. Los viernes

d. La equitación

e. El footing

f. Divertido

g. Los deberes

h. Las tareas domésticas

i. La cama

j. Las compras

k. Aburrido

l. Difícil

7. Categories

interesante	no me gusta	martes	natación
jueves	domingo	boxeo	miércoles
me encanta	aburrido	me gusta	senderismo
buceo	lunes	divertido	sábado

Adjectives	Days of the week	Sports	Phrases to express likes and dislikes

8. Positive or Negative?

a. Me gusta

b. Apasionante

c. Interesante

d. Es agotador

e. Me encanta

f. Es difícil

g. Relajante

h. No me gusta

i. Me encanta

9. Sentence Puzzle

a. Hago todos días boxeo los después colegio del — *I do boxing every day after school*

b. la casi Hago los por mañana footing todos días — *I do jogging nearly every day in the morning*

c. pesas Hago y tres semana la escalada veces a — *I do weights and rock climbing three times a week*

d. buceo Nunca natación hago, pero hago — *I never do scuba diving but I do swimming*

e. hago Nunca aburrido porque senderismo es — *I never do hiking because it is boring*

f. Cada hago hago día, la y después cama yoga — *Every day, I make my bed and then I do yoga*

g. hacer Después los de deberes, footing hago — *After doing my homework I do jogging*

10. Tangled translation: translate into Spanish

a. Hago ***boxing*** todos los ***days***. Me encanta, pero es ***tiring***.

b. No hago ***weights never***. ***I don't like it*** porque es ***boring***.

c. Cada día ***I make*** la ***bed and*** luego ***do sport***. ***I never*** hago ***the house chores.***

d. Después de hacer ***my homework*** hago ***jogging***. Me gusta, ***but it is*** agotador.

e. Hago ***athletics*** tres ***times*** a la ***week with*** mi novia. ¡Es ***exciting***!

f. ***I do*** equitación ***three*** veces a la semana en el ***countryside***. Es muy ***relaxing.***

g. ***All the*** días hago ejercicio ***physical*** con ***my brother*** mayor. ¡Es muy ***hard***!

h. ***Never*** hago buceo ***because*** es ***boring***. Prefiero la ***swimming.***

i. ***I never*** hago ***nothing*** porque ***I am*** perezoso y el deporte es ***tiring*** y ***boring.***

j. Hago las ***chores*** domésticas y después ***I do horse riding*** con mis ***friends***. ¡***I love it***!

11. Listen, complete, then translate into English

a. Me gusta mucho el ciclismo porque es _____________.

b. Me gusta mucho el footing porque es ____________.

c. Hago _______. Me gusta porque es _____________.

d. Me encanta el _________ porque es ______________.

e. Odio la __________ porque es ______________.

f. Me gusta mucho el _________ porque es ___________.

g. No me gusta nada el ________ porque es ____________.

12. Listen and correct the errors

a. Hago deporte de vez de cuando

b. Me encanta porque aburrido

c. Me gusta nada porque es agotador

d. Hago buceo todos días

e. Hago senderismo nunca

f. Hago vela todo los domingo

g. Hago pesos un día la semana

h. Nunca hago físico ejercicio

i. Hago buceo menudo

13. Gapped translation: complete the translation

a. Me enca __ __ __	*I love it*
b. Hago ve __ __	*I do sailing*
c. No me gusta na __ __	*I don't like it at all*
d. Hago bu __ __ __	*I go diving*
e. Me gusta el atlet __ __ __ __	*I like athletics*
f. Todos los d __ __ __	*Every day*
g. Nun __ __ hago dep __ __ __ __	*I never do sport*
h. Hago pes__ __	*I do weights*
i. …de v__ __ en c__ __nd__	*…from time to time*
j. Es m__ __ agot__ __ __ __	*It is very tiring*

14. Translate into Spanish

a. I go jogging and swimming every day

b. I never do athletics because it is boring

c. I do the shopping from time to time

d. I never make my bed

e. I do sport nearly every day

f. I never go hiking because it is boring

g. I do boxing every day

h. I do weights rarely

i. I do sailing from time to time

j. First, I do the house chores and later I do sport

5.3 FULL PRESENT CONJUGATION OF HACER + NOUN + FREQUENCY ADVERB

(SAYING WHAT LEISURE ACTIVITIES YOU DO AND HOW OFTEN)

		atletismo	*athletics*	**a menudo** *often*
		artes marciales	*martial arts*	**de vez en cuando** *from time to time*
		boxeo	*boxing*	**los lunes** *on Mondays*
		buceo	*scuba diving/ snorkelling*	**los martes**
		ciclismo	*cycling*	**los miércoles**
	Hago *I do*	**deporte**	*sport*	**los jueves**
		ejercicio físico	*physical exercise*	**los viernes**
	Haces *You do*	**equitación**	*horse riding*	**los sábados**
(No) *Don't*	**Hace** *He/she does*	**escalada**	*rock climbing*	**los domingos**
		footing	*jogging*	**los fines de semana** *at the weekends*
(Nunca) *Never*	**Hacemos** *We do*	**natación**	*swimming*	**nunca** *never*
		pesas	*weights*	**siempre** *always*
	Hacéis *You guys/ladies do*	**senderismo**	*hiking*	**todos los días** *every day*
		vela	*sailing*	**una vez a la semana** *once a week*
	Hacen *They do*	**la cama**	*(make) the bed*	
		la comida	*(make) food (lunch)*	
		las compras	*the shopping*	
		las tareas domésticas	*the chores*	
		los deberes	*homework*	
		preguntas	*(ask) questions*	
		una pregunta	*(ask) a question*	

No hago nada *I don't do anything* **Nunca hago nada** *I never do anything*

LANGUAGE AWARENESS

HACER – 1st Person Irregular

As you have seen in previous units, in Spanish, depending on the person who is doing the action: I, you, we, they etc., we use a different verb ending. This is known as **verb conjugation**.

In the present indicative tense, ***hacer*** is a **1st person irregular verb**. This means that only the 1st person ***hago (I do)*** is irregular. The rest of the verb (see above) follows the same pattern as a regular ER verb.

The many translations of *hacer*

As you know, there are other ways to translate the verb ***hacer,*** apart from ***"to do"*** and ***"to make"***…

- To **do**:

Hago deporte *I do sport*

- To **make**:

Hacen la cama *They **make** the bed*

- To **go**:

Hace senderismo *He/she **goes** hiking*

- To **ask**:

Hacemos preguntas *We **ask** questions*

1. Faulty translation: fix the English translation

a. Hacemos senderismo	*They go hiking*
b. ¿Qué deportes haces?	*What sports does he do?*
c. Nunca hace pesas	*He never goes swimming*
d. Siempre hacen escalada	*We always go rock climbing*
e. ¿Dónde hacéis equitación?	*Where do I go horse riding?*
f. Hago artes marciales	*He does martial arts*
g. Nunca hacen deporte	*We never do sport*
h. Hacen las compras	*You do the shopping*

2. Broken words

a. Hacemos sende__ __ __ __ __

b. Ellas no hacen na__ __

c. ¿Qué depo__ __ __ haces?

d. Hago nata__ __ __ __

e. ¿Hacéis las comp__ __ __?

f. Mi hermano hace pes__ __

g. ¿Hacéis artes mar__ia__ __ __?

3. Gapped (English) translation

a. Hago senderismo solo	_________ *hiking alone*
b. Hacen deporte	_____________ *sport*
c. ¿Qué haces?	*What do* _____________*?*
d. Hacemos vela	_________ *sailing*
e. ¿Qué deporte hacéis?	*What sport do* ___________*?*
f. Nunca hacen pesas	_________ *never do weights*
g. ¿Hacéis karate?	*Do* ____________ *karate?*
h. No hacen nada	____________ *nothing*
i. ¿Cuándo hacéis escalada?	*When* ________ *rock climbing*
j. Él hace muchas preguntas	*He* _______ *a lot of questions*

4. Match

Escalada	*We do*
Deporte	*On Thursdays*
Hago	*Rock climbing*
Footing	*Never*
Hacemos	*Martial arts*
Los jueves	*Nothing*
Nunca	*Sport*
Hacen	*Swimming*
Natación	*Jogging*
Nada	*They do*
Artes marciales	*I do*

5. Word hunt

a. A day of the week starting with J: El j__ __ __ __ __

b. A sport starting with E: E__ __ __ __ __ __ __ __

c. A time adverb starting with N: N__ __ __ __

d. A sport starting with E: Eq __ __ __ __ __ __ __ __ __

e. A time adverbial with two words: A m__ __ __ __ __ __

f. Opposite of *aburrido*: D__ __ __ __ __ __ __ __ __ __

g. Opposite of *todo*: N__ __ __

¡Hola pingüino!

6. Listen and complete with the missing vowels

a. H__c__m__s __sc__l__d__ t__d__s l__s d__ __s

b. Cua __ __ __ ha __ __ vi __ __ __o hac__ __ __s v__ __ a

c. M__s h__rm__n__s n__ h__c__n n__d__

d. N__nc__ h__c__ f__ __t__ng

e. ¿T__ n__ h__c__s d__p__rt__?

f. ¿D__nd__ h__c__ __s p__s__s v__s__tr__s?

g. Nunca h__g__ v__l__ p__rq __ __ __s __b__rr__d__

h. H__c__m__s c__cl__sm__ p__rque __s __p__s__ __ n__nt__

7. Translate into English

a. No hago mucho deporte

b. Nunca hacen ejercicio

c. Hacemos escalada todos los días

d. Hacemos footing tres veces a la semana

e. ¿Qué hacéis hoy?

f. Esta mañana no hacemos nada

g. ¿Dónde haces natación?

h. Por lo general, hago escalada sola

i. No hago atletismo porque es aburrido

j. ¿Qué deporte hacen?

8. Tangled translation: translate into Spanish

a. Nunca ***does*** deporte porque dice que es ***tiring***

b. Nosotros no ***do nothing***

c. Yo ***never do*** footing porque es ***boring***

d. ***All*** los ***Thursdays*** mis padres ***do*** equitación

e. María ***does*** ejercicio físico ***every day***

f. ¿***What*** deporte ***do*** vosotros?

g. ¡***You*** nunca haces ***physical exercise***!

h. Mi padre ***does*** natación y mi ***mother does*** senderismo

i. Mi primo y yo ***do weights*** dos veces a la semana

j. ¿Qué deporte ***do*** tus padres?

9. Listen and choose the correct verb form

a. No **hace/hago/haces** atletismo

b. Nunca **hacen/hacéis/hacemos** nuestros deberes

c. Casi nunca **hago/hace/haces** vela

d. ¿Qué deporte **hacéis/haces/hace**?

e. ¿**Hacemos/Hacéis/Hacen** equitación?

f. **Hago/Haces/Hacen** senderismo

g. Siempre **hace/hago/hacemos** mi cama

10. Complete the verbs

a. Yo no ha__ __ senderismo nunca

b. Nosotros nunca ha__ __ __ __ __ boxeo

c. Mis padres no ha__ __ __ deporte

d. ¿Qué deporte ha__ __ __ tú?

e. Mi madre y yo ha__ __ __ __ __ las tareas domésticas todos los días

f. Mi hermano no ha__ __ nada

11. Complete the table with the correct forms of *HACER*

Yo	hago
Tú	
Ella	
Él	
Nosotras	
Vosotros	
Ellos	
Ellas	
Mi padre	
Mi padre y yo	

12. Complete with the correct forms of *HACER*

a. Mis padres nunca _________ deporte

b. Mi madre ________ yoga todos los días

c. Mi hermano menor nunca _________ nada

d. Mis hermanos __________ pesas a menudo

e. Mis abuelos siempre __________ preguntas

f. Mi hermana _________ la comida hoy

g. Nunca ________ escalada porque tengo miedo

h. Nosotros _________ mucho deporte

i. ¿Qué deporte_________ (vosotras)?

j. Mi padre y yo ____________ natación juntos

k. Mi hermana y mi hermano nunca _______ nada

13. Translate into Spanish

a. I do rock climbing
b. We do sailing
c. You do weights
d. She does athletics
e. What sport do you do?

f. They make the bed
g. They make questions
h. He does nothing
i. We never do sport
j. She doesn't do the house chores

k. Every day
l. Rarely
m. Often
n. This morning
o. I like it a lot

14. Guided translation

a. *We do weights every day* H_ _ _ _ _ _ _ p_ _ _ _ _ t_ _ _ _ _ l_ _ d_ _ _

b. *They never do sport* N_ _ _ _ _ h_ _ _ _ _ d_ _ _ _ _ _ _

c. *What sport do you do?* ¿Q_ _ d_ _ _ _ _ _ _ h_ _ _ _ _?

d. *I don't do anything* N_ h_ _ _ n_ _ _

e. *My girlfriend and I...* M_ n_ _ _ _ _ y y_...

f. *...(we) never do hiking* …n_ _ _ _ _ h_ _ _ _ _ _ _ s_ _ _ _ _ _ _ _ _ _

g. *My father does boxing and weights* M_ p_ _ _ _ _ h_ _ _ b_ _ _ _ _ y p_ _ _ _ _

h. *My brother does rock climbing* M_ h_ _ _ _ _ _ _ _ h_ _ _ e_ _ _ _ _ _ _ _ _

15. Find the Spanish translation and write it next to the English prompts

h	y	n	o	h	a	c	e	n	a	d	a	g	u	d	l	ñ	s	o	r	n	q	e	a	d	a	l
a	v	e	c	m	n	f	w	o	s	v	a	j	e	b	o	j	e	i	x	o	g	n	k	i	l	m
c	a	s	y	n	u	n	c	a	h	a	g	o	l	a	c	a	m	a	f	h	y	m	c	t	a	r
e	n	u	n	c	a	h	a	c	e	m	o	s	d	e	p	o	r	t	e	a	q	i	g	r	e	l
n	u	n	c	a	h	a	c	e	n	p	e	s	a	s	m	e	j	i	y	g	a	ñ	a	t	u	f
b	c	n	o	h	a	c	e	m	o	s	e	s	c	a	l	a	d	a	q	o	f	r	i	l	g	a
u	p	a	s	q	u	é	h	a	c	e	s	f	o	r	l	u	m	o	ñ	n	a	t	o	s	b	i
c	h	n	o	h	a	c	é	i	s	v	e	l	a	d	u	r	d	a	b	a	s	t	u	k	n	o
e	s	h	t	o	b	a	r	h	a	p	r	y	n	o	h	a	c	e	n	d	e	p	o	r	t	e
o	k	a	s	y	v	e	r	a	d	b	e	l	a	c	h	a	c	e	n	a	t	a	c	i	ó	n
c	n	m	i	z	f	s	d	e	s	n	o	h	a	c	e	m	o	s	n	a	d	a	y	e	n	o

a. I never make the bed
b. You guys don't go sailing
c. They never do weights
d. We don't go rock climbing
e. He does nothing
f. We never do sport

g. I do nothing
h. What do you do?
i. They go scuba diving
j. We do nothing
k. They don't do sport
l. He goes swimming

16. Staircase translation: translate each sentence from memory

a.	I do	sport					
b.	We do	horse riding	rarely				
c.	They do	swimming	often	with us			
d.	We do	sailing	once a week	with our parents.	I like it a lot		
e.	She does	jogging	every day	alone	because	it is relaxing	
f.	They do	sailing	at the weekend	alone.	We never	do sailing.	It's boring

a. ____

b. ____

c. ____

d. ____

e. ____

f. ____

17. Complete with the correct form of *HACER* and possessive adjective

a. (Yo) ______ pesas con ___ mejor amigo

b. (Ella) _______ vela con _____ padres

c. (Nosotros) _______ karate con _______ tío Pepe

d. (Ellas) ________ escalada con _______ novios

e. ¿(Vosotros) _________ boxeo con ________ padre?

f. (Nosotras) Siempre __________ las tareas domésticas con ________ madre

g. (Él) _________ buceo con ___ padre

h. (Tú) Nunca _________ equitación con _____ amigas

i. (Ellas) _________ hacen preguntas a _______ profesores

18. Complete with the correct form of *HACER* and *TENER*

a. Cuando (yo) ____________ tiempo libre, (yo) _________ footing en el parque

b. Cuando (él) ___________ tiempo libre, (él) ____________ pesas conmigo

c. Cuando (ellos) _________ tiempo libre, (ellos) __________ equitación con nosotros

d. Cuando (ella) __________ tiempo libre, (ella) __________ las tareas domésticas

e. Cuando (nosotros) ___________ tiempo libre, __________ boxeo con nuestro tío

f. ¿Qué _________ tú cuando (tú) _________ tiempo libre?

5.4 CUANDO + HACE + NOUN / LLUEVE / NIEVA + PRESENT OF HACER

(SAYING WHAT ONE DOES IN DIFFERENT TYPES OF WEATHER)

Cuando *When*	**hace** *it is*	**buen tiempo** *nice weather* **calor** *hot* **frío** *cold* **mal tiempo** *bad weather* **sol** *sunny* **viento** *windy*
Cuando llueve *When it rains* **Cuando nieva** *When it snows*		

(No) *don't* **(Nunca)** *never* **(Siempre)** *always*	**Hago** *I do* **Haces** *you do* **Hace** *he/she does* **Hacemos** *we do* **Hacéis** *you guys do* **Hacen** *they do*	**atletismo** *athletics* **artes marciales** **boxeo** **buceo** *scuba diving* **ciclismo** **deporte** *sport* **ejercicio físico** *physical exercise* **equitación** *horse riding* **escalada** *rock climbing* **esquí** *ski* **footing** *jogging* **natación** *swimming* **pesas** *weights* **senderismo** *hiking* **vela** *sailing* **windsurf** **yoga**
		la comida *(make) food (lunch)* **las compras** *the shopping* **las tareas domésticas** *the house chores* **los deberes** *homework*
Nunca hacemos nada *We never do anything*		

LANGUAGE AWARENESS

HACER – THE WEATHER MAKER!

¡Hola!

There is one more important use of ***hacer,*** apart from "to do", "to make" and the others seen in the previous units, it is also used for some common weather descriptions.

- **Hace sol** *It is sunny* — Literally It **makes** sun
- **Hace frío** *It is cold* — Literally It **makes** cold

Hace sol y buen tiempo

1. Gapped translation: complete the translation

a. Cuando hace viento, hago vela o windsurf	*When it is ________, I go sailing or surfing*
b. Cuando hace mucho frío, no hago nada	*When it is very cold, I do ____________*
c. Cuando hace buen tiempo, hago footing	*When the weather is ____________, I go jogging*
d. Cuando nieva, hago esquí	*When it _______, I go skiing*
e. Cuando hace mucho calor, hago natación	*When it is very _________ , I go swimming*
f. Cuando llueve, me quedo en casa y…	*When it ________ , I stay at home and...*
g. …hago las tareas domésticas	*...I do the _____________*
h. Cuando hace mal tiempo, hago las compras	*When the weather is _____ , I do the _________*
i. Cuando hace sol y calor, hago buceo	*When it is ______ and ________, I go __________*

2. Complete with the correct present form of *HACER*

a. Cuando hace viento (nosotros) __________ windsurf

b. Cuando hace buen tiempo (ellos) no _________ nada

c. Cuando llueve (yo) ________ las tareas domésticas

d. Cuando hace mucho calor (ellas) _________ buceo

e. ¿Qué (tú) _______ cuando hace mucho calor?

f. Mi madre nunca _______ deporte cuando hace mucho calor

g. Nosotros no _________ escalada cuando hace mal tiempo

h. Mis tíos ______ vela cuando no hace frío

i. Mi hermano _______ yoga cuando hace mal tiempo

3. Listen and complete

a. Cuando hace _ _ _ _ _ _

b. Cuando hace _ _ _ _

c. Cuando hace

_ _ _ _ _ _ _ _ _ _

d. Cuando hace

_ _ _ _ _ _ _ _ _ _

e. Cuando _ _ _ _ _

f. Cuando _ _ _ _ _ _ _

g. Cuando hace _ _ _ _ _ _ _

h. Cuando hace _ _ _

i. Cuando hace

_ _ _ _ _ _ _ _ _ _ _

4. Sentence Puzzle

a. hace Cuando hago viento windsurf	*When it's windy I go windsurfing*
b. Cuando hace hace calor natación	*When it is hot she goes swimming*
c. buceo Cuando hace hacemos sol	*When it is sunny we go diving*
d. esquí Cuando nieva hacen	*When it snows they go skiing*
e. hace Cuando hago frío no nada	*When it's cold I don't do anything*
f. Cuando buen tiempo escalada hace hace	*When the weather's good she goes rock climbing*
g. tiempo Cuando mal hace hacen los deberes	*When the weather is bad they do the homework*
h. ¿tiempo Qué hace haces cuando mal?	*What do you do when the weather is bad?*
i. ¿hacéis cuando Qué hace calor?	*What do you guys do when it is hot?*

5. Translanagrams: unscramble the phrases and translate them into English

a. Hcea ivenot

b. caHe oracl

c. vaNei

d. Hcea neub pmeito

e. aHec los

f. echa írof

g. eLvlue

h. aHec alm pemtoi

6. Listen and translate into English.

a.

b.

c.

d.

e.

f.

g.

h.

i.

7. Find the Spanish translation and write it next to the English prompts

a	t	o	m	g	s	o	l	o	í	d	y	r	a	n
v	m	a	l	t	i	e	m	p	o	f	r	e	d	m
z	a	h	ñ	f	o	s	n	w	b	m	a	t	e	z
a	m	d	e	h	z	c	a	d	u	a	l	i	c	t
m	e	g	r	a	n	a	d	q	e	l	a	d	ó	m
d	s	ó	t	m	a	l	a	b	n	r	e	a	r	b
s	x	i	g	h	e	a	d	a	t	e	i	r	d	o
g	t	a	v	i	q	d	r	e	i	m	é	s	o	d
j	o	g	y	b	j	a	o	h	e	k	a	l	m	j
e	c	a	f	b	s	t	o	g	m	a	n	k	y	o
é	r	r	v	n	n	b	d	u	p	f	r	t	u	s
r	u	x	c	e	h	c	a	l	o	r	a	b	t	o
y	t	f	i	l	l	e	v	b	j	í	l	g	u	e
e	r	v	e	z	h	a	c	a	y	o	g	e	r	l

a. Bad weather

b. Good weather

c. Heat

d. Wind

e. Sailing

f. Rock climbing

g. Hiking

h. Nothing

i. Cold

j. Sun

8. Complete

a. Hace mal ti _ _ _ _ *it's bad weather*

b. Hace _ _ _ _ _ tiempo *it's nice weather*

c. Hace _ _ _ *it's sunny*

d. Hace _ _ _ _ _ *it's hot*

e. Hace _ _ _ _ _ _ *it's windy*

f. Hace _ _ _ _ *it's cold*

g. Hago _ _ _ _ *I go sailing*

h. Hacen los debe_ _ _ *they do homework*

i. Hacemos _ _ _ _ _ *we go skiing*

9. Translate into Spanish

a. When it is hot, I go swimming

b. When it snows, I go skiing

c. When it is cold, I do my homework

d. When it is bad weather, I do the house chores

e. When it is nice weather, I go jogging

f. When it is hot, I do nothing

g. When it is cold, I do weights in the gym

h. When it is windy, I go windsurfing

i. When it rains, I go shopping

5.5 PRESENT OF HACER FALTA + NOUN/VERB *(SAYING WHAT ONE NEEDS)*

No me hace falta *I don't need it*			**No me hace falta nada** *I don't need anything/I need nothing*	
			ayuda	*help*
			dinero	*money*
A mí	**Me hace falta**	*I need*	**comer mejor**	*to eat better*
			descansar	*to rest*
A ti	**Te hace falta**	*You need*	**estudiar más**	*to study more*
A él/ella	**Le hace falta**	*He/she needs*	**hacer más deporte**	*to do more sport*
A nosotros	**Nos hace falta**	*We need*	**un abrigo**	*a coat*
			un lápiz	*a pencil*
A vosotros	**Os hace falta**	*You guys need*	**un libro**	*a book*
A ellos/ellas	**Les hace falta**	*They need*	**un móvil**	*a mobile phone*
			un ordenador	*a computer*
			un sacapuntas	*a sharpener*
			una goma	*a rubber*
Me hace falta mi móvil	*I need my mobile phone*			

LANGUAGE AWARENESS: *HACER* VS *HACER FALTA*

In Spanish there are two main ways of expressing "to need". One is a regular AR verb, ***"necesitar"***, which works the same as all other verbs.

- **Necesito un abrigo** *I need a coat* • **Necesitas estudiar** *You need to study*

The other way, which is **very** common in Spanish, is to use ***"hacer falta"***, which means "to be necessary", but literally **"to do/make lack".**

- **Me hace falta un abrigo** *To me I lack a coat* ***(I need** a coat)*
- **Te hace falta estudiar** *To you you lack to study* ***(You need** to study)*

To say that different people need something **we change the (indirect object) pronoun in front of *hace falta*** as opposed to the verb ***hacer*** itself**:**

- **Me hace falta ayuda** *To me I lack help* ***(I need** help)*

¡A MÍ ME HACE FALTA!

If we want to emphasise the person who needs something, we can add the "*A mí/ A ti/etc*" pronoun to the sentence in front of the indirect object pronoun. It does not mean anything extra, but we just emphasise that the person really needs something!

- **A mí me hace falta un lápiz** *I need a pencil*

1. Match

Me hace falta un abrigo nuevo	*I need money*
Me hace falta dinero	*I need a new coat*
Me hace falta una goma	*I need help*
Me hace falta ayuda	*I need a pencil sharpener*
Me hace falta descansar	*I need to rest*
Me hace falta comer mejor	*I need a rubber*
Me hace falta un libro	*I need a computer*
Me hace falta un sacapuntas	*I need a book*
Me hace falta un ordenador	*I need to eat better*

2. Anagrams

a. inDero *money*
b. escDsaran *to rest*
c. yAuad *help*
d. Un rdeodonar *a computer*
e. nU acaspuntsa *a sharpener*
f. oCerm jomer *to eat better*
g. Un oagrib *a coat*
h. nU oilbr *a book*
i. Una omag *a rubber*

3. Gapped translation: complete the translation

a. Me hace falta una goma ____ *need a rubber*
b. Le hace falta descansar *he needs to* _______
c. Nos hace falta dinero ____ *need money*
d. ¿Qué os hace falta? *What do* ________ *need?*
e. ¡No te hace falta nada! *You don't need* ________*!*
f. Les hace falta un coche nuevo _____ *need a new car*
g. No me hace falta nada *I don't need* _________
h. ¿Qué te hace falta? *What do* ____ *need?*
i. ¿Qué les falta? *What do* ____ *need?*

4. Choose the correct pronoun

a. **Te/Le/Me** hace falta *She needs*
b. **Nos/Os/Les** hace falta *We need*
c. **Les/Nos/Os** hace falta *You guys need*
d. **Me/Te/Le** hace falta *I need*
e. **Os/Te/Nos** hace falta *You need*
f. **Le/Nos/Les** hace falta *He needs*
g. **Les/Nos/Os** hace falta *They need*

5. Find the Spanish and then write it next to the English prompts

s	u	n	a	b	r	i	g	o	e	s	t	f	r	a	m	i
f	g	r	u	d	o	b	e	m	o	s	u	c	n	i	p	a
d	u	n	t	g	d	i	n	e	r	o	n	e	a	s	o	t
k	e	r	o	u	j	a	b	y	s	i	d	u	d	m	x	j
g	j	l	i	v	u	m	e	h	a	c	e	f	a	l	t	a
c	l	i	v	ó	m	n	u	v	o	d	s	a	p	h	o	n
a	i	d	o	n	t	l	a	i	k	a	c	t	u	s	d	y
l	e	h	a	c	e	f	a	l	t	a	a	o	n	d	w	ó
m	i	b	r	o	d	r	i	z	a	l	n	d	a	e	t	s
f	r	o	n	d	h	q	ñ	u	x	u	s	a	g	o	l	e
g	d	c	h	a	k	o	r	d	e	n	a	d	o	r	u	s
b	i	c	n	e	s	u	n	g	n	e	r	o	m	k	p	o
a	d	e	t	i	b	e	a	e	t	x	w	u	a	r	g	y
n	o	s	h	a	c	e	f	a	l	t	a	m	j	d	c	i

a. A coat
b. We need
c. A rubber
d. I need
e. Nothing
f. Money
g. A mobile phone
h. Computer
i. He needs
j. To rest

6. Break the flow

a. Amímehacefaltaunagoma

b. ¿Quétehacefaltaati?

c. Aellosnoleshacefaltanada

d. Anosotrosnoshacefaltamásdinero

e. ¿Quéoshacefaltaavosotras?

f. Amímehacefaltaunbuenamigo

g. Aellalehacefaltauncoche

h. Aéllehacefaltaunabrigonuevo

7. Gapped translation: complete the translation

a. ___ hace ______ un _________ *I need a coat*

b. ___ hace falta _______ mejor *He needs to eat better*

c. ___ nos ____________ nada *We don't need anything*

d. A nosotros ___ hace _________... *We need...*

e. A ellos ____ hace ______ dinero *They need money*

f. A ____ le hace falta... *She needs...*

g. ...un vestido _______ *...a new dress*

h. ¿Qué ____ hace _________? *What do you need?*

8. Listen, complete and translate

a. __ __ __ hace falta dinero

b. __ __ hace falta un abrigo

c. __ __ hace falta un lápiz

d. __ __ __ hace falta descansar

e. ¿Qué __ __ hace falta?

f. ¿Qué __ __ hace falta?

g. __ __ __ hace falta comer mejor

h. ¡No __ __ hace falta nada!

9. Complete with the missing pronoun

a. A mi madre ____ hace falta dinero

b. A mí y a mi hermano ____ hace falta unos abrigos

c. A mi novia ____ hace falta descansar

d. A mis padres ____ hace falta comer mejor

e. A ti ___ hace falta una buena amiga

f. A vosotros ____ hace falta hacer más deporte

g. ¡A mi hermana no ___ hace falta nada!

h. A mí ____ hace falta ayuda

10. Tangled translation: translate into Spanish

a. A mí me ***need money***

b. A ***you guys*** os ***need to rest***

c. A nosotros ***us need*** un buen amigo

d. A ***my sister needs*** nada

e. A mis padres les ***need*** comer ***better***

f. ¿Qué ***you guys need***?

g. A Marcelo ***him*** hace falta un ***coat***

h. A mi madre ***her*** hace falta ***help***

i. A nosotros ***us need*** estudiar ***more***

j. ***You need*** hacer ***more*** deporte

11. Translate into Spanish

a. We need to study more

b. I need to rest more

c. They need to eat better

d. You guys need more money

e. You need a good friend

f. My mother needs help

g. My parents don't need anything

h. My brother and I need to do more sport

i. Pablo needs a pencil

j. I need a rubber

5.6 HACE FALTA + SING. NOUNS OR VERB VS HACEN FALTA + PLURAL NOUNS

(SAYING WHAT ONE NEEDS)

A mí	Me hace falta	*I need*	ayuda	*help*
A ti	Te hace falta	*You need*	dinero	*money*
A él/ella	Le hace falta	*He/she needs*	comer mejor	*to eat better*
A nosotros	Nos hace falta	*We need*	descansar	*to rest*
A vosotros	Os hace falta	*You guys need*	estudiar más	*to study more*
A ellos/ellas	Les hace falta	*They need*	hacer más deporte	*to do more sport*
			un lápiz	*a pencil*
			un libro	*a book*
			un sacapuntas	*a sharpener*
			un abrigo	*a coat*
			un ordenador	*a computer*
			un móvil	*a mobile phone*
			una goma	*a rubber*

Me hace falta mi móvil	*I need **my** mobile*
No me hace falta	*I don't need **it***
No me hace falta nada	*I don't need **anything**/I need **nothing***

No me hacen falta *I don't need them*

A mí	Me hace**n** falta	*I need*	buenos amigos	*good friends*
A ti	Te hace**n** falta	*You need*	unos zapatos nuevos	*new shoes*
A él/ella	Le hace**n** falta	*He/she needs*	unos videojuegos nuevos	*new videogames*
A nosotros	Nos hace**n** falta	*We need*	más pingüinos	*more penguins*
A vosotros	Os hace**n** falta	*You guys need*	más lápices	*more pencils*
A ellos/ellas	Les hace**n** falta	*They need*	más libros	*more books*
			muchas cosas	*many things*

Me hacen falta mis llaves	*I need **my** keys*
No me hacen falta	*I don't need **them***

LANGUAGE AWARENESS

ME HACEN FALTA - PLURALS

If what is needed is something plural, we use ***hacen falta***

- **Nos hacen falta más pingüinos**

We need more penguins

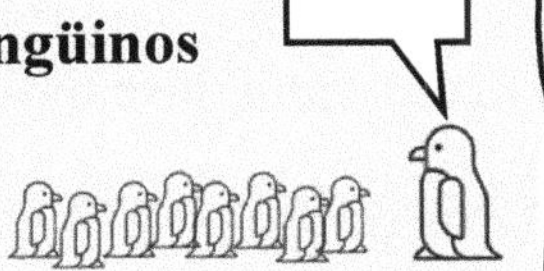

NO ME HACE FALTA

If we use ***no me hace falta*** on its own, we translate it as "I don't need it", even though in Spanish, the word "it" is not a part of the sentence. Some other examples are:

- **Me hace falta** — *I need it*
- **No nos hacen falta** — *We don't need them*
- **No les hacen falta** — *They don't need them*

1. Faulty translation: fix the English translation

a. Me hace falta un abrigo	*We need a coat*
b. Nos hacen falta muchas cosas	*We need more things*
c. ¿Os hace falta ayuda?	*Do you need help?*
d. ¿Qué te hace falta?	*What does he need?*
e. Le hace falta un ordenador	*She needs a mobile phone*
f. Les hace falta una goma	*He needs a rubber*
g. Me hace falta dinero	*I need my mobile phone*
h. Le hace falta más gente	*They need more people*
i. ¿Qué os hace falta?	*What do they need?*
j. Te hacen falta buenos amigos	*You need more friends*

2. Gapped translation

a. ¿__ __ hace falta dinero?
Do you need money?

b. __ __ hacen falta muchas cosas
I need a lot of things

c. ¿Qué __ __ hace falta?
What do you guys need?

d. No __ __ hace falta nada
She doesn't need anything

e. __ __ __ hace falta una goma
They need a rubber

f. __ __ __ hace falta ayuda
We need help

3. Sentence Puzzle

a. abrigo unos hacen Me falta un nuevos y zapatos	*I need a new coat and new shoes*
b. ¿te Qué falta hace?	*What do you need?*
c. muchas Me hacen cosas: todo sobre falta dinero	*I need a lot of things: above all money*
d. falta Os amigos hacen nuevos	*You guys need new friends*
e. hace Le falta más y comer mejor descansar	*He needs to rest more and eat better*
f. A le Marco ordenador hace un falta nuevo	*Marco needs a new computer*
g. Carmen A le hace hacer más falta deporte	*Carmen needs to do more sport*
h. Nos nuevos hacen unos falta zapatos	*We need new shoes*

4. Break the flow

a. Mehacenfaltamuchascosas

b. AJuanlehacenfaltaunagomayunlápiz

c. AMarcelalehacefaltaunvestidonuevo

d. Noshacefaltamásdinero.

e. Atitehacenfaltabuenosamigos

f. Mehacenfaltaunoszapatosnuevos

g. Noshacenfaltamuchascosas

h. Tehacefaltaunordenadornuevo

i. ¿Quéleshacefalta?

5. Listen and complete the words

a. Nos hac__ __ falta mucha__ cos__ __

b. Le hac__ falta un vestid__ nuev__

c. Me hac__ __ falta uno__ zapato__ nuevo__

d. Te hac__ falta un ordenador nuev__

e. ¿Qué le__ hac__ falta?

f. ¿Qué os hac__ falta?

g. Me hac__ falta a__ud__

h. Le hac__ falta descansar

i. Nos hac__ falta hacer más deporte

6. *Me hacen falta* or *me hace falta*?

a. Me **hace/hacen** falta zapatos nuevos

b. No me **hace/hacen** falta nada

c. ¿Qué te **hace/hacen** falta?

d. A Marco le **hace/hacen** falta un ordenador

e. A mí no me **hace/hacen** falta dinero

f. Nos **hace/hacen** falta amigos nuevos

g. Me **hace/hacen** falta una Play nueva

h. Nos **hace/hacen** falta muchas cosas

i. Te **hace/hacen** falta descansar

7. Add an N in the blanks if required or leave blank if not.

a. Me hace__ falta zapatos nuevos

b. No me hace__ falta amigos nuevos

c. Nos hace__ falta dinero

d. A ellos les hace__ falta de todo

e. A mis padres les hace__ falta hacer más deporte

f. A mi hermano le hace__ falta calcetines nuevos

g. ¿Qué les hace__ falta a ellos?

h. A ella le hace__ falta un móvil nuevo

i. Nos hace__ falta muchas cosas

8. Complete with *hace/hacen* as appropriate

a. Me _______ falta un móvil nuevo

b. Me ________ falta unos zapatos nuevos

c. Me ________ falta ayuda

d. Me ________ falta descansar

e. No me ________ falta nada

f. Me ________ falta unos bolígrafos nuevos

g. No me ________ falta calcetines nuevos

h. Me ________ falta videojuegos nuevos

9. Listen, complete and then translate

a. ___ _______ falta un abrigo nuevo

b. ___ _______ falta calcetines

c. ___ _______ falta dinero

d. ___ _______ falta un móvil nuevo

e. ___ ___ _______ falta nada

f. ___ _______ falta zapatos nuevos

g. No ___ _________ falta calcetines nuevos

h. ¿ ___ _________ falta videojuegos nuevos?

10. Guided translation

a. *I need a rubber*	M__ h__ __ __ f__ __ __ __ u__ __ g__ __ __
b. *We need shoes*	N__ __ h__ __ __ __ f__ __ __ __ z__ __ __ __ __ __
c. *They need many things*	L__ __ h__ __ __ __ f__ __ __ __ m__ __ __ __ __ c__ __ __ __
d. *She doesn't need money*	N__ l__ h__ __ __ f__ __ __ __ d__ __ __ __ __
e. *We need to rest*	N__ __ h__ __ __ f__ __ __ __ d__ __ __ __ __ __ __ __
f. *I need a computer*	M__ h__ __ __ f__ __ __ __ u__ o__ __ __ __ __ __ __ __
g. *You need nothing*	N__ t__ h__ __ __ f__ __ __ __ n__ __ __

11. Translate into Spanish

a. I need a new computer

b. We need nothing

c. I need a new dress and new shoes

d. What do you need?

e. We need many things

f. They don't need more money

g. She needs to rest

h. We need a new car

A

ORAL PING PONG

HACER

ENGLISH 1	SPANISH 1	ENGLISH 2	SPANISH 2
Often, I do physical exercise because I am sporty and I love it.	A menudo, hago ejercicio físico porque soy deportista y me encanta.	I rarely make my bed at weekends because I am tired.	
I always do the house chores at the weekends, but I don't like them at all.	Siempre hago las tareas domésticas los fines de semana, pero no me gustan nada.	I go scuba diving from time to time when it is hot and sunny.	
My sister goes swimming from time to time.	Mi hermana hace natación de vez en cuando.	My parents do nothing on Fridays.	
My friends and I go hiking on Fridays when it is nice weather.	Mis amigos y yo hacemos senderismo los viernes cuando hace buen tiempo.	My friends and I go cycling in the park when it doesn't rain.	
I go sailing every day when it is sunny because it is fun.	Hago vela todos los días cuando hace sol porque es divertido.	Do you go sailing when it is windy?	
We never do anything at weekends.	Nunca hacemos nada los fines de semana.	We need our mobile phones.	
I need to do more sport when it is nice weather.	A mí me hace falta hacer más deporte cuando hace buen tiempo.	I need to do more sport.	
She needs to study more.	A ella le hace falta estudiar más.	They need to go to the cinema more.	

INSTRUCTIONS - You are **PARTNER A.** Work in pairs. Each of you has two sets of sentences - one set has already been translated for you. You will ask your partner to translate these. The other set of sentences have not been translated. Your partner will ask you to translate these.
HOW TO PLAY - Partner A starts by reading out his/her/their first sentence in English. Partner B must translate. Partner A must check the answer and award the following points: **3 points** = perfect, **2 points** = 1 mistake, **1 point** = mistakes but the verb is accurate. If they cannot translate correctly, Partner A will read out the sentence so that Partner B can learn what the correct translation is.
Then Partner B reads out his/her/their first sentence, and so on.
OBJECTIVE - Try to win more points than your partner by translating correctly as many sentences as possible.

B

ORAL PING PONG

HACER

ENGLISH 1	SPANISH 1	ENGLISH 2	SPANISH 2
Often, I do physical exercise because I am sporty and I love it.		I rarely make my bed at weekends because I am tired.	Raramente hago la cama los fines de semana porque estoy cansado.
I always do the house chores at the weekends, but I don't like them at all.		I go scuba diving from time to time when it is hot and sunny.	Hago buceo de vez en cuando, cuando hace calor y sol.
My sister goes swimming from time to time.		My parents do nothing on Fridays.	Mis padres no hacen nada los viernes.
My friends and I go hiking on Fridays when it is nice weather.		My friends and I go cycling in the park when it doesn't rain.	Mis amigos y yo hacemos ciclismo en el parque cuando no llueve.
I go sailing every day when it is sunny because it is fun.		Do you go sailing when it is windy?	¿Haces vela cuando hace viento?
We never do anything at weekends.		We need our mobile phones.	A nosotros nos hacen falta nuestros móviles.
I need to do more sport when it is nice weather.		I need to do more sport.	A mí me hace falta hacer más deporte.
She needs to study more.		They need to go to the cinema more.	A ellos/ellas les hace falta ir al cine más.

INSTRUCTIONS - You are **PARTNER B.** Work in pairs. Each of you has two sets of sentences - one set has already been translated for you. You will ask your partner to translate these. The other set of sentences have not been translated. Your partner will ask you to translate these.
HOW TO PLAY - Partner A starts by reading out his/her/their first sentence in English. Partner B must translate. Partner A must check the answer and award the following points: **3 points** = perfect, **2 points** = 1 mistake, **1 point** = mistakes but the verb is accurate. If they cannot translate correctly, Partner A will read out the sentence so that Partner B can learn what the correct translation is.
Then Partner B reads out his/her/their first sentence, and so on.
OBJECTIVE - Try to win more points than your partner by translating correctly as many sentences as possible.

No Snakes No Ladders

HACER

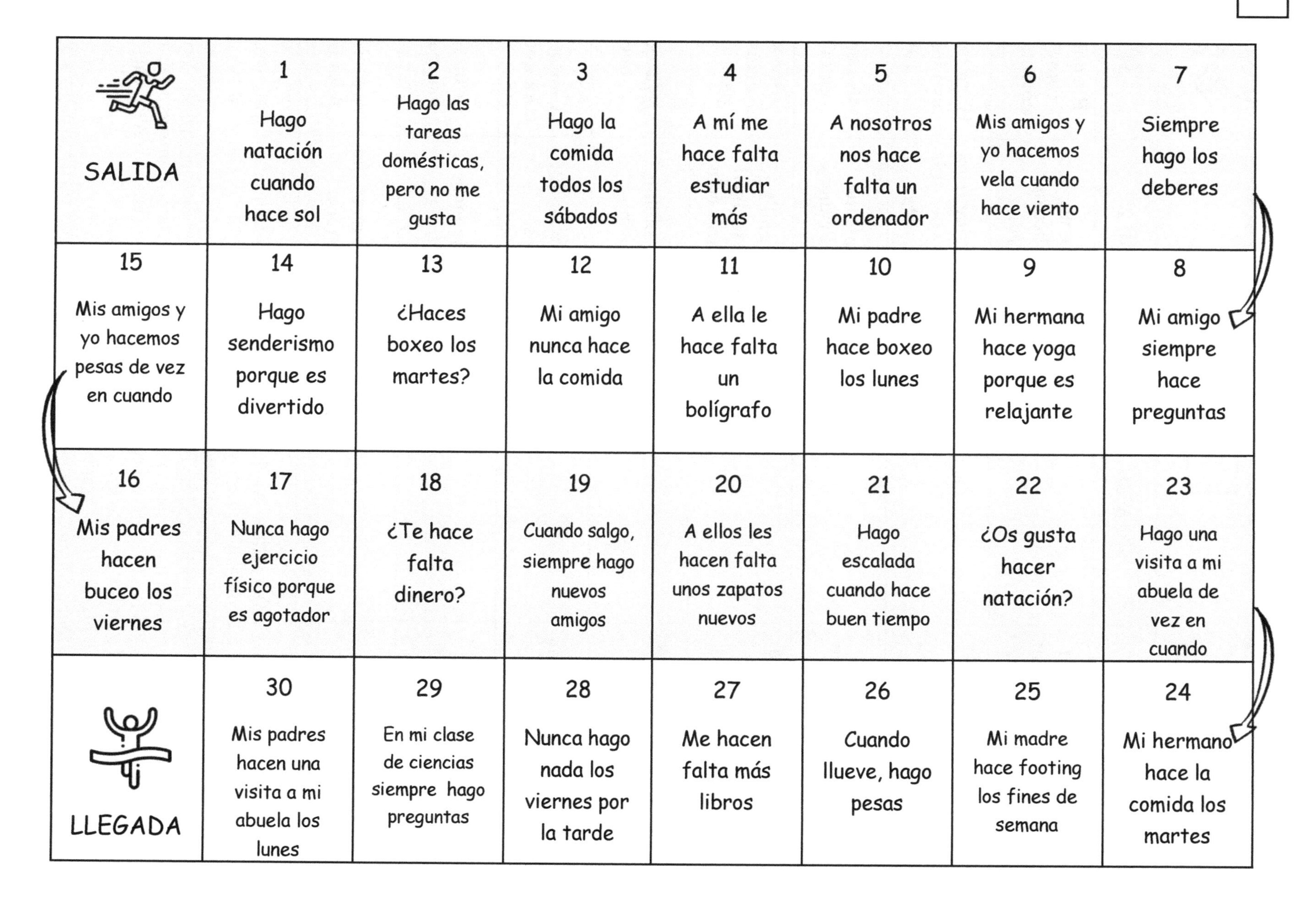

SALIDA	1 Hago natación cuando hace sol	2 Hago las tareas domésticas, pero no me gusta	3 Hago la comida todos los sábados	4 A mí me hace falta estudiar más	5 A nosotros nos hace falta un ordenador	6 Mis amigos y yo hacemos vela cuando hace viento	7 Siempre hago los deberes
15 Mis amigos y yo hacemos pesas de vez en cuando	14 Hago senderismo porque es divertido	13 ¿Haces boxeo los martes?	12 Mi amigo nunca hace la comida	11 A ella le hace falta un bolígrafo	10 Mi padre hace boxeo los lunes	9 Mi hermana hace yoga porque es relajante	8 Mi amigo siempre hace preguntas
16 Mis padres hacen buceo los viernes	17 Nunca hago ejercicio físico porque es agotador	18 ¿Te hace falta dinero?	19 Cuando salgo, siempre hago nuevos amigos	20 A ellos les hacen falta unos zapatos nuevos	21 Hago escalada cuando hace buen tiempo	22 ¿Os gusta hacer natación?	23 Hago una visita a mi abuela de vez en cuando
LLEGADA	30 Mis padres hacen una visita a mi abuela los lunes	29 En mi clase de ciencias siempre hago preguntas	28 Nunca hago nada los viernes por la tarde	27 Me hacen falta más libros	26 Cuando llueve, hago pesas	25 Mi madre hace footing los fines de semana	24 Mi hermano hace la comida los martes

No Snakes No Ladders

HACER

SALIDA	1 I *go* swimming when it is sunny	2 I do house chores, but I don't like it	3 I make lunch every Saturday	4 I need to study more	5 We need a computer	6 My friends and I go sailing when it is windy	7 I always do my homework
15 My friends and I do weights from time to time	14 I *go* hiking because it is fun	13 Do you do boxing on Tuesdays?	12 My friend never makes lunch	11 She needs a pen	10 My dad does boxing on Mondays	9 My sister does yoga because it is relaxing	8 My friend always asks questions
16 My parents *go* scuba diving on Fridays	17 I never do physical exercise because it is tiring	18 Do you need money?	19 When I go out, I always make new friends	20 They need some new shoes	21 I do rock climbing when it is nice weather	22 Do you guys like *going* swimming?	23 I pay a visit to my grandmother from time to time
LLEGADA	30 My parents pay a visit to my grandmother on Mondays	29 In my science lesson I always ask questions	28 I never do anything on Fridays in the evening	27 I need more books	26 When it rains, I do weights	25 My mother *goes* jogging at weekends	24 My brother makes lunch on Tuesdays

PYRAMID TRANSLATION

HACER

Translate each part of the pyramid out loud with your partner, then write it into the spaces provided below.

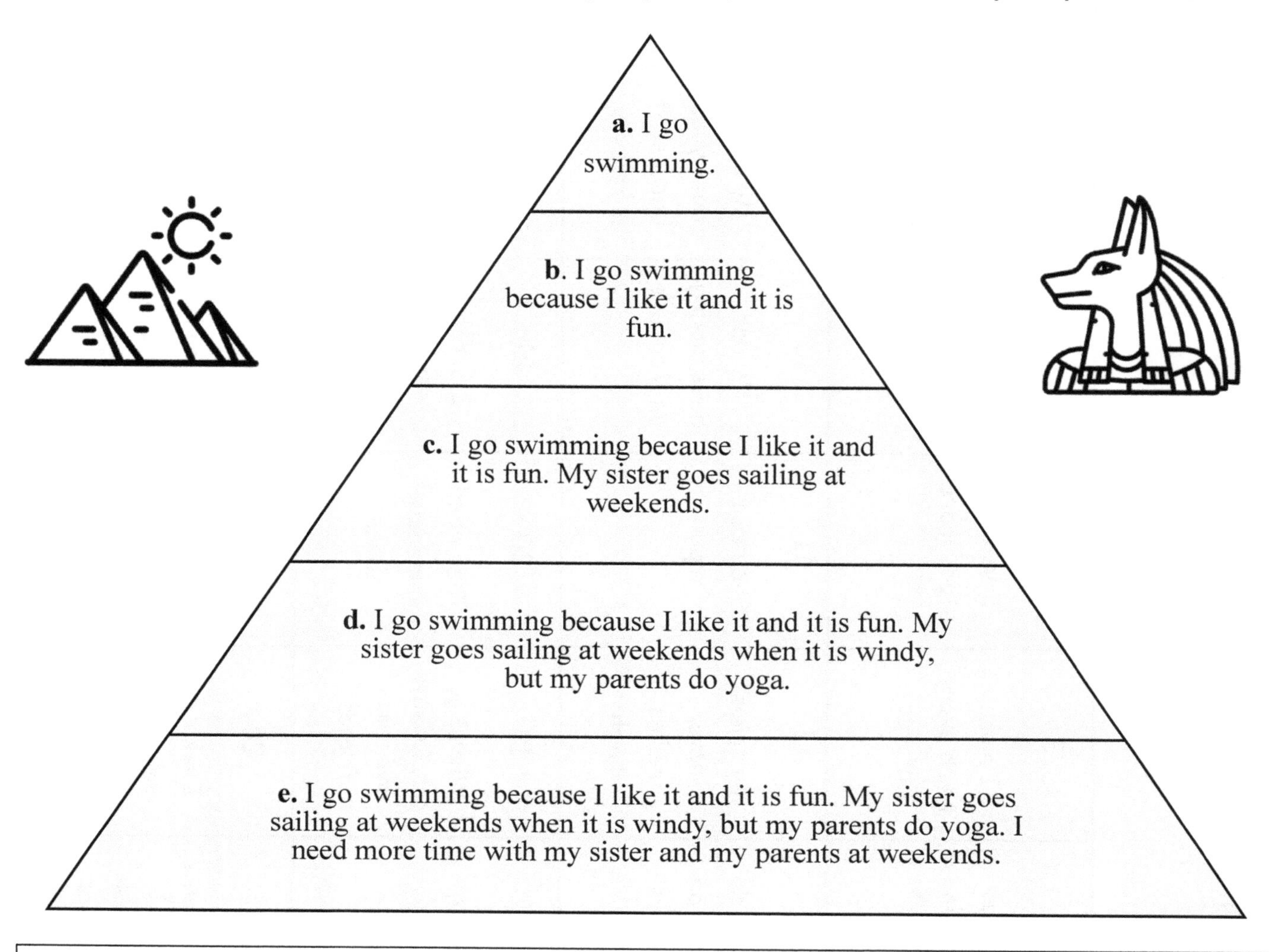

Write your translation here

SOLUTION: Hago natación porque me gusta y es divertido. Mi hermana hace vela los fines de semana cuando hace viento, pero mis padres hacen yoga. A mí me hace falta más tiempo con mi hermana y mis padres los fines de semana.

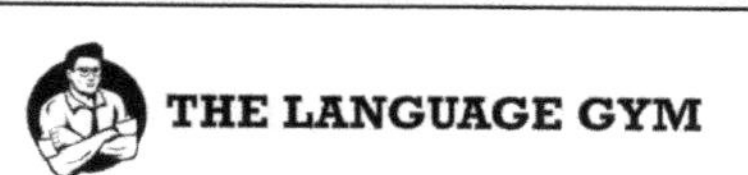

UNIT 6 – GUSTAR

A mí	Me	
A ti	Te	
A él / ella	Le	**gusta**
A nosotros / as	Nos	
A vosotros / as	Os	
A ellos / as	Les	

6.1 ME GUSTA/ENCANTA + PLACES + WHO WITH + LO HAGO + TIME ADVERBIALS *(SAYING WHAT ACTIVITIES WE DO WITH PEOPLE)*

		ciclismo	*cycling*		**mi familia**
		deporte	*sport*		**mi mejor amigo/a**
	hacer	**equitación**	*horse riding*		*my best friend*
Me gusta	*to do*	**escalada**	*rock climbing*		
I like	*(to go)*	**nada**	*nothing/anything*		**mi novio**
		natación	*swimming*		*my boyfriend*
No me gusta		**senderismo**	*hiking*		**mi novia**
I don't like		**yoga**	*yoga*		*my girlfriend*
		al baloncesto	*basketball*	**con**	**mi pareja**
Me gusta mucho	**jugar**	**al fútbol**	*football*	*with*	*my partner*
I really like	*to play*	**al tenis**	*tennis*		
		a las cartas	*cards*		**mi primo/a**
Me encanta		**a los videojuegos**	*videogames*		*my cousin*
I love		**al cine**	*to the cinema*		
	ir	**al estadio**	*to the stadium*		**mis amigos**
	to go	**al parque**	*to the park*		*my friends*
		a la playa	*to the beach*		**mis amigas**
		a la piscina	*to the pool*		*my (girl) friends*
No me gusta hacer <u>nada</u> con <u>nadie</u>	*I don't like to do anything with anyone*				

	a menudo	*often*
	de vez en cuando	*from time to time*
	después del colegio	*after school*
Lo hago	**los lunes**	*on Mondays*
I do it	**los miércoles**	*on Wednesdays*
	los viernes	*on Fridays*
No lo hago	**los sábados**	*on Saturdays*
I don't do it	**los fines de semana**	*at the weekends*
	siempre	*always*
	todos los días	*every day*
	una vez a la semana	*once a week*
No lo hago <u>nunca</u>	*I never do it*	

LANGUAGE AWARENESS: GUSTAR – PART 1

Gustar is a **verb of psychological affection**; we use it when talking about what things / activities / people we like. We do not conjugate ***gustar*** like most other verbs, where the **verb ending** changes depending on the person who does the action, like ***hacer (hago/haces/hace/etc.)***

Instead of conjugating the ending of ***gustar***, we only change the **indirect object pronoun (*me/te/le/etc.*)** in front of ***gustar*** to show **who** is doing the liking:

- **<u>Me</u> gusta hacer ciclismo** — *<u>I</u> like to do/go cycling*
- **<u>Te</u> gusta hacer ciclismo** — *<u>You</u> like to do/go cycling*

1. Match

Hacer ciclismo	*To do rock climbing*
Hacer senderismo	*To do nothing*
Jugar a las cartas	*To do horse riding*
Ir a la playa	*To play videogames*
Jugar a los videojuegos	*To do cycling*
Ir al estadio	*To go to the stadium*
Hacer equitación	*To go to the beach*
No hacer nada	*To go hiking*
Hacer escalada	*To do swimming*
Hacer natación	*To play cards*

2. Anagrams

a. *I like* — eM asgut

b. *I love* — eM acnenat

c. *To do yoga* — rcHae gyoa

d. *To do swimming* — cHare ótanaicn

e. *Once a week* — naU zve a al amaesn

f. *To play cards* — rJgua a als tacsra

g. *Videogames* — osL voiesdgjeou

h. *To go to the beach* — rI a al aplya

i. *From time to time* — eD zev ne ucadno

3. Break the flow

a. Megustairalaplayaconmifamilialosfinesdesemanaporqueesdivertido.

b. Meencantairalcentrocomercialparaverunapelículaporqueesrelajante.

c. Meencantahacerequitaciónconmimejoramigolosfinesdesemana.

d. Megustajugaralfútbolconmisamigosporqueesapasionante.

e. Megustairalestadioconmimejoramigodevezencuando.

f. Megustajugaralbaloncestoconmiprimaloslunesporqueesrelajante.

g. Megustajugaralascartasconmiabuelotodoslosdías.

h. Nomegustahacernadalossábados.

i. Nomegustahacerequitaciónconmipadre.Nolohagonunca.

4. Draw a circle around the time expressions and underline the hobbies

a. A menudo

b. Senderismo

c. Videojuegos

d. Siempre

e. Natación

f. Nunca

g. Deporte

h. Escalada

i. De vez en cuando

5. Listen and translate

a.

b.

c.

d.

e.

f.

g.

h.

i.

6. Gapped translation: complete the translation

a. No me gusta hacer nada — *I don't like to do* ____________

b. Me encanta ir a la piscina — *I love going to the* ___________

c. Lo hago a menudo — *I do it* _______________

d. Me gusta hacer deporte — *I like doing* _____________

e. Me encanta jugar a las cartas — *I* ___________ *playing cards*

f. Lo hago de vez en cuando — *I do it* _______________

g. Me encanta hacer equitación — *I love doing* _______________

h. Nunca lo hago — *I* _______________ *do it*

7. Faulty translation: fix the Spanish translation

a. *I like to do swimming*	Me gusta hacer nada
b. *I like going to the cinema*	Me encanta ir al cine
c. *I love going to the park*	Me encanta ir al estadio
d. *I love going to the pool*	Me gusta ir a la playa
e. *I do it every day*	Lo hago todos los lunes
f. *With my boyfriend*	Con mi novia
g. *I never do it*	Siempre lo hago
h. *I always do it*	Lo hago de vez en cuando

8. Rearrange the sentences in the correct order

a. senderismo Me hacer encanta

b. hago Lo de en vez cuando

c. a la No playa gusta ir me

d. hago los Lo todos días

e. baloncesto jugar al los lunes Me gusta

f. ir No la a piscina gusta me

g. hago Lo raramente mi con hermano

9. Gapped translation: complete the translation

a. Me gusta _______ natación. Lo hago a ____________.	*I like doing swimming. I do it often.*
b. No me _______ jugar a los ______________.	*I don't like playing videogames.*
c. Nunca lo ________.	*I never do it.*
d. Me _________ jugar a las _________.	*I love playing cards.*
e. Lo _____ todos los fines ____ semana.	*I do it every weekend.*
f. Me encanta ________ pesas. Lo hago los ____________.	*I love doing weights. I do it on Tuesdays.*
g. No me _________ hacer footing. No lo hago _________.	*I don't like going jogging. I never do it.*
h. _____ me gusta ________ _______.	*I don't like doing anything.*
i. Me _________ ir a la _________.	*I like going to the beach.*
j. ____ hago una vez a la ____________.	*I do it once a week.*
k. Me gusta ______ ____________.	*I like doing rock-climbing.*

10. Listen and complete the words with the missing vowels

a. N__ m__ g__st__ __r __ l__ pl__y__ c__n m__ f__m__l__ __. N__ l__ h__ g__ n__nc__.

b. M__ __nc__nt__ __r __l c__ntr__ c__n m__s __m__g__s. L__ h__g__ l__ __ d__m__ng__s.

c. M__ __nc__nt__ __r __l c__ntr__ c__m__rc__ __l c__n m__ m__j__r __m__g__.

d. M__ g__st__ h__c__r __sc__l__d__ c__n m__ p__dr__. L__ h__g__ d__ v__z __n c__ __nd__.

e. M__ g__st__ j__g__r __ l__s c__rt__s c__n m__ m__dr__. L__ h__g__ l__s l__n__s.

f. M__ g__st__ j__g__r __l t__n__s, p__r__ __s d__r__. L__ h__g__ t__d__s l__s d__ __s.

g. N__ m__ g__st__ h__c__r n__d__ c__n m__ f__m__l__ __ l__s v__ __rn__s.

h. N__ m__ g__st__ __r __l c__ntr__ c__m__rc__ __l c__n m__ m__dr__. N__ l__ h__g__ n__nc__.

11. Listen and correct the mistakes

a. Lo hago un vez al semana

b. No me gusta mucho hacer cartas

c. Lo nunca hago

d. Todos los fines semana

e. Me encanta ir natación

f. Me gusta ir en el cine con mi novia

g. Me gusta jugar cartas con mi hermano o mi madre

h. Me gusta ir al playa con mis tío

12. Translation

a. I like

b. I love

c. I don't like

d. Much

e. Often

f. On Fridays

g. On weekends

h. I like doing hiking

i. I love doing weights

j. I do it often

k. I like going to the beach

l. I love doing swimming

m. I like a lot

n. I never do it

o. I like going to the park

p. With my brother

q. With my father

r. With my girlfriend

13. Guided translation

a. *I don't like to do homework with my friend. I never do it.* N__ m__ g__ __ __ __ h__ __ __ __ l__ __ d__ __ __ __ __ __ __ c__ __ m__ a__ __ __ __. N__ l__ h__ __ __ n__ __ __ __.

b. *I like to do swimming with my friends. I do it at weekends.* M__ gu __ __ __ h__ __ __ __ n__ __ __ __ __ __ __c__ __ m__ __ a__ __ __ __ __. L__ h__ __ __ l__ __ f__ __ __ __ d__ sem __ __ __.

c. *I like to play cards with my grandfather. I always do it.* M__ g__ __ __ __ j__ __ __ __ a l__ __ c__ __ __ __ __ __ c__ __ m__ a__ __ __ __ __ __. L__ h__ __ __ s__ __ __ __ __ __ __.

d. *I love to go to the stadium and play football with my friends. I do it once a week.* M__ e__ __ __ __ __ __ i__ a__ e__ __ __ __ __ __ __ y j__ __ __ __ a__ f__ __ __ __ __ c__ __ m__ __ a__ __ __ __ __. L__ h__ __ __ u__ __ v__ __ a l__ s__ __ __ __ __ __.

e. *I love to do horse riding with my best friend (f). I do it on Saturdays.* M__ e__ __ __ __ __ __ __ h__ __ __ __ e__ __ __ __ __ __ __ __ __ __ __ c__ __ m__ m__ __ __ __ __ a__ __ __ __. L__ h__ __ __ l__ __ s__ __ __ __ __ __.

14. Translate into Spanish

a. I don't like to go swimming with my father. I do it once a week.

b. I like going to the park with my friends. I do it nearly (*casi*) every day.

c. I love going to the beach with my girlfriend. I do it every weekend.

d. I don't like going horse riding with my mother. I do it every Sunday.

e. I don't like much playing cards with my family.

f. I like a lot going to the cinema with my boyfriend. I do it once a week.

g. I like doing rock climbing with my brother. I do it three times a week.

h. I love playing basketball with my best friend. I do it every day after school (*después del colegio*).

6.2 PRESENT OF GUSTAR + INFINITIVE OF HACER + NOUN. OBJECT PRONOUN + PRESENT OF HACER + TIME ADVERBIALS

(SAYING WHAT ONE LIKES/DISLIKES DOING AND HOW OFTEN THEY DO IT)

A mí (no) me gusta *I (don't) like* **A ti (no) te gusta** *You (don't) like* **A él/ella/ mi hermano (no) le gusta** *He/she/my brother likes (doesn't like)* **A nosotros (no) nos gusta** *We (don't) like* **A vosotros (no) os gusta** *You guys (don't) like* **A ellos/ellas (no) les gusta** *They (don't) like* **A mis padres (no) les gusta** *My parents (don't) like*	**hacer** *to do* *(to go)*	**ciclismo** *cycling* **deporte** *sport* **equitación** *horse riding* **escalada** *rock climbing* **nada** *nothing (to not do anything)* **natación** *swimming* **senderismo** *hiking* **yoga** *yoga*
	jugar *to play*	**al baloncesto** *basketball* **al fútbol** *football* **al tenis** *tennis* **a las cartas** *cards* **a los videojuegos** *videogames*
	ir *to go*	**al centro comercial** *to the shopping centre* **al cine** *to the cinema* **al estadio** *to the stadium* **a la playa** *to the beach* **a la piscina** *to the swimming pool*

Lo hago	*I do it*	**a menudo**	*often*
Lo haces	*You do it*	**de vez en cuando**	*from time to time*
Lo hace	*He/she does it*	**los lunes**	*on Mondays*
Lo hacemos	*We do it*	**los martes**	*on Tuesdays*
Lo hacéis	*You guys/ladies do it*	**los miércoles**	*on Wednesdays*
Lo hacen	*They do it*	**los jueves**	*on Thursdays*
		los viernes	*on Fridays*
No lo hago	*I* ***don't*** *do it*	**los sábados**	*on Saturdays*
No lo haces	*You* ***don't*** *do it*	**los domingos**	*on Sundays*
No lo hace	*He/she* ***doesn't*** *do it*	**los fines de semana**	*at the weekends*
No lo hacemos	*We* ***don't*** *do it*	**nunca**	*never*
No lo hacéis	*You guys/ladies* ***don't*** *do it*	**siempre**	*always*
No lo hacen	*They* ***don't*** *do it*	**todos los días**	*every day*
		una vez a la semana	*once a week*

LANGUAGE AWARENESS

NADA, NUNCA & NADIE

When we use ***nunca, nadie*** or ***nada*** with a verb, we must use ***no*** in front of such verb.

Remember that in Spanish we negate twice!

- **No hago nada** *I don't do nothing/anything*
- **No lo hago nunca** *I never do it*

And sometimes even three times!

- **Nunca hago nada con nadie**

I never do anything with anyone

Literally: *I never do nothing with no-one*

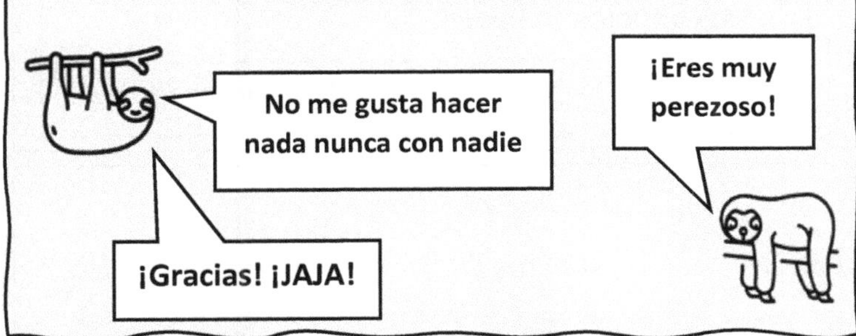

EXTRA EMPHASIS

You can add the extra pronoun ***"A mí/ti/él/ella/etc."*** if you want to make your sentence more emphatic:

- **A mí me gusta hacer ciclismo**

I like to do/go cycling

- **A ella le gusta jugar al tenis**

She likes to play tennis

This would be the equivalent of raising the pitch & volume of "I" / "she" in the above sentences to make it really clear who it is that likes either cycling or tennis.

IT IS PLEASING TO ME!

One way to help understand this structure is to think of ***gustar*** as meaning **'to please'.** It is sometimes referred to as a **backwards verb** because the structure works backwards compared to the English. Instead of "I like to do cycling" it is more like "to do cycling is pleasing to me"

	A mí	**me gusta**	**hacer**	**ciclismo**
Literal translation	*To me*	*it is pleasing*	*to do*	*cycling*
Translation	*I like*		*to do*	*cycling*

A MI PADRE LE GUSTA...

When we mention the person who likes to do something, we also use the **Personal *A*** in front of the noun:

- **A mi padre le gusta ir al cine**

My dad likes to go to the cinema

Literally it means: *going to the cinema is pleasing "to" my dad!*

POSSESSIVE ADJECTIVES

Remember that *mi familia/mi amigo/mi primo*/etc. will change to *tu, su, nuestro/a* or *vuestro/a* depending on the person we are talking about:

- **Nos gusta hacer equitación con nuestro amigo**

*We like to do horse riding with **our** friend*

- **Les gusta ir al parque con sus amigos**

*They like to go to the park with **their** friends*

1. Match

A mí me gusta	*Do you ladies like?*
A mi hermano le gusta	*We (f) like*
A nosotros nos gusta	*They (m) like*
A mi abuela le gusta	*My parents like*
¿A ti te gusta?	*You guys like*
A vosotros os gusta	*I like*
A ellos les gusta	*My brother likes*
A mis padres les gusta	*Do you like?*
¿A vosotras os gusta?	*We (m) like*
A nosotras nos gusta	*My grandmother likes*

2. Complete the table

Español	Inglés
	We do it
Lo hacen	
Vosotros lo hacéis	
	You do it
	He does it
Mi abuela lo hace	
	My uncles do it
Mis abuelos lo hacen	
	You ladies do it

3. Anagrams

a. A ím em asgut *I like*
b. ¿eT asgut? *Do you like?*
c. oL ehac *He does it*
d. osN ustga *We like*
e. Lo ogha *I do it*
f. oL mhaecos *We do it*
g. eL asgut *He likes*
h. oL ahecn *They do it*
i. ¿sO atusg? *Do you guys like?*
j. oL ahsce *You do it*
k. A im ahemran le asgut *My sister likes*
l. ¿A it et asgut? *Do you like?*

4. Gapped translation: complete the translation

a. _____ gusta jugar en el ordenador. Lo _______ a menudo.
I like playing on the computer. I do it often.

b. No ___ gusta ir a la piscina. Lo _________ raramente.
We don't like going to the swimming pool. We do it rarely.

c. A mis padres no ___ gusta ir al cine. No lo _______ nunca.
My parents don't like going to the cinema. They never do it.

d. ¿Qué __ gusta hacer el fin de semana? A mí no __ gusta hacer nada.
What do you like doing at the weekend? I don't like doing anything.

e. A Elena ___ gusta hacer escalada. Lo ______ tres días a la semana.
Elena likes going rock climbing. She does it three times a week.

f. ¿Adónde ___ gusta ir el fin de semana? A nosotros ___ gusta hacer natación.
Where do you like going at the weekend? We like to go swimming.

g. A mi novia y a mí _____ gusta jugar al tenis. Lo _______ casi todos los días.
My girlfriend and I like playing tennis. We do it nearly every day.

5. Break the flow

a. Nomegustairalaplayaconmifamilialosfinesdesemanaporqueesaburrido.

b. Amímegustairalcineconmisamigoslosfinesdesemana.

c. Amisamigoslesgustahaceryoga.Lohacenamenudo.

d. Amispadreslesgustairalsupermercadoamenudo.Lohacenlossábados.

e. ¿Atitegustairalcinecontusamigoslosfinesdesemana?

f. ¿Osgustahacernataciónconvuestrafamiliadevezencuando?

g. Legustahacersenderismoconsupadre.Lohacelosdomingos.

h. Nosgustairalestadioamenudo.Lohacemoslossábados.

i. Amisabuelosnolesgustahacernadalosjueves.

6. Listen, complete and translate

a. ___ ___ gusta

b. ___ ___ ___ gusta

c. ___ ___ gusta

d. ___ ___ ___ gusta

e. ___ ___ gusta

f. ___ ___ gusta

g. ___ ___ hago

h. ___ ___ hacen

i. ___ ___ hacemos

7. Listen and complete the table

	Person	Pronoun+gusta	Infinitive	Verb to do	Time expression
Ejemplo	*A mí*	*me gusta*	*ir al cine*	*Lo hago*	*de vez en cuando*
a.					
b.					
c.					
d.					
e.					
f.					
g.					

8. Sentence Puzzle

a. gusta Nos deporte y hacer lo hacemos a menudo — *We like doing sport and we do it often*

b. gusta las Me jugar a cartas lo y todos los hago días — *I like playing cards and I do it every day*

c. Le playa gusta la ir a — *She likes going to the beach*

d. Lo sábados hace los — *She does it on Saturdays*

e. gusta Les vela hacer — *They like going sailing*

f. ¿gusta Qué el hacer te semana fin de? — *What do you like doing at the weekend?*

g. ¿os Dónde gusta natación hacer? — *Where do you guys like to go swimming?*

h. no me semana A mí gusta nada fin hacer el de — *I don't like doing anything at the weekend*

i. ¿Con baloncesto jugar gusta quién les al? — *Who do they like to play basketball with?*

j. madre Play jugar A gusta mi le a la conmigo — *My mother likes playing PlayStation with me*

k. hacemos los domingos Lo todos sábados y — *We do it every Saturday and Sunday*

9. Choose the correct pronoun

a. **Me/Te/Le** gusta ir al cine con mis amigos

b. **Les/Os/Nos** gusta hacer equitación con nuestro padre

c. A ellos **te/os/les** gusta ir al supermercado los viernes

d. A mi tía **me/le/nos** gusta hacer yoga los domingos con su hija

e. ¿**Te/Le/Les** gusta jugar al fútbol con tus primos?

f. ¿A vosotras **les/nos/os** gusta jugar a las cartas con vuestros hermanos?

g. A mí **te/le/me** gusta jugar a los videojuegos con mi abuelo

h. A ella **os/nos/le** gusta jugar a las cartas con su madre

i. A ellos **nos/os/les** gusta ir al cine de vez en cuando

10.Translate into English

a. Nos encanta ir al cine

b. Les gusta mucho hacer deporte

c. Le encanta jugar al baloncesto

d. ¿Qué te gusta hacer los fines de semana?

e. ¿Os gusta jugar al tenis?

f. Nos gusta mucho ir al parque

g. Lo hacemos todos los días

h. Lo hacen raramente

i. Lo hace todos los lunes

11. Choose the correct word from the options given in the table below

a. Me gusta ir al cine con mis amigos. Lo __________ de vez en cuando.

b. A mi hermano ___ gusta ir al estadio y jugar al fútbol.

c. A mis hermanos y a mí nos gusta jugar a los videojuegos. Lo ________ los fines de semana.

d. ¿A vosotros ____ gusta hacer equitación con vuestra familia?

e. A ellos les gusta ir a la playa con su padre. Lo ___________ a menudo.

f. A ti te gusta ir al centro comercial con tu amigo. Lo __________ los fines de semana.

g. ¿A ti _______ gusta ir a la piscina los miércoles?

h. A mis padres ________ gusta hacer la comida juntos.

haces	hago	hacen	les	le	os	hacemos	te

12. Correct the mistake in each sentence and then listen to check

a. A mí te gusta ir al cine con mis amigos. Lo hago los fines de semana.

b. A nosotros no os gusta hacer nada los fines de semana.

c. A mi hermano le gusta jugar a los videojuegos. Lo hacen los viernes.

d. ¿A ti os gusta ir al cine con tu hermano?

e. ¿A vosotras les gusta ir al supermercado que está en el centro?

f. A mi abuelo le gusta jugar a las cartas. Lo hacéis a menudo.

g. A mis amigos nos gusta jugar al fútbol. Lo hacen los martes.

h. A mi abuela le gusta hacer natación. Lo hago una vez a la semana.

13. Translate to Spanish

a. I like

b. We like

c. I do it

d. They do it

e. She likes

f. They do it

g. Do you like it?

h. What do you like?

i. We do it

j. Do you guys like it?

14. Guided translation

a. *I like to go to the cinema with my sister. We do it at the weekends.*

M___ g_______ i__ a____ c_____ c____ m__ h_______. L___ h______ l___ f_______ d___ s___________.

b. *Do you guys like going to the beach from time to time?*

¿A v_______ o___ g_______ i_____ a l___ p______ d___ v____ e__ c_________?

c. *My sister likes to play cards with my mum. They do it often.*

A m___ h_________ l__ g_______ j_______ a l___ c__________ c___ m____ m_____. L__ h____ a m__________.

d. *My brothers like to play videogames because it is fun. They do it at weekends.*

A m____ h_________ l___ g________ j______ a l___ v___________ p_______ e__ d__________. L___ h_______ l___ f_____ d__ s__________.

15. Listen. Spot the missing pronoun. Write it in and then translate into English

a. A mí no gusta hacer nada los viernes por la tarde.

b. A vosotros gusta hacer deporte. Lo hacéis los fines de semana.

c. A mi padre gusta ir al supermercado con mi madre. Lo hacen los viernes.

d. A mí gusta ir al cine con mis amigos.

e. A ellos gusta hacer equitación con sus amigos. Lo hacen una vez a la semana.

f. ¿A vosotras gusta ir a la playa con vuestros amigos?

16. Translate the following words/phrases into Spanish

a. Hiking
b. Beach
c. Chess
d. Never
e. To play cards
f. Nothing
g. My father
h. Weekends
i. My sister
j. We do it
k. Saturdays
l. Your friends
m. Often
n. Because
o. Fridays
p. I do it
q. Swimming
r. He does it

17. Translate the sentences into Spanish

a. We like to go to the beach with our friends because it is fun. We do it often. Do you like it?

b. My brother likes to play chess with my father. They do it on Fridays and Saturdays.

c. I don't like to do anything at weekends because I am tired. What do you do?

d. Do you like to go to the cinema with your friends at weekends? I don't like it much. I rarely do it.

e. We don't like to do horse riding. We never do it. We like a lot playing videogames.

f. My sister doesn't like to do hiking. She never does it. She loves doing swimming and boxing.

g. My parents don't like playing videogames. They never do it. They love playing cards.

6.3 INDIRECT OBJECT PRONOUN + GUSTA/GUSTAN + NOUN + PORQUE + ES/SON + ADJECTIVE *(TALKING ABOUT FOOD LIKES AND DISLIKES)*

<table>
<tr><td>(A mí)</td><td>*(no)
Me
I</td><td rowspan="3">gusta
like(s)</td><td rowspan="2">el arroz rice
el pollo chicken
el pescado fish
el café coffee</td><td rowspan="3">porque es
because it is

pero es
but it is</td><td rowspan="2">sabroso
tasty
asqueroso
disgusting
saludable
healthy
dulce
sweet</td></tr>
<tr><td>(A ti)</td><td>Te
You</td></tr>
<tr><td>(A él/ella)
(A mi hermano)</td><td>Le
He/She
My brother</td><td>la leche milk
la miel honey
la pizza pizza
la carne meat</td><td>sabrosa
asquerosa
saludable
dulce</td></tr>
<tr><td>(A nosotros)
(A nosotras)</td><td>Nos
We</td><td rowspan="3">gustan
like(s)</td><td rowspan="2">los bocadillos de queso
cheese sandwiches
los helados
ice creams
los tomates
tomatoes
los huevos fritos
fried eggs
los dulces
sweets</td><td rowspan="3">porque son
because they are

pero son
but they are</td><td rowspan="2">sabrosos
asquerosos
saludables
dulces</td></tr>
<tr><td>(A vosotros)
(A vosotras)</td><td>Os
You guys</td></tr>
<tr><td>(A ellos/ellas)
(A mis padres)</td><td>Les
They
My parents</td><td>las verduras
(the) vegetables
las patatas fritas
(the) chips/crisps
las hamburguesas
(the) burgers</td><td>sabrosas
asquerosas
saludables
dulces</td></tr>
</table>

Author's note:
*To make the negative form we say *"No me gusta" / "No le gusta"* etc.

LANGUAGE AWARENESS: *GUSTAR* – PART 2

Unlike most of the other verbs we've seen, ***gustar*** usually conjugates in the 3rd person.

SINGULAR NOUNS

If the noun being liked is a singular noun, we use ***gusta*** (3rd person singular of ***gustar***)

- **Me gusta el pollo** — *I like chicken*
- **A Esme le gusta el pollo** — *Esme likes chicken*

PLURAL NOUNS

If the noun being liked is a plural noun, we use ***gustan*** (3rd person plural of ***gustar***)

- **Me gustan los tomates** — *I like tomatoes*
- **A Esme le gustan los tomates** — *Esme likes tomatoes*

ME GUSTA + NOUNS/VERBS

Gustar is nearly always followed either by the **definite article** (*el/la/los/las*) or a **possessive adjective** (*mi/mis/tu/tus/su/sus/nuestro/a/os/as/vuestro/a/os/as*) or an **infinitive verb.**

If Gianfranco wants to talk about his pet chicken:

- **Me gusta la gallina** — *I like the chicken*
- **Me gusta mi gallina** — *I like my chicken*
- **Me gusta hablar con mi gallina** — *I like talking to my chicken*

1. Match

A mí me gusta la leche	*They (m) like fish*
A él le gusta la leche	*They (f) like vegetables*
No nos gustan las verduras	*Do you like burgers?*
A ellos les gusta el pescado	*I like milk*
A mí me gusta el pescado	*Do you guys like burgers?*
A nosotros nos gusta la leche	*He likes milk*
¿Te gustan las hamburguesas?	*We like milk*
¿Os gustan las hamburguesas?	*I like fish*
A ellas les gustan las verduras	*We don't like vegetables*

2. Complete the table with the missing English or Spanish word

Saludable	
	Fish
Dulce	
	Tomatoes
Sabroso	
	Ice creams
Asqueroso	
	Burgers
Las verduras	
	Milk
La carne	

3. Translate into English

a. Me gusta la leche

b. No me gustan los bocadillos

c. No le gustan los tomates

d. Les gustan los helados

e. ¿No te gustan las patatas fritas?

f. ¡Os gustan mucho los huevos fritos!

g. A nosotros nos gusta la pizza

h. A mis padres les gusta la pasta

i. A nosotros no nos gustan los dulces

4. Choose the correct verb then translate the sentence into English

a. Me **gusta/gustan** el arroz

b. A mi hermana le **gustan/gusta** los helados

c. A nosotros nos **gustan/gusta** la leche

d. ¿A vosotros os **gusta/gustan** las hamburguesas?

e. A mi padre le **gusta/gustan** los bocadillos de queso

f. A mis padres les **gustan/gusta** el pescado

g. No nos **gusta/gustan** mucho el pescado

h. A mis hermanos no les **gusta/gustan** los tomates

5. Listen and then: (1) complete with the correct pronoun; (2) choose the correct verb; (3) translate into English

a. __ __ **gusta/gustan** la leche

b. __ __ __ **gustan/gusta** el pollo

c. __ __ __ **gustan/gusta** las hamburguesas

d. ¿__ __ **gustan/gusta** las patatas fritas?

e. __ __ **gusta/ gustan** los huevos fritos

f. __ __ **gusta/gustan** la carne

g. __ __ __ **gusta/gustan** los dulces

h. No __ __ **gusta/gustan** el pescado

6. Anagrams

a. eL sguta al echle

b. sO ngtusa asl ashumusagbre

c. eLs gaust le cdepsao

d. osN aguts le zorar

e. eL sguta al zazpi

f. eM agsut al necra

g. eM sguat le éfac

h. sO stugna ols obacidlols ed souqe

i. ¿eT sugtna ols vheuso tofirs?

7. Faulty Translation: fix the English translation

a. Me gustan las hamburguesas, pero no son muy saludables
I like burgers because they are very tasty

b. A mi hermano le gusta el arroz porque no es dulce
My sister likes fish because it is not sweet

c. A mí me gustan los helados, pero son demasiado dulces
I like ice creams because they are quite sweet

d. A nosotros nos gustan los bocadillos de queso porque son bastante sabrosos
We love cheese sandwiches, but they are not very tasty

e. A mis abuelos les gustan los huevos fritos, pero en mi opinión son bastante asquerosos
My parents like cheese sandwiches, but in my opinion they are very disgusting

f. ¿Qué te gustan más: las verduras o los dulces?
What do you like more: vegetables or meat?

8. One of three

		1	2	3
a.	Saludable	*tasty*	*healthy*	*sweet*
b.	Los huevos fritos	*meat*	*fried eggs*	*sandwiches*
c.	Los helados	*honey*	*ice creams*	*vegetables*
d.	Dulce	*sweet*	*salty*	*tasty*
e.	El café	*milk*	*fish*	*coffee*
f.	Las patatas fritas	*ice creams*	*chips*	*milk*
g.	Asqueroso	*salty*	*tasty*	*disgusting*
h.	La miel	*honey*	*sandwich*	*milk*
i.	La leche	*meat*	*milk*	*fish*
j.	Los dulces	*tomatoes*	*sweets*	*sweet*
k.	Sabroso	*salty*	*disgusting*	*tasty*
l.	El pescado	*meat*	*vegetables*	*fish*

9. Complete with *gusta* or *gustan* as appropriate

a. A mí no me _________ la pizza

b. A nosotros nos ________ la miel

c. A ellos les ________ los helados

d. A mi madre le _______ la carne

e. A mí no me _________ los tomates

f. A ellas les ________ las verduras

g. ¿Os _________ los dulces?

h. ¿Te _________ el pescado?

i. A mi padre le _______ el pollo

j. A ella no le ________ el café

10. Sentence Puzzle

a. el es gusta porque pescado Me saludable — *I like fish because it is healthy*

b. nosotros A los gustan nos fritos huevos… — *We like fried eggs…*

c. …muy pero son no saludables — *…but they are not very healthy*

d. mi le A hermano patatas gustan las fritas… — *My brother likes chips…*

e. …porque bastante sabrosas son — *…because they are quite tasty*

f. ¿gusta Te arroz el? — *Do you like rice?*

g. ¿gustan verduras las Os? — *Do you guys like vegetables?*

h. A gusta mí me sabrosa porque carne la muy es — *I like meat because it is very tasty*

i. padre A mi muy gusta le la miel dulce es porque — *My father likes honey because it is very sweet*

11. Spot the mistakes, correct them, and then listen to check

a. A mí me gusta el arroz porque son delicioso
I like rice because it is delicious

b. A mi hermano les gusta el pescado porque es saludables
My brother likes fish because it is healthy

c. Nos gustan el azúcar, pero dulce
I like sugar, but it is sweet

d. Mi abuelo me gusta los bocadillos de queso porque son sabrosos
My grandfather likes cheese sandwiches because they are tasty

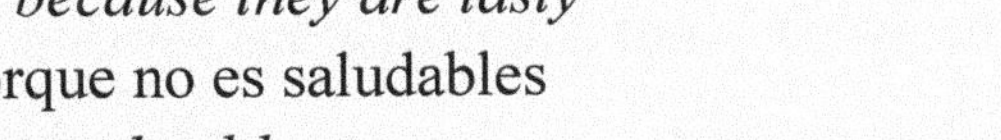

e. A ellos no le gusta las hamburguesas porque no es saludables
They don't like burgers because they are not healthy

f. ¿Te gustan la leche? *Do you guys like milk?*

12. Tangled translation: translate into Spanish

a. A ***me*** no me ***like*** las patatas ***fried because they are not*** saludables

b. A ***us*** nos ***like*** la leche ***because*** es deliciosa

c. A ***them*** (f) les ***like*** los helados ***because are*** dulces

d. A ***you guys*** os ***like*** las hamburguesas porque son ***tasty***

e. A ***me*** no me ***like*** las ***vegetables*** porque son ***disgusting***

f. ***We do not*** gustan los ***eggs*** fritos porque son ***disgusting***

g. A ellos ***do not like*** el pescado ***because*** es ***disgusting***

h. ***I like*** la carne ***and*** el pollo porque son ***tasty***

i. A ellas ***do not like tomates***, pero ***are healthy***

13. Translate into Spanish

a. I like honey

b. We like rice

c. They like ice creams

d. We like burgers

e. She likes tomatoes

f. I like fried eggs

g. We like chips

h. I like coffee

i. We like pizza

14. Guided Translation

a. M___ g__________ l____ t____________ p___________ s______ s__________

I like tomatoes because they are tasty

b. A m_____ h___________ l__ g_________ l___ h______________, p________ n___ s_____ s____________

My brother likes burgers, but they are not very healthy

c. A n__________ n_____ g____________ l____ b____________ d___ q________ p__________ s___ b__________ s____________

We like cheese sandwiches because they are quite tasty

d. M___ g______ m_______ l__ m_____ p_____ e__ d______

I like honey a lot because it is sweet

e. N__ l____ g_______ l___ h______ f______ p_____ n__ s___ s___________

They do not like fried eggs because they are not healthy

f. N__ l__ g________ e__ p_______ p______ n__ e__ s__________

She doesn't like chicken because it is not tasty

15. Translate into Spanish. Emphasise the verb *GUSTAR* where you can!

a. I like tomatoes because they are healthy, but my father doesn't like tomatoes because they are not very tasty.

b. We like burgers, but they are not healthy. My sister loves burgers because they are tasty.

c. Do you guys like coffee?

d. Do you guys like chicken and chips?

e. My parents like cheese sandwiches because they are tasty, but I don't like them.

f. They (f) like meat because it is not disgusting, but we don't like meat because it is not tasty.

g. I like chips because they are tasty, but they are not healthy.

h. My best friend doesn't like fish because it is disgusting, but it is very healthy.

6.4 INDIRECT OBJECT PRONOUN + GUSTA/GUSTAN + NOUNS + ES + ADJECTIVE
(SAYING HOW MUCH I LIKE PEOPLE AND WHY)

<table>
<tr><td>(A mí)</td><td>*(no)
Me
I</td><td rowspan="4">gusta
like(s)</td><td rowspan="2">mi mejor amigo
my best friend (m)
mi novio
my boyfriend
mi tío
my uncle
mi profesor de español
my Spanish teacher
mi profesor de inglés
my English teacher</td><td rowspan="4">porque
es
because
he/she is</td><td rowspan="2">pesado annoying
trabajador
hard-working
listo clever
perezoso lazy
simpático nice
callado reserved
alegre cheerful
paciente patient</td></tr>
<tr><td>(A ti)</td><td>Te
You</td></tr>
<tr><td>(A él/ella)
(A mi hermano)</td><td>Le
He/She
My brother</td><td rowspan="2">mi mejor amiga
my best friend (f)
mi novia
my girlfriend
mi tía
my aunt
mi profesora de inglés
my English teacher
mi profesora de arte
my art teacher</td><td rowspan="2">pesada
trabajadora
lista
perezosa
simpática
callada
alegre
paciente</td></tr>
<tr><td>(A nosotros)
(A nosotras)</td><td>Nos
We</td></tr>
<tr><td>(A vosotros)
(A vosotras)</td><td>Os
You guys</td><td rowspan="2">gustan
like(s)</td><td>mis amigos
my friends (m or m+f)
mis padres
my parents
mis abuelos
my grandparents
mis profesores
my teachers</td><td rowspan="2">porque
son
because
they are</td><td>pesados
trabajadores
listos
perezosos
simpáticos
callados
alegres
pacientes</td></tr>
<tr><td>(A ellos/ellas)
(A mis padres)</td><td>Les
They
My parents</td><td>mis amigas
my friends (f)
mis hermanas
my sisters
mis primas
my cousins (f)</td><td>pesadas
trabajadoras
listas
perezosas
simpáticas
calladas
alegres
pacientes</td></tr>
</table>

LANGUAGE AWARENESS: PLURAL NOUNS

In Spanish, when we use a **masculine plural noun**, it can refer to two or more male people/animals, but it can also refer to a mixture of male and female people/animals.

- **Mis padres** — *My parents* — Literally: My fathers
- **Mis abuelos** — *My grandparents* — Literally: My grandfathers

When we talk about a group of friends, if we say *mis amigos*, we are referring to a group of friends that is either **all male** or a **mixture of male & females:**

- **Mis amigos** — *My friends (masc. or mixed)* — Literally: My male friends

In fact, in Spanish, if we have a group of friends containing several girls and one boy, we use the **masculine, plural** noun: *amigos*. This can be considered an example of a **neutral form** being used for **linguistic economy.** If we are talking about a group that is composed **entirely** of **females,** only then we do use the female plural noun:

- **Mis amigas** — *My girl friends* — Literally: My girl friends (100% female group)

1. Match

Me gusta mi amigo	*Do you guys like your Spanish teacher?*
Te gusta tu amigo	*He likes his friend*
Nos gusta nuestra tía	*Do you like your aunt?*
A ella le gusta su hermano	*I like my friend*
¿Te gusta tu tía?	*I like my Spanish teacher*
A él le gusta su amigo	*We like our aunt*
Me gusta mi profesora de español	*You like your friend*
¿Os gusta vuestra profesora de español?	*She likes her brother*

2. Complete the sentence with the correct pronoun and possessive adjective

a.___ gusta ___ profesor de matemáticas
I like my maths teacher

b. ___ gustan _________ profesores generalmente
We generally like our teachers

c. ___ gustan _____ hermanos a veces
She likes her brothers sometimes

d. ¿___ gusta ___ profesor de ciencias?
Do you like your science teacher?

e. ¿___ gustan ________ profesores?
Do you guys like your teachers?

3. Translate into English

a. Mi hermana es perezosa

b. Me gustan mis hermanos

c. Mi tía es demasiado callada

d. Mis abuelos son simpáticos

e. A ella le gusta su tía

f. Su madre es demasiado callada

g. Nos gustan nuestros profes

h. Les gustan sus profesores

4. Break the flow and translate the sentences into English

a. Megustamiprofesordeinglésporqueeslisto

b. Amiamigolegustansusabuelosporquesondivertidos

c. Aéllegustasupadreporqueesdivertidoyhacenequitaciónjuntos

d. Nomegustamihermanoporqueesperezosoynohacelacamanunca

e. Anosotrosnosgustanuestroprofesordeespañolporqueessimpático

f. ¿Tegustantusprofesores?Síperodevezencuandosonpesados

g. Aellalegustasutíaporqueesalegreysimpática

5. Sentence Puzzle

a. gusta ella A le profesor su matemáticas de es porque no perezoso

She likes her maths teacher because he is not lazy

b. nosotros pacientes A gustan nos son divertidas hacen padres nuestros porque muy actividades y

We like our parents because they are patient and do very fun activities

c. mi A hermana muy porque gusta y le tía nuestra es alegre simpática

My sister likes our aunt because she is cheerful and very nice

d. ellos les A gustan profesores sus son porque listos

They like their teachers because they are clever

e. ¿gusta Te hermano tu? me No gusta es porque perezoso casa no en

Do you like your brother? No, I don't like him because he is lazy at home

6. Listen and translate into English

a.

b.

c.

d.

e.

f.

g.

h.

i.

7. Gapped Translation: complete the translation

a. ____ gusta mi ________, pero ___ perezoso porque no _______ la _____ nunca.

I like my brother, but he is lazy because he never makes the bed.

b. A ______ amigos ____ gusta ____ profesor de _______ porque ___ listo.

Our friends like their English teacher because he is clever

c. A ___ padre ___ gusta ___ amigo porque no ___ perezoso y siempre _______ escalada los fines de _____________.

My father likes his friend because he is not lazy and they always do rock climbing at the weekends.

d. A ____ abuelos les _____ jugar a las ______. A mí ____ gustan mis _______ porque son _______.

My grandparents like to play cards. I like my grandparents because they are fun.

8. Listen and fill in the gaps

a. Nos gustan __________ profesores porque son ___________

b. A _____ le ______ su novio porque es _________

c. A nosotros nos _______ nuestros __________

d. ¿ ____ gustan tus hermanos?

e. A _____ no le gusta su profesor de ________________

f. Mis padres son demasiado __________ y habladores

g. No _____ gusta tu hermano porque es ________ arrogante

h. A mi hermano no _____ gusta su profesor de inglés porque es muy __________ y un poco ______________

9. Anagrams

a. eosprezo

b. elarge

c. osámpicti

d. ¿so stgua ovustre pdera?

e. em sguat im ovnio

f. ¿et tgsua ut rfpreoors ed lésngi?

g. el usgta us lbuaeo

h. ons usgta unetsro mpiro

i. els usgta us moaig

j. ¿so tgsua avustre mdera?

10. Staircase translation – Translate each sentence from memory

a.	I like	my boyfriend				
b.	Our parents	are	patient			
c.	We like	our teachers	because they are	clever		
d.	They like	their teachers	because they are	nice and	fun	
e.	She doesn't like	her sister	because she is	lazy	and doesn't do	chores

a. ______________________________

b. ______________________________

c. ______________________________

d. ______________________________

e. ______________________________

11. Translate into Spanish

a. Do you guys like your teachers? Generally, we like them, but from time to time they are annoying.

b. I like my maths teacher because he is not lazy and he is quite nice.

c. My brother doesn't like his English teacher because she is too quiet and boring.

d. We like our friends because they are not lazy. We like going rock climbing at weekends.

e. I like my father because we like to play cards together (*juntos*). We do it on Sundays.

f. Do you guys like your parents? We like our parents, but they are annoying from time to time.

g. My sister likes her boyfriend, but he is too quiet. They like to go to the cinema. They do it on Fridays.

h. My friend likes his teachers because they are nice and patient.

i. My brothers like to go to the cinema at weekends with my grandfather. They do it often.

j. We don't like our science teacher because she is annoying.

k. Do you like your maths teacher? Yes, I like him because he is cheerful and hard-working.

6.5 NOUN + VERBS LIKE GUSTAR + PORQUE + ES/SON + ADJECTIVES

(SAYING HOW I FEEL ABOUT PEOPLE AND WHY)

<table>
<tr>
<td>**El deporte** *sport*
El español *Spanish*
La geografía *geography*
La historia *history*
La política *politics*

Mi novia *my girlfriend*
Mi novio *my boyfriend*
Mi padre *my father*
Mi profesor *my teacher*</td>
<td>**me aburre**
bores me
me chifla
I am crazy about
me encanta *I love*
me importa
matters to me
me interesa
interests me
me molesta
annoys me</td>
<td rowspan="2">**porque es**
because it is</td>
<td rowspan="2">**aburrido/a** *boring*
apasionante *exciting*
arrogante *arrogant*
difícil *difficult*
divertido/a *fun*
estúpido/a *stupid*
fácil *easy*
fascinante *fascinating*
inteligente *intelligent*
interesante *interesting*
pesado/a *annoying*</td>
</tr>
<tr>
<td colspan="2">**Paco me cae bien/mal**
I get along well/badly with Paco</td>
</tr>
<tr>
<td>**Las matemáticas** *maths*
Las ciencias *science*
Los idiomas *languages*

Mis abuelos
My grandparents
Mis hermanas
My sisters
Mis hermanos
My brothers/siblings
Mis padres
My parents
Mis primos
My cousins
Mis vecinos
My neighbours</td>
<td>**me aburren**
me chiflan
me encantan
me importan
me interesan
me molestan</td>
<td rowspan="2">**porque son**
because they are</td>
<td rowspan="2">**aburridos/as**
apasionantes
arrogantes
difíciles
divertidos/as
estúpidos/as
fáciles
fascinantes
inteligentes
interesantes
pesados/as</td>
</tr>
<tr>
<td colspan="2">**Mis vecinos me caen bien/mal**
I get along well/badly with my neighbours</td>
</tr>
</table>

LANGUAGE AWARENESS: *CAER BIEN/MAL*

To say that you like or get along well/badly with someone, you can use ***caer bien / mal.*** Unlike ***gustar***, which is a generic "to like", this expression can only be used with people, and is best used specifically with acquaintances or people that you meet (as opposed to parents/siblings).

- **A mi amigo le cae bien su profesor** *My friend likes / gets along well with his teacher*
- **Me caen mal mis vecinos** *I don't like / get along badly with my neighbours*
- **Mis compañeros de clase me caen bien** *I like / get along well with my classmates*

1. Match

Mi profesor me cae bien	*I love languages*
Mis vecinos me caen mal	*History matters to me*
Mis amigos me caen bien	*History bores me*
La historia me interesa	*My teacher bores me*
La historia me aburre	*I don't get along with my neighbours*
Mi profesor me aburre	*History interests me*
La historia me importa	*I get along with my friends*
Me encantan los idiomas	*I get along with my teacher*

2. Anagrams

a. ols maidios em aubrenr

b. im ovecni em eca alm

c. al tshioira em anitrees

d. al fíargegoa em pormiat

e. im ovnoi em porimat

f. sim ovencis em ecan nbie

g. al opilitac em asomelat

h. ims loubaes em flanhci

i. ols masidio em anietersn

j. em cnenaat le ñolspea

3. Break the flow and translate the sentences into English

a. Lapolíticameinteresaporqueesfascinante

b. Meencantalageografíaporqueesapasionante

c. Misvecinosmecaenbienporquesonsimpáticos

d. Miprofesordehistoriamecaemalporqueesarrogante

e. Lageografíameinteresaporqueesfácil

f. Minoviomemolestaavecesporqueespesado

g. Lascienciasmeinteresanporquesonfascinantes

4. Listen and fill in the gaps

a. ______________ me interesa porque es ____________

b. Mi vecino _________________ porque es _______________

c. La geografía ______________ porque es _______________

d. ________________ mis hermanos porque ______ divertidos

e. Los idiomas _________________

5. Gapped Translation: please complete

a. La geografía ______________ porque es __________

History interests me because it is easy

b. Mis vecinos _____________, pero a veces _______________

I get along with my neighbours, but sometimes they annoy me

c._______________ los idiomas porque _______ apasionantes

I love languages because they are exciting

d. Las matemáticas ________________ porque _______ fáciles

I am crazy about mathematics because they are easy

6. Translate into English

a. Me caen bien mis vecinos porque son simpáticos

b. Mi vecino me molesta porque es arrogante

c. Los idiomas me interesan porque son fascinantes

d. La historia me aburre porque es difícil

e. Me chiflan los idiomas porque son apasionantes

f. Mi primo me cae mal porque es pesado

g. Mi vecino me cae bien porque es simpático

h. Mis amigos me caen bien porque son fascinantes

7. Faulty translation: fix the English translation

a. El deporte me aburre porque es difícil
Geography bores me because it is difficult

b. La política me interesa porque es fascinante
Politics matters to me because it is fascinating

c. Mi primo me cae mal porque es pesado
I get along with my cousin because he is nice

d. La historia me encanta porque es apasionante
I care about sport because it is exciting

e. Los idiomas me interesan porque son importantes
Languages matter to me because they are interesting

f. Las ciencias me aburren porque son muy difíciles
Science annoys me because it is not difficult

8. Tangled translation: into Spanish

a. La geografía me ***interests*** porque es ***exciting***

b. Los idiomas ***matter to me*** porque son ***interesting***

c. Mi vecino ***I get along*** porque es ***nice***

d. Mi ***cousin*** me cae mal ***because he is arrogant***

e. La ***politics*** me interesa porque ***is*** importante

f. Las matemáticas ***bore me*** porque son ***difficult***

g. Me encanta el ***sport because*** es ***exciting***

h. Mis padres ***annoy me*** porque ***are*** pesados

9. Correct the mistakes and listen to check 

a. Mis primas me cae bien porque es divertido

b. La política me interesan porque es apasionantes

c. Los idiomas me chifla porque es fáciles

d. Las ciencias me importa porque es fascinantes

e. Mi hermano me molestan porque son muy pesado

f. Mis padres me aburre porque es estrictos

g. La geografía me interesa porque son apasionantes

h. Mi profesor de inglés me aburren porque es pesado

i. El novio de mi hermana me molesta porque es arroganto

j. Mis profesores me cae bien porque es trabajador

10. Choose the correct words

a. La geografía me **encanta/encantan** porque no es **difícil/difíciles**

b. Mis vecinos me **cae/caen** mal porque son **aburridos/aburridas**

c. Los idiomas me **chifla/chiflan** porque son **apasionantes/apasionante**

d. Mi padre me **molesta/molestan** porque es **aburrido/aburrida** a veces

e. El deporte me **interesa/interesan** porque es **apasionantes/apasionante**

f. Las matemáticas me **aburre/aburren** porque son **pesados/pesadas**

g. Mi madre me **molesta/molestan** a veces

11. Translate into Spanish

a. Politics interest me because it is exciting

b. I am crazy about languages

c. I get along with my dad because he is nice

d. History interests me because it is fun

e. I love my granddad because he is nice

f. I like my neighbours because they are nice

g. Sport matters to me because it is fun and easy

h. I don't get along with my teacher because he is strict

i. Maths bores me because it is difficult

j. I get along with my uncle because he is cheerful

ORAL PING PONG

GUSTAR

ENGLISH 1	SPANISH 1	ENGLISH 2	SPANISH 2
I like to play basketball with my friends in the park.	Me gusta jugar al baloncesto con mis amigos en el parque.	I like my friends because they are nice.	
My brother likes to go swimming. He does it on Fridays.	A mi hermano le gusta hacer natación. Lo hace los viernes.	I like to go to the swimming pool with my cousin. I do it every day.	
We like to go to the cinema. We do it at the weekends.	A nosotros nos gusta ir al cine. Lo hacemos los fines de semana.	My friends like to play tennis. They do it from time to time.	
My parents don't like to play videogames. They never do it	A mis padres no les gusta jugar a los videojuegos. No lo hacen nunca.	My sister doesn't like to play cards. She never does it.	
Do you like to go to the beach in the summer?	¿A ti te gusta ir a la playa en el verano?	Do you guys like to go cycling in the park at weekends?	
My friends and I like sweets, but they are not healthy.	A mis amigos y a mí nos gustan los dulces, pero no son saludables	My mum likes vegetables because they are healthy, but I don't like them.	
My dad doesn't like honey because it is too sweet.	A mi padre no le gusta la miel porque es demasiado dulce.	My sister doesn't like tomatoes because they are disgusting.	
I get along with my English teacher because she is cheerful and hard-working.	Me cae bien mi profesora de inglés porque es alegre y trabajadora.	My brothers and I like our grandparents, but they are annoying sometimes.	

INSTRUCTIONS - You are **PARTNER A.** Work in pairs. Each of you has two sets of sentences - one set has already been translated for you. You will ask your partner to translate these. The other set of sentences have not been translated. Your partner will ask you to translate these.
HOW TO PLAY - Partner A starts by reading out his/her/their first sentence in English. Partner B must translate. Partner A must check the answer and award the following points: **3 points** = perfect, **2 points** = 1 mistake, **1 point** = mistakes but the verb is accurate. If they cannot translate correctly, Partner A will read out the sentence so that Partner B can learn what the correct translation is.
Then Partner B reads out his/her/their first sentence, and so on.
OBJECTIVE - Try to win more points than your partner by translating correctly as many sentences as possible.

ORAL PING PONG

GUSTAR

ENGLISH 1	SPANISH 1	ENGLISH 2	SPANISH 2
I like to play basketball with my friends in the park.		I like my friends because they are nice.	Me gustan mis amigos porque son simpáticos.
My brother likes go swimming. He does it on Fridays.		I like to go to the swimming pool with my cousin. I do it every day.	Me gusta ir a la piscina con mi primo/a. Lo hago todos los días.
We like to go to the cinema. We do it often at the weekend.		My friends like to play tennis. They do it from time to time.	A mis amigos les gusta jugar al tenis. Lo hacen de vez en cuando.
My parents don't like to play videogames. They never do it.		My sister doesn't like to play cards. She never does it.	A mi hermana no le gusta jugar a las cartas. Nunca lo hace.
Do you like to go to the beach in the summer?		Do you guys like to go cycling in the park at weekends?	¿Os gusta hacer ciclismo en el parque los fines de semana?
My friends and I like sweets, but they are not healthy.		My mum likes vegetables because they are healthy, but I don't like them.	A mi madre le gustan las verduras porque son saludables, pero a mí no me gustan.
My dad doesn't like honey because it is too sweet.		My sister doesn't like tomatoes because they are disgusting.	A mi hermana no le gustan los tomates porque son asquerosos.
I get along with my English teacher because she is cheerful and hard-working.		My brothers and I like our grandparents, but they are annoying sometimes.	A mis hermanos y a mí nos gustan nuestros abuelos, pero son pesados a veces.

INSTRUCTIONS - You are **PARTNER B.** Work in pairs. Each of you has two sets of sentences - one set has already been translated for you. You will ask your partner to translate these. The other set of sentences have not been translated. Your partner will ask you to translate these.
HOW TO PLAY - Partner A starts by reading out his/her/their first sentence in English. Partner B must translate. Partner A must check the answer and award the following points: **3 points** = perfect, **2 points** = 1 mistake, **1 point** = mistakes but the verb is accurate. If they cannot translate correctly, Partner A will read out the sentence so that Partner B can learn what the correct translation is.
Then Partner B reads out his/her/their first sentence, and so on.
OBJECTIVE - Try to win more points than your partner by translating correctly as many sentences as possible.

GUSTAR

No Snakes No Ladders

SALIDA	1 We like chips	2 I like to go to the beach in the summer	3 She likes to do hiking. She does it often	4 Do you like to do rock climbing?	5 I like to play tennis. I do it at weekends	6 I like my English teacher because she is cheerful	7 My mum likes my sister because she is hard-working
15 I like my best friend because she is not lazy	14 My sister loves ice creams, but they are not healthy	13 Do you like to go to the cinema?	12 We like to do rock climbing. We do it often	11 She likes to do rock climbing. She does it once a week	10 They like to play football. They do it every day	9 We like our friends because they are nice	8 We like our grandfather because he is patient
16 I like to go swimming. I do it often	17 We like chicken because it is quite healthy	18 Do you guys like to play videogames?	19 They like to play cards. They do it once a week	20 We like to play tennis at weekends	21 I like my aunt because she is nice	22 They do not like to play cards	23 My girlfriend likes her mum
LLEGADA	30 We do not like burgers	29 I don't like to do anything at weekends	28 She likes to play football. She does it on Fridays	27 We like fried eggs and chips	26 I do not like my cat because she is annoying	25 We don't like to do anything at weekends	24 I like chips because they are tasty

GUSTAR

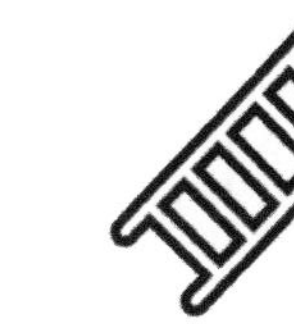

No Snakes No Ladders

SALIDA	1 A nosotros nos gustan las patatas fritas	2 Me gusta ir a la playa en verano	3 A ella le gusta hacer senderismo. Lo hace a menudo	4 ¿Te gusta hacer escalada?	5 A mí me gusta jugar al tenis. Lo hago los fines de semana	6 Me gusta mi profesora de inglés porque es alegre	7 A mi madre le gusta mi hermana porque es trabajadora
15 Me gusta mi mejor amiga porque no es perezosa	14 A mi hermana le gustan los helados, pero no son saludables	13 ¿Te gusta ir al cine?	12 A nosotros nos gusta hacer escalada.	11 A ella le gusta hacer escalada. Lo hace una vez a la semana	10 A ellos les gusta jugar al fútbol. Lo hacen todos los días	9 A nosotros nos gustan nuestros amigos porque son simpáticos	8 Nos gusta nuestro abuelo porque es paciente
16 Me gusta hacer natación. Lo hago a menudo	17 A nosotros nos gusta el pollo porque es bastante saludable	18 ¿Os gusta jugar a los videojue-gos?	19 A ellos les gusta jugar a las cartas. Lo hacen una vez a la semana	20 A nosotros nos gusta jugar al tenis los fines de semana	21 A mí me gusta mi tía porque es simpática	22 A ellos no les gusta jugar a las cartas	23 A mi novia le gusta su madre
LLEGADA	30 A nosotros no nos gustan las hamburgue-sas	29 No me gusta hacer nada los fines de semana	28 A ella le gusta jugar al fútbol. Lo hace los viernes	27 A nosotros nos gustan los huevos fritos y las patatas fritas	26 A mí no me gusta mi gata porque es pesada	25 No nos gusta hacer nada los fines de semana	24 A mí me gustan las patatas fritas porque son sabrosas

PYRAMID TRANSLATION

GUSTAR

Translate each part of the pyramid out loud with your partner, then write it into the spaces provided below.

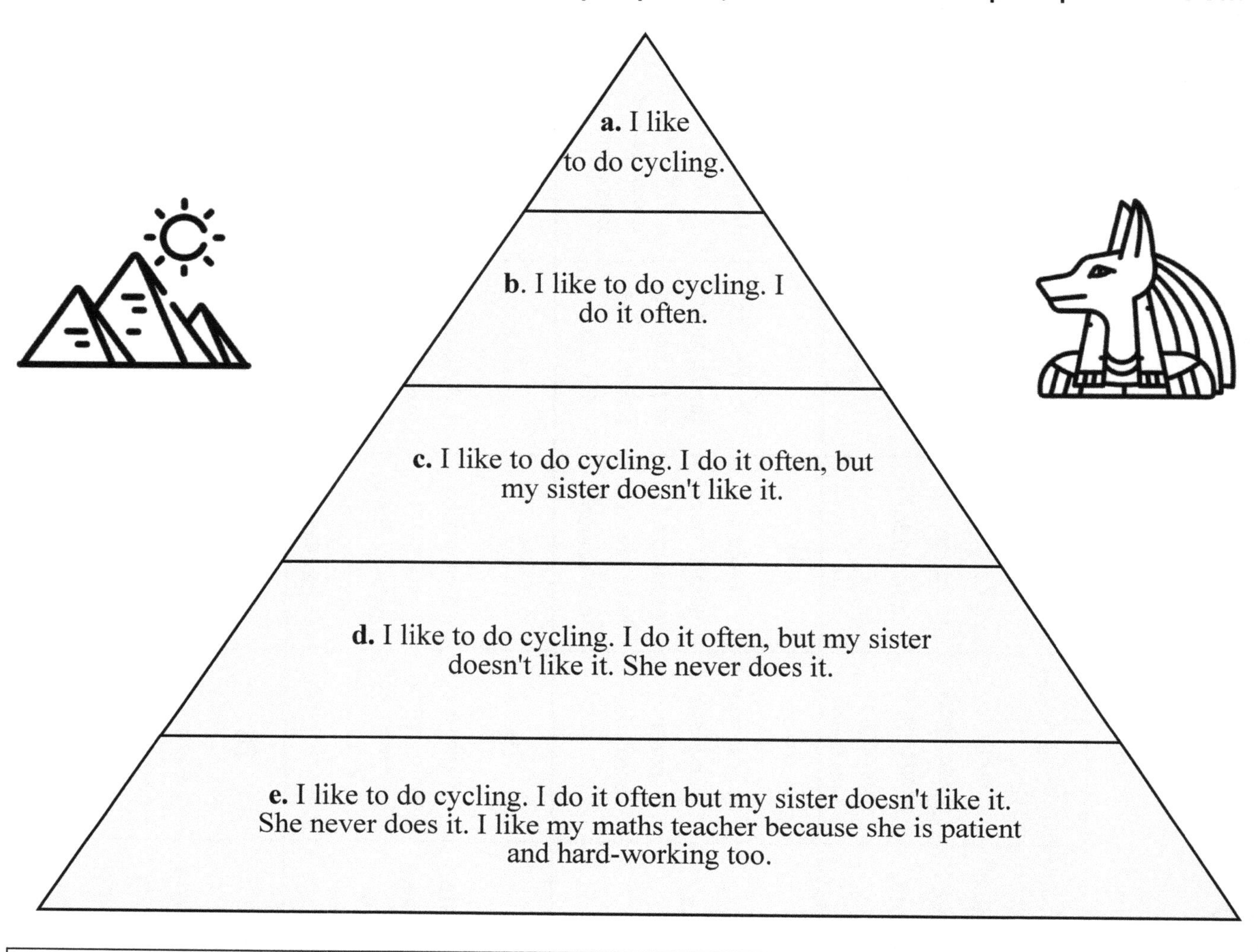

Write your translation here

SOLUTION: Me gusta hacer ciclismo. Lo hago a menudo, pero a mi hermana no le gusta. Nunca lo hace. Me gusta mi profesora de matemáticas porque es paciente y trabajadora también.

UNIT 7 – JUGAR Vs TOCAR

Yo	Juego	Toco
Tú	Juegas	Tocas
Él / Ella	Juega	Toca
Nosotros / as	Jugamos	Tocamos
Vosotros / as	Jugáis	Tocáis
Ellos / as	Juegan	Tocan

7.1 TIME MARKER + JUEGO + A/AL/A LA/EN + NOUN + CON + NOUN. AFFECTIVE VERB + PORQUE + ES + ADJECTIVE.
(SAYING WHAT GAMES I PLAY, WITH WHOM AND HOW I FEEL ABOUT THEM)

Cuando tengo tiempo *When I have time* **Los fines de semana** *At the weekends* **Los lunes** *On Mondays*	**juego** *I play*	**al ajedrez** *chess* **al baloncesto** *basketball* **al fútbol** *football* **al tenis** *tennis* **a la Play** *on the PlayStation* **a las cartas** *cards* **a los videojuegos** *video games* **en el ordenador** *on the computer* ***en el móvil** *on my mobile phone*	**con** *with*	**mi familia** **mi mejor amigo/a** *my best friend* **mi novio/a** *my boyfriend/girlfriend* **mi primo/a** *my cousin* **mis amigos** *my friends* **mis amigas** *my (girl) friends*

No me gusta *I don't like it* **Me gusta** *I like it* **Me encanta** *I love it* **Lo odio** *I hate it*	**porque es** *because it is*	**aburrido** *boring* **agotador** *tiring* **apasionante** *exciting* **divertido** *fun* **duro** *hard* **gracioso** *funny* **la leche** *awesome* **la caña** *amazing*

Lo hago *I do it* **Lo hacemos** *We do it*	**a menudo** *often* **de vez en cuando** *from time to time* **los fines de semana** *at the weekends* **(casi) todos los días** *(almost) every day* **una vez a la semana** *once a week*
No lo hago nunca *I never do it*	**No lo hacemos nunca** *We never do it*

***Author's note:** *"en el móvil"* and *"en mi móvil"* both mean "on my mobile phone" and are interchangeable!

LANGUAGE AWARENESS: *JUGAR A* + ARTICLE

When talking about what games (including sport games) we play, we need to say: ***juego a* + article + activity**. Depending on whether the activity is masculine/feminine and singular/plural, the phrase is formed differently:

- Juego **al** fútbol — *I play football* — (Masculine singular activity)
- Juego **a la** Play — *I play on the PlayStation* — (Feminine singular activity)
- Juego **a los** videojuegos — *I play videogames* — (Masculine singular activity)
- Juego **a las** cartas — *I play cards* — (Feminine singular activity)

This structure functions in the same way as ***ir* + *a* + place** that you saw earlier in the book (Page 95):

- Voy **al** museo y **a la** playa *I go to the museum and to the beach*

1. Match

No me gusta	*Once a week*
Me encanta	*Tiring*
Odio	*Basketball*
Juego	*I hate*
Ajedrez	*From time to time*
Baloncesto	*I play*
Una vez a la semana	*Chess*
De vez en cuando	*I don't like*
Agotador	*I love*

2. Complete with a suitable word

a. _ _ _ lunes juego al ajedrez con mi padre

b. No me _ _ _ _ _ porque es aburrido

c. _ _ hago a menudo

d. Me _ _ _ _ _ _ _ porque es divertido

e. Juego al _ _ _ _ _ _ _ _ _ _ todos los días

f. Odio el tenis porque es _ _ _ _ _ _ _ _

g. Lo _ _ _ _ _ _ _ de vez en cuando

h. Juego a las _ _ _ _ _ _ los fines de semana

3. Slalom translation: use one item from each column of the table to translate each sentence

Juego al ajedrez	todos los días.	Lo hago	muchísimo.	tiempo libre.
Juego a las cartas	con mi padre.	Lo hacemos	todos los días	porque es divertido.
Juego a los videojuegos	con mi mejor amigo.	una vez a la semana.	No me gusta	pero es agotador.
Juego al baloncesto	con mi familia.	de vez en cuando	tengo	porque es la leche
Juego a la Play	con mi primo.	Lo hacemos a menudo.	Me encanta	porque es aburrido.
Juego en mi móvil	con mis compañeros de clase.	Me gusta	Me gusta mucho,	Lo hago con mi hermano.
Juego al tenis	Lo hago	cuando	casi todos los días	porque es la caña

a. *I play chess with my father once a week. I don't like it because it is boring.*

b. *I play cards with my family. We do it often. I love it because it is fun.*

c. *I play videogames with my cousin. I do it every day because it is amazing.*

d. *I play basketball with my classmates. We do it nearly every day because it is awesome.*

e. *I play on the PlayStation every day. I like it a lot. I do it with my brother.*

f. *I play on my mobile phone. I do it when I have free time.*

g. *I play tennis with my best friend from time to time. I like it a lot, but it is tiring.*

LANGUAGE AWARENESS: *LO HAGO/HACEMOS*

To say that we do something we say:

- **Lo hago** *I do it*
- **Lo hacemos** *We do it*

In this structure the ***lo*** *(it)* is known as a **Masculine Direct Object Pronoun.** This is super-heavy grammar, so read the following carefully: It is called a **Direct Object Pronoun** because it replaces the **noun** (here it is the **Direct Object**) in the sentence. For example:

- Juego **al fútbol** *I play **football***
- **Lo** juego a menudo *I play **it** often*

ADVERBS OF FREQUENCY

We use adverbs of frequency, such as ***siempre*** (always) and ***nunca*** (never) to say how often we do an activity. Sometimes these work better at the **start** of the sentence:

- **Siempre** juego al tenis *I **always** play tennis*

...and sometimes at the **end**:

- Juego al tenis **todos los días** *I play tennis **every day***
- Lo hago **una vez a la semana** *I do it **once a week***

NEGATIVE FORM

There are two ways to phrase the negative form, to say that you never do something:

- **Nunca** juego al golf *I **never** play golf*
- **Nunca** lo hago *I **never** do it*
- **No** lo hago **nunca** *I **don't** do it '**never**'*

4. Complete with the missing letters

a. J__ __ __o a la Play a men__ __ __

b. Cuando tengo tie__ __ __ juego al ajedr __ __

c. No me gu__ __ __ porque es aburr__ __ __

d. Lo hac__ __ __ __ los lu__ __ __

e. Me gusta po__ __ __ __ es apasiona__ __ __

f. Lo o__ __ __ porque es muy agota__ __ __

g. Juego a las car__ __ __ con mi fami__ __ __

h. No ju__ __ __ al balonce__ __ __ a menudo

5. Tick the expressions in the list below which refer to time and cross the adjectives

a. A menudo	h. Divertido
b. Apasionante	i. Los lunes
c. Aburrido	j. Raramente
d. De vez en cuando	k. Todos los días
e. Los fines de semana	l. Duro
f. Nunca	m. Gracioso
g. Agotador	n. Una vez a la semana

6. Complete with *a, al, con, por, los* or *en*

a. Juego ____ mi familia

b. Juego ____ baloncesto

c. Lo hago todos _____ días

d. Juego ___ tenis ___ el colegio

e. Lo hago ____ menudo

f. Juego ____ mi hermano

g. Juego ___ la Play ___ la tarde

h. Juego ____ la cartas

i. ____ lunes juego ___ ajedrez

7. Listen and complete with a suitable word

a. Los lunes _______ al baloncesto con mis amigos.

b. Por lo general, juego al ________ con mi padre.

c. Juego a la Play casi todos los ________.

d. Juego a las cartas con mi madre. ____ hacemos a menudo.

e. Juego al tenis, pero no lo __________ a menudo porque es ___________.

f. Me _______ mucho el fútbol porque es divertido.

g. Nunca juego a los ______________.

h. ¡________ el golf porque es aburridísimo!

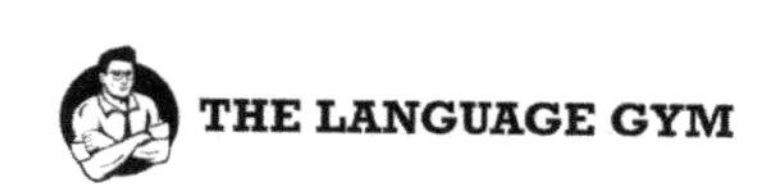

8. Guided translation; then listen and check your answers

a. N_ m_ g____ e_ b________. C____ n_____ l___ h_____. *I don't like basketball. I hardly ever do it.*

b. L_ h_________ u____ v____ p____ s___________. *We do it once a week.*

c. O_____ e__ g_______. E_ m___ a_____________. *I hate golf. It is very boring.*

d. J______ a l___ c_______ c___ m_ f___________. *I play cards with my family.*

e. L_ h____ t______ l___ d_____. *I do it every day.*

f. N_______ j________ e__ m__ m________. *I never play on my mobile phone.*

g. C____ n___ j______ a_ t_____. *I hardly ever play tennis.*

h. J______ a l_ P_____ a m________. E__ l__ l________. *I play on the Play often. It's awesome.*

9. Translate into Spanish

a. Once a week

b. Often

c. Basketball

d. Cards

e. Never

f. Boring

g. Tiring

h. Awesome *(the milk)*

i. Computer

j. Mobile phone

10. Tangled translation: translate into Spanish

a. ***I don't*** juego al ***tennis***. No me ***like it*** porque ***it is*** aburrido.

b. Juego al ***football***. Me ***like it because*** es ***exciting***.

c. Nunca ***I play*** a las ***cards***. No me ***like it*** porque no es ***fun***.

d. Juego ***on my*** móvil. Me ***love it*** porque ***is awesome***.

e. ***I don't*** juego al ***football***. ***I don't like it*** porque ***is tiring***.

f. Juego en el ***computer***. ***I like it*** porque ***is*** divertido.

g. ***I play*** al ***chess*** con ***my friends***. Me ***like it*** porque ***is exciting***.

h. ***I play*** al ***football***. Lo ***I do*** todos los días.

i. Juego a los ***videogames with*** mis ***friends***. ***It*** hacemos ***often***.

11. Translate into Spanish

a. I don't play tennis. I don't like it because it is boring.

b. I play basketball often. I love it because it is exciting.

c. I play on the Play every day. I like it a lot because it is fun.

d. I play cards with my family. We do it every Saturday.

e. I play videogames with my best friend. We do it every day.

f. I love tennis because it is fun. However (*Sin embargo*), it is quite tiring.

g. I never play golf. I hate it because it is very boring.

h. I play on my mobile phone all the time. It is a lot of fun.

i. I play football every day after school. I love it. It is awesome.

7.2 PRESENT OF JUGAR + A/AL/A LA/EN + NOUN + EN + NOUN + DIRECT OBJECT PRONOUN + HACER + FREQUENCY ADVERBS

(SAYING WHERE ONE PLAYS GAMES AND HOW OFTEN ONE DOES IT)

Cuando tengo tiempo	*When I have time*	**Los fines de semana**	*At the weekends*
Los lunes / martes / miércoles / jueves / viernes / sábados /domingos			

(Yo) *I*	**Juego** *I play*	**al ajedrez** *chess* **al baloncesto** **al billar** *snooker* **al fútbol** **al tenis** **a la Play** **a las cartas** **a juegos en línea** *online games* **en el ordenador** *on the computer* **en el móvil**	**en** *in*	**el**	**colegio** **jardín** **estadio** **parque** **polideportivo**
(Tú) *Yo*	**Juegas** *You play*				
(Mi amigo/a) **(Mi hermano/a)**	**Juega** *He/She plays*				
(Mi amigo/a y yo) *My friend and I* **(Nosotros/nosotras)**	**Jugamos** *We play*			**la**	**biblioteca** **habitación** **piscina** **playa**
(Vosotros/vosotras) *You guys*	**Jugáis** *You guys play*				
(Mis amigos) *My friends* **(Mis padres)** *My parents*	**Juegan** *They play*				

Lo	**hago**	*I do it*	**a menudo**	*often*
	haces	*you do it*	**de vez en cuando**	*from time to time*
	hace	*he she does it*	**los fines de semana**	*at the weekends*
	hacemos	*we do it*	**todos los días**	*every day*
	hacéis	*you guys do it*	**una vez a la semana**	*once a week*
	hacen	*they do it*		

No lo hago nunca / Nunca lo hago	*I never do it*	**No lo hacemos nunca / Nunca lo hacemos**	*We never do it*

LANGUAGE AWARENESS: RADICAL CHANGING VERBS

Jugar (to play) is a Radical Changing verb. This means that it conjugates differently to regular AR verbs because the stem changes from **jug** to **jueg** in the I/you/he/she/they forms.

See the side-by-side comparison on the right to see the difference between jugar and hablar.

A good way to remember these verbs is to picture a boot in which the radical changing forms **(1-2-3-6)** fit inside. The regular forms (nosotros and vosotros) are outside the boot. See the picture on the top right. This is why these verbs are also referred to, informally, as **"Boot Verbs"** (as well as **1-2-3-6 verbs**).

Jugar: Radical Changing Verb

Juego *I play*	**Jug**amos *We play*
Juegas *You play*	**Jug**áis *You (guys) play*
Juega *He/she plays*	**Jueg**an *They play*

Regular AR verb (stem is "HABL")

Hablo *I talk*	**Habl**amos *We talk*
Hablas *You talk*	**Habl**áis *You guys talk*
Habla *He/she talks*	**Habl**an *They talk*

1. Choose the correct option

a. (Yo) **Juega/Juego/Juegas** al rugby todos los lunes

b. (Nosotros) Nunca **juegan/jugáis/jugamos** al tenis

c. (Ellas) **Jugan/Juega/Juegan** a las cartas

d. Los domingos, (ellos) **juega/juegan/jugamos** al golf

e. ¿(Vosotras) A qué **jugáis/juegas/juegan** hoy?

f. ¡(Tú) Siempre **juegas/juega/jugas** a la Play!

g. Mis padres nunca **juegan/jugan/jugáis** al ajedrez

h. ¿A qué **juego/juegas/juega** tú?

2. Complete

a. (Yo) Nunca jueg__ al tenis

b. (Nosotros) No jugamo__ al rugby

c. Ellos siempre juega__ a la Play

d. Mi padre ju__ga al golf a menudo

e. (Vosotros) ¿A qué jugái__ ahora?

f. Mis hermanos ju__gan al ajedrez

g. Tú siempre juega__ al futbol

h. (Nosotros) Juga__os al baloncesto

3. Faulty translation: fix the English translation

a. Jugamos al tenis en el polideportivo	*They play tennis at school*
b. Juegan al golf todos los jueves	*She plays tennis every Sunday*
c. ¿Dónde juegas al baloncesto? ¿En el colegio?	*Where do you guys play basketball? At home?*
d. Mi padre y yo jugamos al billar en mi casa	*My father and I play videogames at home*
e. Los domingos juegan al rugby en el parque	*On Sundays we play rugby at the park*
f. Siempre juega a la Play en su habitación	*I always play on the PlayStation in my room*
g. Jugáis a juegos en línea de vez en cuando	*We play online games often*
h. Todavía juegan con muñecas	*She still plays with dolls*

4. Broken translation

a. *They play football*	Jueg__ __ a__ fút__ __ __
b. *We never play rugby*	Nun__ __ juga__ __ __ a__ rugby
c. *I don't play chess*	N__ ju__ __ __ a__ ajedr __ __
d. *My friends never play basketball*	Mi __ amig __ __ nu__ __ __ jue__ __ __ al balonces __ __
e. *On Sundays I play cards*	Lo__ domin__ __ __ ju__ __ __ a l__ __ car__ __ __
f. *He plays tennis every day*	Ju __ __ __ a__ te__ __ __ tod__ __ l__ __ dí__ __
g. *We play rugby in the countryside*	Jugam__ __ a__ r__ __ __ __ e__ e__ cam__ __
h. *They play handball…*	Jueg__ __ a__ bal__ __ __ __ __ __ __
i. *…in the sports centre*	…e__ e__ po__ __ __epo__ __ __ v__
i. *Do you guys play on the PlayStation?*	¿Jug__ __ __ a l__ Play?
j. *You guys always play cards!*	¡Vosot__ __ __ siemp__ __ jug__ __ __ a la__ cart__ __ !

5. Match

En el campo	*At the sports centre*
En la montaña	*At his/her house*
En la piscina	*In my room*
En el polideportivo	*In the swimming pool*
En mi casa	*At (my) home*
En la playa	*In the park*
En mi habitación	*In the mountain*
En su casa	*On the beach*
En el parque	*In the countryside*

6. Listen and Complete

a. Nosotras __________ al fútbol

b. Ellos ___________ al golf

c. Ella __________ al rugby

d. Yo nunca __________ a la Play

e. Ellas ___________ con las muñecas

f. Él ___________ al baloncesto

g. ¿Á qué ____________ vosotros?

h. ¿Á qué ___________ tú?

i. Mis padres ___________ al rugby

7. Sentence Puzzle

a. lunes jugamos Los Paco y a la yo Play. Lo casa mi en hacemos.

On Mondays, Paco and I play on the PlayStation. We do it in my house.

b. amigos baloncesto Los, mis al viernes juegan. hacen Lo mi en colegio.

On Fridays, my friends play basketball. They do it in my school.

c. fines Los semana de, hermano mi juega fútbol al. hace Lo polideportivo en el.

At weekends, my brother plays football. He does it at the sports centre.

d. ¿Los juegas sábados, golf al con padre tu? ¿lo Dónde haces?

On Saturdays, do you play golf with your father? Where do you do it?

e. Los de padre semana mi fines juegan y mayor hermano mi al ajedrez. hacen Lo en jardín el.

At weekends, my father and my older brother play chess. They do it in the garden.

8. Tangled translation: translate into Spanish

a. Los fines de ***week he plays*** al ***chess*** con mi ***father*** en ***the*** campo.

b. Los ***Thursdays*** juego con mi perro. ***I do it*** en el ***countryside***.

c. De vez en cuando ***we play*** a las ***cards*** con nuestros ***parents***. Lo ***we do*** en mi casa.

d. ¿***On*** sábados, ***do you guys play tennis*** en el club de tenis ***near*** de vuestra ***house***?

e. ***On Mondays*** y miércoles ***they play*** a ***games*** en línea. Lo ***they do*** en ***house*** de Paco.

f. Pedro ***plays*** a la Play ***every day***. ***It*** hace en su ***room***.

g. Mi madre y sus ***friends play*** a las ***cards*** todos los ***Tuesdays***. ***It*** hacen en la ***house*** de Marta.

h. ***On Fridays***, mi ***sister*** mayor ***plays*** al squash con mi ***father***. Lo ***does*** en el ***sports centre***.

9. Listen and Fill in each gap with the correct word

a. Los ___________ mi _________ y yo _________ al baloncesto. Lo ________ en el polideportivo.

b. Los fines de __________, mis hermanos _________ al fútbol en el ______________.

c. ___ viernes, después del colegio, mis _____________ de clase ________ al fútbol. Lo _________ en el ___________ de fútbol del colegio.

d. Mi madre y sus amigas __________ a las cartas todos los ________. Lo ________ en mi casa.

e. Pedro ________ a juegos en línea todos los ______ con su ________ amigo. Lo hace en su ______.

f. Los ___________ mis hermanos ________ al rugby para su colegio. _____ hacen en el estadio.

10. Guided translation

a. *I play tennis* J__ __ __ __ a__ t__ __ __ __

b. *We play cards* Juga __ __ __ a l__ __ cart__ __

c. *With my father* C__ __ m__ p__ __ __ __

d. *In the countryside* E__ e__ c__ __ __ __

e. *They play football* Jue__ __ __ a__ f__ __ __ __ __

f. *At weekends* Lo __ fin __ __ d__ sem __ __ __

g. *Do you play rugby?* ¿Jue__ __ __ a__ r__ __ __ __ ?

h. *I do it at my home* L__ h__ __ __ e__ m__ c__ __ __

i. *I still play* To__ __ __ __ __ ju __ __ __

11. Complete the table

Pronoun	Verb Jugar	Verb Hacer + lo
Yo	Juego	Lo hago
Tú	Juegas	
Él		Lo hace
Ella	Juega	
Nosotros		Lo hacemos
Vosotros	Jugáis	
Ellos		Lo hacen
Ellas	Juegan	

12. Translate into Spanish

a. In the countryside

b. We do it

c. They play cards

d. I do it

e. On the beach

f. They play snooker

g. She plays football

h. At weekends

i. In the sports centre

j. She does it

k. They do it

13. Translate into Spanish

a. At weekends, she plays chess with my father in my house.

b. On Sundays, I play with my dog. I do it in the countryside.

c. On Saturdays, we play cards with our uncles. We do it at their house.

d. On Mondays, do you guys still play tennis at the tennis club near your house?

e. They play online games every day. They do it at Paco's house.

f. Pedro plays on the PlayStation all the time. He does it in his room.

g. My father and his friends play cards on Tuesdays. They do it at the house of their friend Mario.

h. On Fridays, my younger brother plays volleyball with my older brother. They do it at the sports centre near my house.

7.3 PRESENT OF JUGAR + A/AL/A LA + NOUN + MEJOR/PEOR QUE + NOUN/PRONOUN
(SAYING HOW WELL ONE PLAYS GAMES COMPARED TO OTHERS)

<table>
<tr><td>(Yo)
I</td><td>Juego
I play</td><td rowspan="5">al ajedrez chess
al baloncesto basketball
al billar snooker
al fútbol
al voleibol
al rugby
al tenis
a la Play Playstation
a las cartas cards
a juegos en línea online games
a los videojuegos</td><td rowspan="5">mejor que
better than

peor que
worse than</td><td rowspan="5">yo *me
tú *you
él *him
ella *her
mi amigo/a
mi hermano/a
nosotros/as *us
vosotros/as *you guys
ellos/as *they
mis amigos/as my friends
nuestros amigos our friends</td></tr>
<tr><td>(Tú)
You</td><td>Juegas
You play</td></tr>
<tr><td>(Mi amigo/a)
My friend
(Mi hermano/a)
My brother/sister</td><td>Juega
He/She plays</td></tr>
<tr><td>(Mi amigo/a y yo)
My friend and I
(Nosotros/nosotras)
We</td><td>Jugamos
We play</td></tr>
<tr><td>(Mis amigos)
My friends
(Mis padres)
My parents</td><td>Juegan
They play</td></tr>
<tr><td colspan="5">*Author's note: for more info about why these pronouns translate as "me" and not "I", etc. See below!</td></tr>
</table>

LANGUAGE AWARENESS: COMPARATIVES

When we use comparatives in Spanish ***mejor que*** (better than) or ***peor que*** (worse than), the structure used in Spanish is almost the same as English.

- **Yo juego al tenis mejor que *tú*** *I play tennis better than you*

In this sentence above, the structure is identical to English. However, depending on whom the second part of the comparison is about ***(yo, tú, él/ella, nosotros/as, vosotros/as, ellos/as)***, the English translation is slightly different.

- **Tú juegas al tenis mejor que *yo*** *You play tennis better than me*
- **Él juega mejor que *ella*** *He plays better than her*

OBJECT PRONOUNS

The reason for this change is that the **Subject Pronouns** used in Spanish at the end of the sentence are translated into English by **Object Pronouns**

- **...mejor que *él / ella / nosotros / ellos*** Subject Pronouns
- *...better than him / her / us / them* Object Pronouns

JUGAR + "A" UNTRANSLATABLE PREPOSITIONS

Have you noticed that the verb ***jugar*** is always followed by ***a*** (or **al / a la / a los / a las**)?

In Spanish, ***a*** is a preposition. It can sometimes be translated as *"to"* in English

- **Voy a la playa** *I go to the beach*

But in the context of **"*jugar a*"** plus sports or activities the ***a*** **doesn't have an English translation.**

- **Juego a las cartas** *I play ... cards*

Just remember **"jugar a"** + sports/activities.

1. Match

Juego al voleibol	*Better than them*
Mejor que él	*They play volleyball*
Jugamos al voleibol	*Worse than me*
Mejor que ellos	*Worse than her*
Mejor que yo	*I play volleyball*
Juegan al voleibol	*He/she plays volleyball*
Peor que yo	*Better than me*
Peor que ella	*Better than him*
Juega al voleibol	*We play volleyball*

2. Listen and unjumble the words 

a. yo que al billar hermano mi juega mejor

b. nosotros ellos peor juegan que rugby al

c. abuelo que al juega mi ajedrez mejor yo

d. hermanos mis al juegan fútbol yo mejor que

e. ¿tú a cartas las juegas que mejor él?

f. ellos videojuegos a juegan los que peor ella

g. madre mejor mi tenis al mi juega que padre

h. primo mi peor juega yo que tenis al

3. Faulty translation: fix the English translation

a. Mi hermano juega al fútbol mejor que yo — *My sister plays rugby better than me*

b. Ella juega al billar mejor que su novio — *He plays snooker better than his girlfriend*

c. Nosotros jugamos al tenis mejor que tú — *They play tennis better than you*

d. Mis padres juegan a las cartas peor que yo — *My grandparents play videogames better than me*

e. Mi hermana juega al ajedrez mejor que yo — *My brother plays chess worse than me*

f. Ellos juegan a las cartas mejor que su padre — *We play cards better than our father*

g. Mi tío juega al fútbol mejor que mi padre — *My aunt plays football better than my uncle*

4. Listen and complete the table 

	Person	Verb	Comparative	Possessive	Noun
e.g.	*Yo*	*juego al voleibol*	*mejor que*	*nuestro*	*padre*
a.		juegas al tenis		mi	
b.	Ellos		peor que		
c.					padre
d.		juega al baloncesto			
e.	Mis padres			mis	
f.		juega a las cartas	peor que		
g.	Vosotros			mi	hermana
h.	Ellos		peor que		
i.		juega al fútbol			primo
j.	Mi prima		mejor que		
k.			mejor que		abuelo

5. Guided translation

a. *I play tennis better than my brother. I do it often.* J__________ a____ t_______ m_______ q_______ m____ h__________. L___ h________ a m__________.

b. *We play cards worse than our grandfather. We do it rarely.* N___________ j__________ a l_____ c________ p_________ q_____ n__________ a___________. L__ h___________ r__________.

c. *My parents play videogames worse than me. I do it every day.* M_____ p__________ j________ a l___ v________ p________ q___ y___. L__ h____ t_____ l___ d___.

d. *My sister plays chess better than my father. She does it often.* M____ h________ j______ a___ a____________ m_____ q___ m___ p________. L__ h________ a m_________.

e. *Do you play rugby better than her?* ¿J__________ a____ r_____________ m_____ q____ e____?

6. Break the flow

a. Nosotrosjugamosaltenismejorqueellos

b. Ellosjueganalrugbymejorquemispadres

c. Mihermanojuegaalosvideojuegosmejorqueyo

d. Misabuelosjueganalascartaspeorquemimadre

e. Mihermanajuegalajedrezmejorquemipadre

f. Miabuelojuegaalrugbymejorquemipadre

g. Ellajuegaalvoleibolmejorquenosotros

h. Nosotrosjugamosalrugbymejorqueél

i. Mihermanojuegaajuegosenlíneamejorqueyo

7. Choose the correct word

a. Nosotros **jugamos/juegan/juega** a las cartas mejor que ellos

b. Yo **juega/juego/juegan** al billar mejor que ella

c. Mis amigos y yo **juegas/jugamos/juegan** al fútbol mejor que tú

d. Ella **jugamos/juego/juega** al billar mejor que yo

e. Mi abuelo **juega/jugamos/juegan** al billar

f. Mis tíos **juego/juegan/jugamos** al rugby

g. Mi amigo **juego/jugamos/juega** al baloncesto mejor que yo

8. Translate into English

a. Mi madre juega al fútbol mejor que mi padre

b. Mi hermano juega a los videojuegos mejor que yo

c. Nosotros jugamos al fútbol mejor que ellos

d. Mi madre no juega al baloncesto

e. Ella juega al voleibol mejor que sus padres

f. Nuestro hermano pequeño juega al fútbol mejor que yo

g. Mi hermana juega al ajedrez mejor que mi hermano

9. Translate into Spanish

a. My sister plays football better than me

b. I play cards worse than my father

c. My grandparents play snooker better than my parents

d. My sister plays online games better than us

e. I play chess worse than my grand father

f. Do you play chess better than him?

g. My sister plays basketball better than her.

h. My parents play on the PlayStation better than me

7.4 PRESENT OF TOCAR + NOUN VS PRESENT OF JUGAR + A/AL/A LA/EN + NOUN + TIME MARKER *(SAYING WHAT INSTRUMENT AND GAMES ONE PLAYS)*

Toco	*I play*	**el bajo**	*the bass*	**a menudo** *often*
Tocas	*You play*	**el chelo**	*the cello*	**de vez en cuando** *from time to time*
Toca	*He/She plays*	**el órgano**	*the organ*	**todos los días** *every day*
Tocamos	*We play*	**el saxo**	*the saxophone*	**raramente** *rarely*
Tocáis	*You guys play*	**el violín**		**una vez a la semana** *once a week*
Tocan	*They play*	**la batería**	*the drums*	**dos veces a la semana** *twice a week*
		la flauta	*the flute*	
		la guitarra		
		la trompeta		
Juego	*I play*	**al baloncesto**	*basketball*	
Juegas	*You play*	**al fútbol**	*football*	
Juega	*He/She plays*	**al tenis**		
Jugamos	*We play*	**a la Play**	*on the PlayStation*	
Jugáis	*You guys play*	**a las cartas**	*cards*	
Juegan	*They play*	**a juegos en línea**	*online games*	
		a los videojuegos		

USING ADVERBS – *BIEN / MAL*

Toco bien la guitarra **Toco la guitarra bien**	*I play guitar well*	**Juego mal al fútbol** **Juego al fútbol mal**	*I play football badly*

The adverbs ***bien*** (well) and ***mal*** (badly) can go either **after the <u>verb (1)</u>**, or **after the <u>noun (2)</u>**.

1) Toco bien la guitarra 2) Toco la guitarra bien • *I play guitar well*

In Spanish it sounds more natural when placed directly after the verb ***(toco bien)***, but in English it can **only** go after the noun. You will hear and see both the above Spanish forms in this unit.

LANGUAGE AWARENESS: *JUGAR VS TOCAR*

In Spanish we have two verbs for the verb "**to play" in English.**

If we are talking about playing a sport or a game, we use ***jugar a*** + **article** (see P187).

• **Juego al fútbol** *I play football*

If we are talking about playing an instrument, we must use ***tocar*** *(literally **"to touch"**)*. Please, note that ***tocar*** is followed by the definite article ***el/la***.

• **Toco el violín** *I play the violín*

1. Choose the correct sentence

	Tocar	Jugar
a.	Toco la guitarra	Juego a la guitarra
b.	Toco el ajedrez	Juego al ajedrez
c.	Toco la Play	Juego a la Play
d.	Toco las cartas	Juego a las cartas
e.	Toco la batería	Juego a la batería
f.	Toco el baloncesto	Juego al baloncesto
g.	Toco juegos en línea	Juego a juegos en línea
h.	Toco el piano	Juego al piano
i.	Toco el saxo	Juego al saxo
j.	Toco la flauta	Juego a la flauta

2. Faulty translation: fix the English translation

a. Tocamos la guitarra	*They play the guitar*
b. ¿Qué instrumento tocas?	*What instrument do I play?*
c. Él juega al ajedrez bien	*We play chess badly*
d. Tocan la batería muy bien	*He plays the flute very well*
e. Nunca toca el bajo	*He never plays the flute*
f. Jugamos al fútbol muy bien	*I play football very well*
g. Juegan al tenis muy mal	*He plays football very badly*
h. ¿Tocas el saxo?	*Do we play the saxophone?*
i. ¡Jugáis al baloncesto…	*We play basketball…*
j. …todos los días!	*…every weekend!*
k. No toca ni el saxo ni la flauta	*I neither play sax nor flute*

3. Listen and complete the words

a. Toc__ __ __ __ la guitarra

b. Toc__ el piano

c. Toc__ el violín

d. Toc__ __ la flauta

e. ¿Toc__ __ el saxo?

f. ¿Qué instrumento tocá __ __?

g. Toc__ la trompeta

h. Toc__ __ __ __ la flauta

i. Toc__ __ el chelo

j. Toc__ __ el violín

4. Guided translation

a. *We play the guitar very well*	T________ l__ g________ m____ b_______
b. *They play football badly*	J________ a__ f________ m_______
c. *I don't play the piano*	N__ t______ e__ p_______
d. *They play the trumpet badly*	T________ l__ t________ m_______
e. *We play videogames*	J________ a l__ v________
f. *I don't play the drums well*	N__ t______ l__ b________ b______
g. *You always play on the PlayStation*	S______ j________ a l___ P_______
h. *I never play the bass guitar*	N____ t_______ e__ b________

5. Tangled translation: translate into Spanish

a. ***I play*** la trompeta muy ***badly***

b. ***We play*** el piano ***very*** mal

c. ***They play*** la batería muy ***well***

d. ***I*** nunca ***play the*** bajo

e. ***My*** hermano ***plays*** el chelo ***very badly***

f. ***My*** padres no ***play instruments*** musicales

g. ¿Qué ***instruments*** musicales ***do you guys play***?

h. ***Do you play*** el violín?

6. Translate into Spanish

a. We play the guitar very well

b. I never play the piano

c. We play football and play the saxophone

d. I play the trumpet and I play online games

e. She plays videogames and the drums

f. My father plays the violin very well

g. What instrument do you play?

h. My sister plays the bass and the guitar well

7.5. INTERLEAVING JUGAR, HACER, TOCAR, IR & VERBS LIKE GUSTAR

(SAYING WHAT I DO IN MY FREE TIME AND HOW I FEEL ABOUT IT)

En mi tiempo libre *In my free time*	**juego** **juegas** **juega** **jugamos** **jugáis** **juegan**	*I play* *you play* *he/she plays* *we play* *you guys play* *they play*	**al baloncesto** **al fútbol** **al golf** **al tenis** **a la Play** **a las cartas** **a juegos en línea** **a los videojuegos**	*basketball* *football* *golf* *tennis* *on the PlayStation* *cards* *online games* *video games*

hago *I do* **haces** *you do* **hace** *he/she does* **hacemos** *we do* **hacéis** *you guys do* **hacen** *they do*	**artes marciales** *martial arts* **atletismo** **boxeo** **deporte** *sports* **escalada** *climbing* **footing** *jogging* **pesas** *weights*	**toco** *I play* **tocas** *you play* **toca** *he/she plays* **tocamos** *we play* **tocáis** *you guys play* **tocan** *they play*	**el bajo** *the bass* **el chelo** **el saxo** **el violín** **la batería** *the drums* **la flauta** **la guitarra** **la trompeta**	y	**voy** *I go* **vas** *you go* **va** *he/she goes* **vamos** *we go* **vais** *you guys go* **van** *they go*	**al centro comercial** *to the shopping centre* **al cine** *to the cinema* **al parque** *to the park* **a la piscina** *to the pool* **al polideportivo** *to the sports centre*

Verbs like GUSTAR						
***Me** **Te** **Le** **Nos** **Os** **Les**	**aburre** **chifla** **encanta** **gusta** **molesta**	*'bore'* *'crazy about'* *'love'* *'like'* *'annoy'*	**hacer** **ir** **jugar** **tocar**	*to do* *to go* *to play* *to play*	**deporte** **a la piscina** **al baloncesto** **el piano**	**footing** **al cine** **a los videojuegos** **la guitarra**

LANGUAGE AWARENESS: VERBS LIKE *GUSTAR*

The five** verbs listed above (aburre, chifla, etc.) work in the same way as ***gustar. They are different from the other irregular verbs encountered in previous units. These verbs all work in the **third person** and we change the **Indirect Pronoun** in front of the verb to talk about different people, and not the verb itself.

- **<u>Me</u> gusta hacer footing** — ***<u>I</u>*** *like doing jogging*
- **<u>Te</u> encanta tocar el saxo** — ***<u>You</u>*** *love playing sax*
- **<u>Le</u> encanta tocar la guitarra** — ***<u>He</u>*** *loves playing the guitar*
- **<u>Nos</u> chifla ir al cine** — ***<u>We</u>*** *are crazy about going to the cinema*
- **<u>Os</u> aburre hacer boxeo** — ***<u>You guys</u>*** *find boxing boring*
- **<u>Les</u> molesta el reguetón** — ***<u>They</u>*** *find reguetón 'music' annoying*

When speaking about a third person, we need to add the **Personal *a*** if we are mentioning the person who likes something (as opposed to just "**he/she** likes"). See **Page 165** for more information about this!

- **<u>A</u> mi hermano <u>le</u> encanta tocar la guitarra** — ***<u>My brother</u>*** *loves playing guitar*

1. Match

Juego al fútbol	*It bores you to play the piano*
Jugamos al fútbol	*They do weights*
Jugáis al fútbol	*It bores me to play the piano*
Tocáis la guitarra	*I play football*
Hago pesas	*We do weights*
Hacemos pesas	*We play football*
Hacen pesas	*It bores us to play the piano*
Me aburre tocar el piano	*You guys play the guitar*
Le aburre tocar el piano	*I do weights*
Nos aburre tocar el piano	*They play the piano*
Te aburre tocar el piano	*It bores him/her to play the piano*
Tocan el piano	*You guys play football*

2. Listen and complete

a. ___________al fútbol. ___ gusta jugar al fútbol.

b. __________ el violín. _____ aburre tocar el violín.

c. ___________ pesas. ______ encanta ______ pesas.

d. __________ al centro comercial. _____ encanta ______ al centro _____________.

e. ___________ footing porque _____ encanta _____ footing.

f. _________ escalada porque ___ chifla ______ escalada.

g. ____________ boxeo, pero ____ aburre ____________ boxeo todos los días.

h. __________ a la piscina porque ___ encanta.

i. _________ al ___________ porque _____ chifla _____ todos los domingos.

3. Faulty translation: fix the English translation

a. En nuestro tiempo libre hacemos pesas todos los días. Nos encanta hacer pesas.

In their free time they do athletics every day. They love doing weights.

b. En su tiempo libre mi hermano va a la piscina y hace natación. Le chifla ir a la piscina.

In her free time my sister goes to the gym and does nothing. She loves to go to the gym.

c. En mi tiempo libre toco el piano y juego a los videojuegos. Sin embargo, me aburre tocar la flauta.

In our free time we play the piano and play videogames. However, playing the flute bores us.

d. En su tiempo libre mi padre juega al tenis, hace escalada y va a la piscina. Le encanta hacer deporte.

In their free time my friends play tennis, do climbing and go to the pool. They love to do sports.

e. En tu tiempo libre, ¿haces deporte y tocas un instrumento?

In your free time, do you guys do sports and play an instrument?

4. Break the flow

a. Enmitiempolibrehagoescaladajuegoalfútbolyvoyalcentrocomercialconmisamigos.

b. Ensutiempolibremihermanojuegaalosvideojuegosyhaceequitación.Leencantahacerequitación.

c. Amipadreleaburrehacerescaladatodoslosdías.

d. Amímeaburretocarlaflautaperohagoartesmarciales.

e. MiamigojuegaalaPlayporquelechiflajugarconvideojuegos.

f. Mispadreshacendeportedevezencuandoperonolesgustahacerescalada.

g. Meaburretocarelsaxotodoslosdíasperolohago.

5. Choose the correct word, then listen and check 

a. Mi hermano **juega/hacemos/juegan** al fútbol.

b. En mi tiempo libre **vamos/van/voy** a la piscina. **Me/Nos/Les** encanta ir a la piscina.

c. Mis padres **tocáis/tocas/tocan** el piano mejor que yo porque **nos/os/les** encanta.

d. Mis amigos **tocan/hacen/juegan** pesas todos los días, pero **le/nos/les** aburre.

e. En su tiempo libre mi abuelo **hace/juegas/juega** a las cartas. **Me/Te/Le** chifla.

f. En su tiempo libre **hace/juega/toca** el violín.

6. Staircase translation – Translate each sentence from memory

a.	My dad	does martial arts				
b.	Our parents	go to the swimming pool	and they play tennis			
c.	In my free time	I play piano and the flute,	but my mother	does jogging		
d.	It bores me	to do sport	every day	I do it	rarely	
e.	She doesn't like	to play the drums,	but she plays the guitar	and goes to the shopping centre	because she loves	to go shopping

a. ____

b. ____

c. ____

d. ____

e. ____

7. Guided translation

a. *My dad plays the guitar and goes to the swimming pool. He loves going to the swimming pool.*

M______ p_________ t________ l___ g________ y v______ a l___ p___________. L__ e____________ i___ a la p_____________.

b. *My friends do weights and martial arts. They do it every day, but doing weights bores them.*

M_____ a___________ h_________ p________ y a_______ m_____________. L__ h__________ t_______ l____ d_____, p______ h_________ p__________ l____ a_____________.

c. *My grandfather loves playing cards. He does it at weekends. He also goes to the shopping centre.*

A m___ a__________ l___ e____________ j___________ a l_____ c____________. L___ h_________ l____ f_______ d__ s_____________. T____________ v___ a___ c__________ c________________.

d. *In our free time we play tennis with our uncle and go to the sports centre. We love going to the sports centre because it is fun.*

E__ n__________ t__________ l____________ j____________ a__ t__________ c___ n___________ t_____ y v_______ a__ p____________________. N____ e_____________ i__ a__ p________________________ p_________ e____ d_______________.

8. Translate into English

a. Mi madre juega al baloncesto, toca el piano y va a la piscina todos los fines de semana. Le encanta hacer cosas (*things*).

b. Mis amigos van a la playa cuando hace calor porque les chifla hacer natación. Sin embargo, ni tocan un instrumento ni hacen boxeo.

c. Mis padres ni hacen escalada ni juegan al tenis. No hacen nada porque les aburre hacer deporte.

d. En nuestro tiempo libre mis hermanos y yo hacemos pesas en el gimnasio. También tocamos la batería. Nos encanta tocar un instrumento.

e. Mis primos ni hacen buceo ni hacen vela, pero tocan la flauta. Les encanta tocar música.

9. Translate into Spanish

a. In my free time I do climbing, I play the guitar and I go to the swimming pool in order to swim. I love doing things (*cosas*).

b. My brother is very sporty. He plays tennis and does boxing, but he doesn't play the drums. It bores him to play an instrument.

c. My grandparents play chess at weekends with my brother. My grandfather plays better than my brother. My grandfather is crazy about playing chess.

d. My sister loves to play the piano. She does it every day, but never does sport or plays football.

A

ORAL PING PONG

JUGAR

ENGLISH 1	SPANISH 1	ENGLISH 2	SPANISH 2
When I have time, I play chess with my dad. We do it at weekends.	Cuando tengo tiempo, juego al ajedrez con mi padre. Lo hacemos los fines de semana.	I play basketball with my friends. We do it often at weekends.	
My friend plays handball with his cousins. They do it often in the sports centre.	Mi amigo juega al balonmano con sus primos. Lo hacen a menudo en el polideportivo.	My sister plays football with our cousins. They do it from time to time.	
On Fridays my grandparents play cards with my older brother in my house.	Los viernes mis abuelos juegan a las cartas con mi hermano mayor en mi casa.	My parents play tennis better than my brother and me.	
My sister plays tennis better than me, but I play videogames better than her.	Mi hermana juega al tenis mejor que yo, pero yo juego a los videojuegos mejor que ella.	I play cards worse than my grandfather, but I play chess better than him.	
Do you play the violin? I play the drums, but I play tennis better.	¿Tocas el violín? Yo toco la batería, pero juego al tenis mejor.	I play the flute better than my sister.	
My family and I play the guitar very well, but we never do it.	Mi familia y yo tocamos la guitarra muy bien, pero nunca lo hacemos.	My cousins like playing the cello. They do it every day.	
In my free time I play basketball, I do climbing and I play the bass.	En mi tiempo libre juego al baloncesto, hago escalada y toco el bajo.	My mum goes to the cinema, does martial arts and plays the sax because she likes it.	
My dad plays golf and goes to the swimming pool because he likes going swimming.	Mi padre juega al golf y va a la piscina porque le gusta hacer natación.	Do you play the drums? I play the piano, but it bores me.	

INSTRUCTIONS - You are **PARTNER A.** Work in pairs. Each of you has two sets of sentences - one set has already been translated for you. You will ask your partner to translate these. The other set of sentences have not been translated. Your partner will ask you to translate these.
HOW TO PLAY - Partner A starts by reading out his/her/their first sentence in English. Partner B must translate. Partner A must check the answer and award the following points: **3 points** = perfect, **2 points** = 1 mistake, **1 point** = mistakes but the verb is accurate. If they cannot translate correctly, Partner A will read out the sentence so that Partner B can learn what the correct translation is.
Then Partner B reads out his/her/their first sentence, and so on.
OBJECTIVE - Try to win more points than your partner by translating correctly as many sentences as possible.

B

ORAL PING PONG

JUGAR

ENGLISH 1	SPANISH 1	ENGLISH 2	SPANISH 2
When I have time, I play chess with my dad. We do it at weekends.		I play basketball with my friends. We do it often at weekends.	Juego al baloncesto con mis amigos. Lo hacemos a menudo los fines de semana.
My friend plays handball with his cousins. They do it often in the sports centre.		My sister plays football with our cousins. They do it from time to time.	Mi hermana juega al fútbol con nuestros primos. Lo hacen de vez en cuando.
On Fridays my grandparents play cards with my older brother in my house.		My parents play tennis better than my brother and me.	Mis padres juegan al tenis mejor que mi hermano y yo.
My sister plays tennis better than me, but I play videogames better than her.		I play cards worse than my grandfather, but I play chess better than him.	Juego a las cartas peor que mi abuelo, pero juego al ajedrez mejor que él.
Do you play the violin? I play the drums, but I play tennis better.		I play the flute better than my sister.	Toco la flauta mejor que mi hermana.
My family and I play the guitar very well, but we never do it.		My cousins like playing the cello. They do it every day.	A mis primos les gusta tocar el chelo. Lo hacen todos los días.
In my free time I play basketball, I do climbing and I play the bass.		My mum goes to the cinema, does martial arts and plays the sax because she likes it.	Mi madre va al cine, hace artes marciales y toca el saxo porque le gusta.
My dad plays golf and goes to the swimming pool because he likes going swimming.		Do you play the drums? I play the piano, but it bores me.	¿Tocas la batería? Yo toco el piano, pero me aburre.

INSTRUCTIONS - You are **PARTNER B.** Work in pairs. Each of you has two sets of sentences - one set has already been translated for you. You will ask your partner to translate these. The other set of sentences have not been translated. Your partner will ask you to translate these.
HOW TO PLAY - Partner A starts by reading out his/her/their first sentence <u>in English</u>. Partner B must translate. Partner A must check the answer and award the following points: **3 points** = perfect, **2 points** = 1 mistake, **1 point** = mistakes but the verb is accurate. If they cannot translate correctly, Partner A will read out the sentence so that Partner B can learn what the correct translation is.
Then Partner B reads out his/her/their first sentence, and so on.
OBJECTIVE - Try to win more points than your partner by translating correctly as many sentences as possible.

No Snakes No Ladders

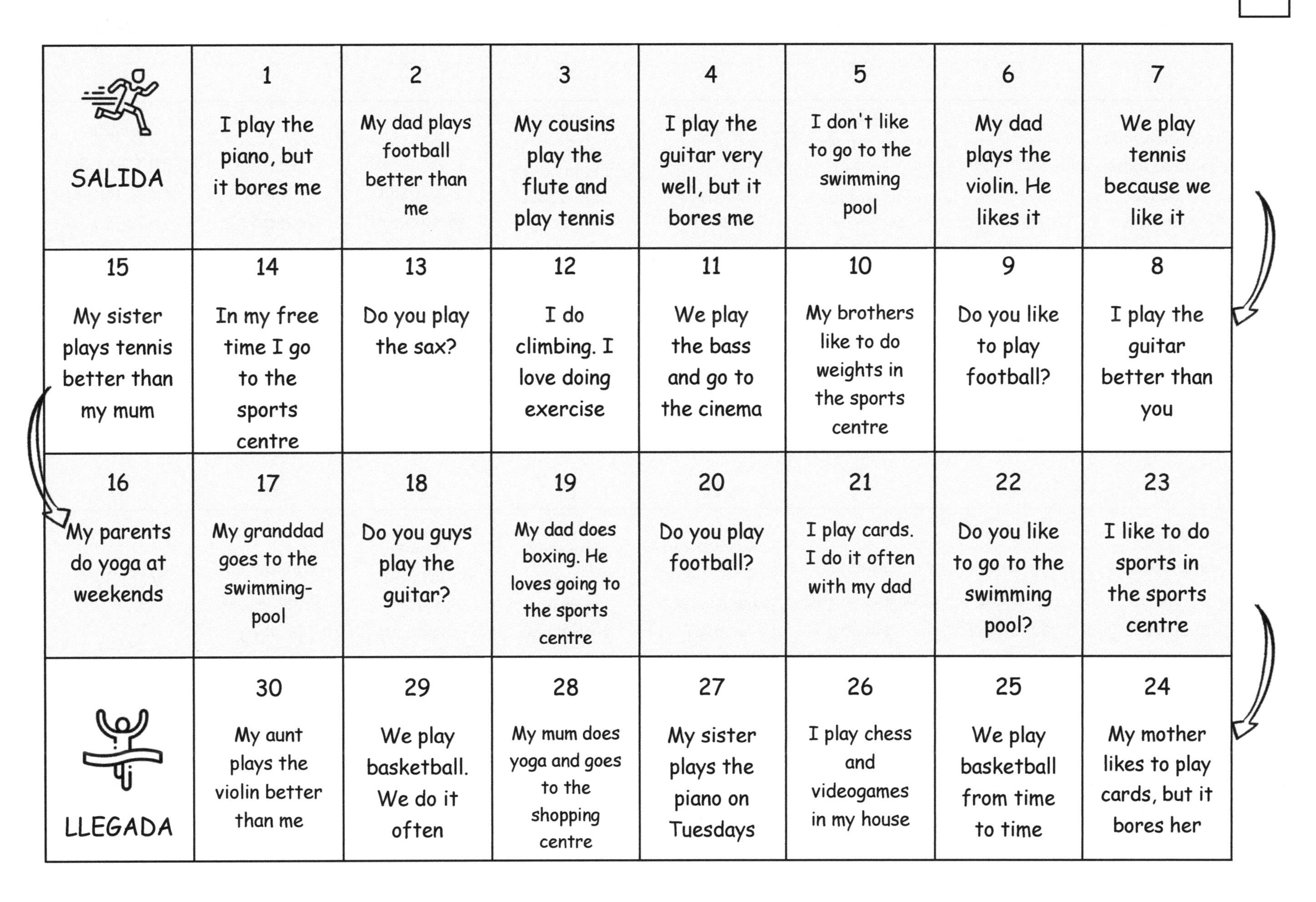

SALIDA	1 I play the piano, but it bores me	2 My dad plays football better than me	3 My cousins play the flute and play tennis	4 I play the guitar very well, but it bores me	5 I don't like to go to the swimming pool	6 My dad plays the violin. He likes it	7 We play tennis because we like it
15 My sister plays tennis better than my mum	14 In my free time I go to the sports centre	13 Do you play the sax?	12 I do climbing. I love doing exercise	11 We play the bass and go to the cinema	10 My brothers like to do weights in the sports centre	9 Do you like to play football?	8 I play the guitar better than you
16 My parents do yoga at weekends	17 My granddad goes to the swimming-pool	18 Do you guys play the guitar?	19 My dad does boxing. He loves going to the sports centre	20 Do you play football?	21 I play cards. I do it often with my dad	22 Do you like to go to the swimming pool?	23 I like to do sports in the sports centre
LLEGADA	30 My aunt plays the violin better than me	29 We play basketball. We do it often	28 My mum does yoga and goes to the shopping centre	27 My sister plays the piano on Tuesdays	26 I play chess and videogames in my house	25 We play basketball from time to time	24 My mother likes to play cards, but it bores her

No Snakes No Ladders

JUGAR

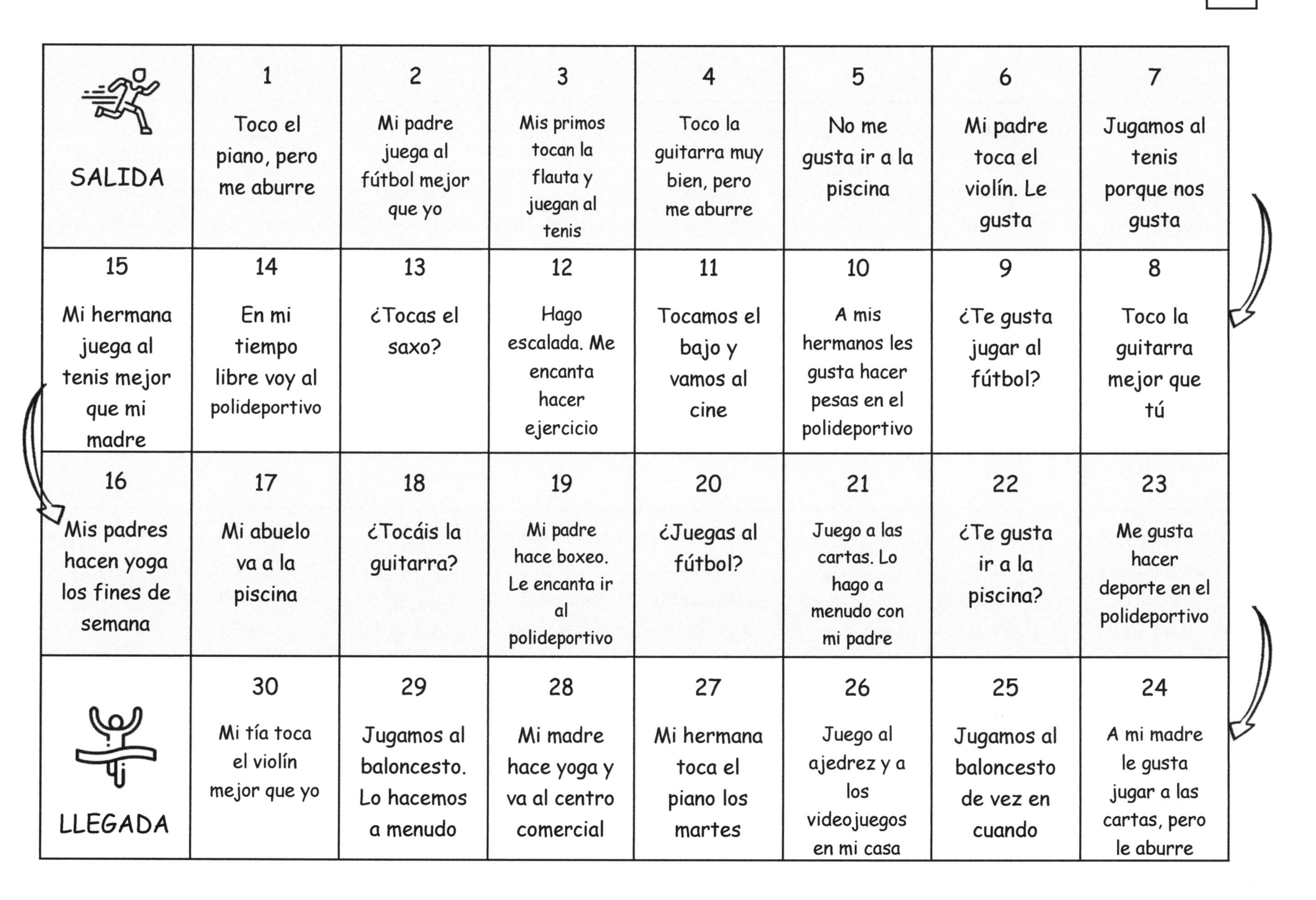

SALIDA	1 Toco el piano, pero me aburre	2 Mi padre juega al fútbol mejor que yo	3 Mis primos tocan la flauta y juegan al tenis	4 Toco la guitarra muy bien, pero me aburre	5 No me gusta ir a la piscina	6 Mi padre toca el violín. Le gusta	7 Jugamos al tenis porque nos gusta
15 Mi hermana juega al tenis mejor que mi madre	14 En mi tiempo libre voy al polideportivo	13 ¿Tocas el saxo?	12 Hago escalada. Me encanta hacer ejercicio	11 Tocamos el bajo y vamos al cine	10 A mis hermanos les gusta hacer pesas en el polideportivo	9 ¿Te gusta jugar al fútbol?	8 Toco la guitarra mejor que tú
16 Mis padres hacen yoga los fines de semana	17 Mi abuelo va a la piscina	18 ¿Tocáis la guitarra?	19 Mi padre hace boxeo. Le encanta ir al polideportivo	20 ¿Juegas al fútbol?	21 Juego a las cartas. Lo hago a menudo con mi padre	22 ¿Te gusta ir a la piscina?	23 Me gusta hacer deporte en el polideportivo
LLEGADA	30 Mi tía toca el violín mejor que yo	29 Jugamos al baloncesto. Lo hacemos a menudo	28 Mi madre hace yoga y va al centro comercial	27 Mi hermana toca el piano los martes	26 Juego al ajedrez y a los videojuegos en mi casa	25 Jugamos al baloncesto de vez en cuando	24 A mi madre le gusta jugar a las cartas, pero le aburre

PYRAMID TRANSLATION

JUGAR

Translate each part of the pyramid out loud with your partner, then write it into the spaces provided below.

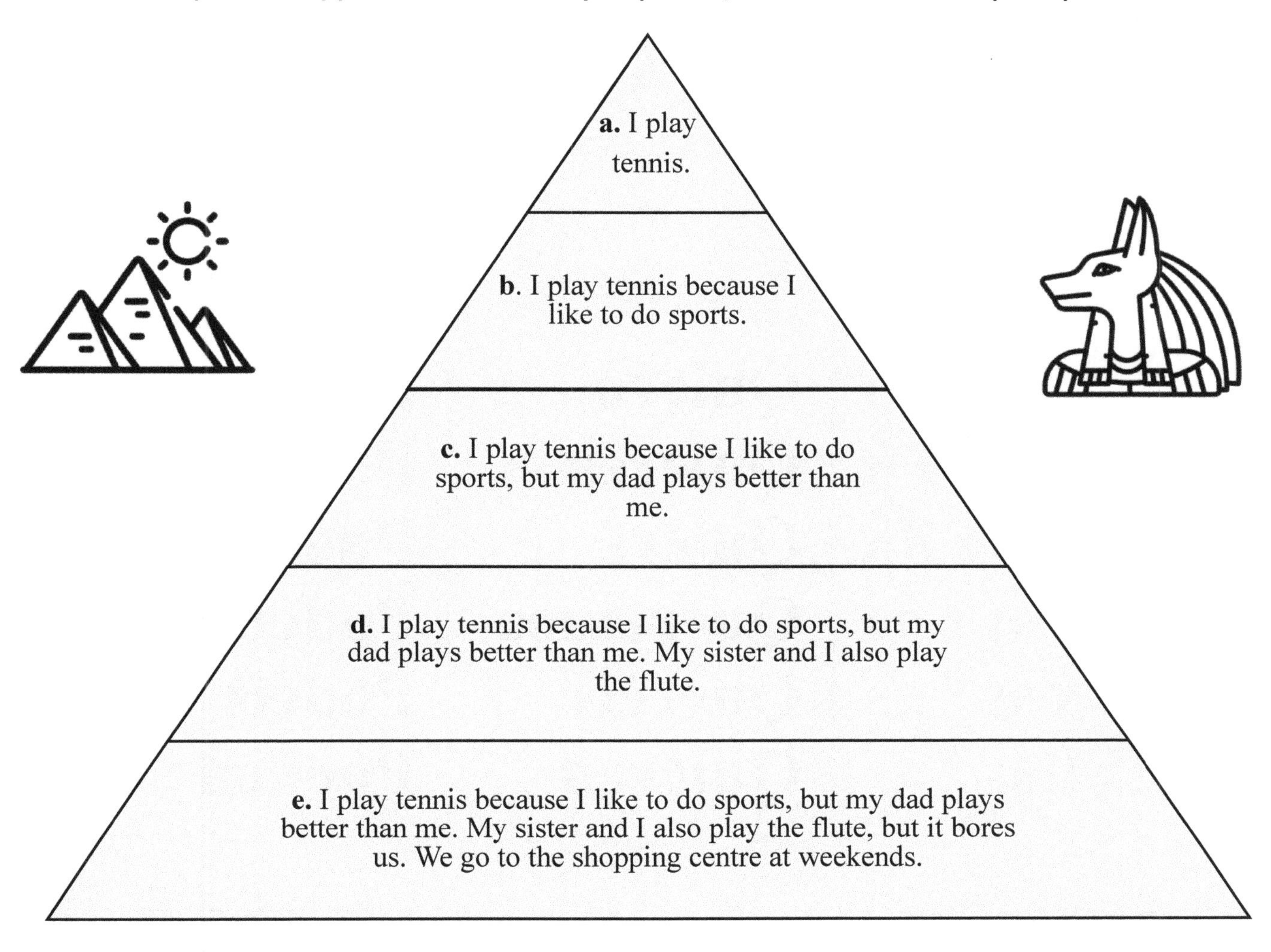

Write your translation here

SOLUTION: Juego al tenis porque me gusta hacer deporte, pero mi padre juega mejor que yo. Mi hermana y yo también tocamos la flauta, pero nos aburre. Vamos al centro comercial los fines de semana.

UNIT 8 – MODAL VERBS
QUERER & PODER

Yo	Quiero	Puedo
Tú	Quieres	Puedes
Él / Ella	Quiere	Puede
Nosotros / as	Queremos	Podemos
Vosotros / as	Queréis	Podéis
Ellos / as	Quieren	Pueden

8.1 EN + MI + NOUN + PUEDO + HACER/IR/JUGAR + NOUN/PREPOSITIONAL PHRASE + TIME MARKER

(SAYING WHAT I CAN DO AND PLAY AND WHERE I CAN GO)

<table>
<tr><td colspan="5">En mi colegio In my school
En mi instituto In my (secondary) school</td></tr>
<tr><td rowspan="3">Puedo
I can</td><td>hacer
to do</td><td>teatro
natación
pesas
atletismo
gimnasia
los deberes</td><td>drama
swimming
weights

homework</td><td rowspan="3">a menudo
often
de vez en cuando
from time to time
los lunes
on Mondays
los martes
los miércoles
los jueves
los viernes
los sábados
los domingos
siempre
always
todos los días
every day
una vez a la semana
once a week
después de las clases
after lessons</td></tr>
<tr><td>ir
to go</td><td>a la biblioteca
a clases de baile
al club de español
al club de ciencias
al club de ajedrez
al taller de teatro</td><td>to the library
to dance lessons
to the Spanish club
to the Science club
to the chess club
to the drama workshop</td></tr>
<tr><td>jugar
to play</td><td colspan="2">al tenis
al fútbol
al rugby</td></tr>
<tr><td>No puedo
I can't</td><td>comer chicle
correr
ser maleducado/a
beber alcohol
beber refrescos
usar el móvil
fumar
llevar joyas
llevar maquillaje
hacer novillos</td><td>chew gum
run
be rude
drink alcohol
drink soft drinks
use my mobile
smoke
wear jewellery
wear make-up
skip lessons</td><td colspan="2">en las aulas
in the classrooms
en los pasillos
in the corridors</td></tr>
<tr><td colspan="5">No puedo comer chicle nunca I can never chew gum</td></tr>
</table>

1. Match

Ir a la biblioteca	*To play rugby*
Ir al club de ajedrez	*To be rude*
Hacer teatro	*To run*
Llevar maquillaje	*To skip lessons*
Llevar joyas	*To go to the library*
Hacer natación	*To chew gum*
Hacer novillos	*To do drama*
Usar el móvil	*To go to the chess club*
Correr	*To wear make-up*
Comer chicle	*To wear jewellery*
Jugar al rugby	*To do swimming*
Ser maleducado	*To use my mobile*

3. Sentence Puzzle

a. biblioteca a a ir una Puedo semana la la vez *I can go to the library once a week*

b. No fumar colegio en puedo mi *I can't smoke in my school*

c. maquillaje clases puedo en llevar No las nunca *I can never wear make-up in lessons*

d. novillos No hacer puedo nunca *I can never skip lessons*

e. Puedo después deberes la los las de hacer en biblioteca clases *I can do homework in the library after lessons*

f. clases de Después las los atletismo puedo hacer miércoles *After lessons I can do athletics on Wednesdays*

g. No refrescos mi puedo beber en instituto nunca *I can never drink soft drinks in my school*

2. Complete the words with the missing vowels, then listen and check

a. N__ p__ __d__ h__c__r n__v__ll__s
I can't skip lessons

b. N__ p__ __d__ c__rr__r __n l__s p__s__ll__s
I can't run in the corridors

c. N__ p__ __d__ ll__v__r m__q__ __ll__j__
I can't wear make-up

d. P__ __d__ j__g__r __l f__tb__l
I can play football

e. P__ __d__ __r a__ cl__b d__ __j__dr__z
I can go to the chess club

f. P__ __d__ h__c__r p__s__s
I can do weights

g. N__ p__ __d__ __s__r __l m__v__l
I can't use my mobile

h. P__ __d__ h__c__r g__mn__s__ __
I can do gymnastics

i. P__ __d__ __r __ cl__s__s d__ b__ __l__
I can go to dance lessons

j. P__ __d__ __r __l t__ll__r d__ t__ __tr__
I can go to the drama workshop

k. N__ p__ __d__ f__m__r
I can't smoke

4. Listen and underline the words you hear 

a. Puedo ir al club de **ajedrez/español/ciencias** después de las clases **todos los días/los lunes/una vez a la semana**

b. No puedo **fumar/llevar maquillaje/llevar joyas** en mi colegio nunca

c. Puedo hacer **natación/atletismo/gimnasia** después de las clases **a menudo/una vez a la semana/los lunes**

d. No puedo **usar el móvil/ser maleducado/correr** en los pasillos

e. Puedo **jugar al fútbol/jugar al rugby/ir al club de ciencias** después de las clases **los lunes/una vez a la semana/los martes**

5. Faulty translation: fix the English translation

a. Puedo ir al club de español una vez a la semana después de las clases

I can go to the chess club twice a week after lessons.

b. En mi colegio puedo hacer natación todos los días después de las clases

In my school I can do weights once a week after lessons

c. No puedo llevar maquillaje ni correr en los pasillos

I cannot wear jewellery nor run in the classrooms

d. En las clases no puedo usar el móvil nunca

In lessons I can never chew gum

e. En mi instituto puedo ir a la biblioteca para hacer los deberes después de las clases

In my school I can go to the drama workshop to do homework before lessons

f. En mi colegio puedo hacer teatro los lunes y atletismo los viernes

In my school I can do swimming on Thursdays and gymnastics on Mondays

6. Gapped translation: complete the translation

a. En mi colegio _________ hacer _______________...	*In my school I can do homework...*
b. ...en la biblioteca __________ de las __________	*...in the library after lessons*
c. Después de las clases ___________ _____ a...	*After lessons I can go to...*
d. __ _______________ para _________ los deberes	*... the library in order to do homework*
e. __________ ir ___ __________ __ ciencias	*I can go to the science club....*
f. ...de vez en cuando ____ ______________	*...from time to time on Fridays*
g. No puedo __________ novillos nunca	*I can never skip lessons*
h. __ puedo __________ ni ___________ en los pasillos	*I can't smoke or run in the corridors*
i. En ___ ______ no _________ comer ___________	*In the classrooms I can't chew gum*
j. En mi colegio puedo ir al _____________ de teatro	*In my school I can go to the drama workshop*

7. Complete with the correct verb

a. No puedo ________ chicle

b. Puedo ________ al taller de teatro

c. Puedo ________ mis deberes en la biblioteca

d. No puedo _________ cigarrillos

e. No puedo _________ novillos

f. No puedo _________ el móvil

g. Puedo __________ a la clase de baile

h. Puedo _______ agua en clase

i. No puedo __________ en los pasillos

j. No puedo _________ maquillaje ni joyas

k. Puedo ________ al club de ciencias

l. No puedo _________ maleducado

m. No puedo _________ Coca-Cola en clase

n. Puedo __________ atletismo

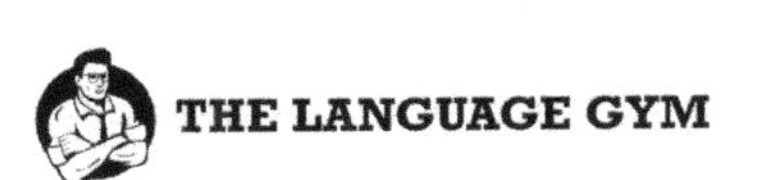

8. Find the Spanish translation and write it next to the English prompts

j	q	r	t	y	u	t	e	m	k	e	z	a	c	t	i	u	m	n	v	s	u	g	h	n
h	e	l	p	u	e	d	o	h	a	c	e	r	p	e	s	a	s	b	o	r	i	n	g	o
g	u	d	y	a	s	e	n	o	p	u	e	d	o	f	u	m	a	r	c	a	n	u	t	p
s	j	a	z	o	m	a	k	i	y	a	j	e	p	a	t	u	f	e	i	s	p	a	v	u
x	p	n	o	p	u	e	d	o	l	l	e	v	a	r	m	a	q	u	i	l	l	a	j	e
b	b	u	w	b	n	u	p	e	u	d	i	m	o	s	y	o	s	a	r	e	l	m	i	d
n	t	r	l	j	i	n	o	p	u	e	d	o	u	s	a	r	e	l	m	ó	v	i	l	o
o	r	e	x	f	c	a	r	r	i	d	e	s	p	ñ	l	s	t	r	a	n	s	f	b	c
n	o	p	u	e	d	o	l	l	e	v	a	r	j	o	y	a	s	r	o	d	e	b	s	o
e	i	b	w	r	m	o	n	i	f	r	u	w	d	e	h	t	n	u	m	s	i	c	a	r
p	t	u	n	o	p	u	e	d	o	h	a	c	e	r	n	o	v	i	l	l	o	s	a	r
ñ	r	e	j	h	u	m	j	n	a	j	g	h	s	q	u	e	a	r	u	m	n	o	t	e
a	s	d	r	n	o	p	u	e	d	o	c	o	m	e	r	c	h	i	c	l	e	b	s	r

a. I cannot chew gum

b. I cannot skip lessons

c. I cannot run

d. I cannot wear jewellery

e. I cannot use my mobile phone

f. I cannot wear make-up

g. I cannot smoke

h. I can do weights

9. Tangled translation: translate into Spanish

a. No puedo ***wear make-up***

b. Puedo ir ***to the*** club de ***chess***

c. No ***can*** correr en los ***corridors***

d. No puedo ***smoke***

e. Puedo hacer ***weights***

f. ***I cannot*** comer ***chewing gum***

g. Puedo ***go*** al club de informática

h. No puedo ***wear*** joyas

i. No ***can*** hacer ***truancy***

j. No puedo ***be impolite***

k. Puedo hacer ***my homework*** en la ***library***

l. Puedo hacer ***swimming***

10. Translate into English

a. No puedo correr en los pasillos

b. Puedo ir al club de ciencias todos los días

c. Puedo ir a la biblioteca y hacer los deberes después de las clases

d. Puedo hacer teatro o atletismo los lunes

e. No puedo hacer novillos nunca

f. No puedo comer chicle o ser maleducado

g. No puedo llevar maquillaje

h. No puedo fumar ni beber alcohol

11. Translate into Spanish

a. I can't either smoke or drink alcohol

b. I can never wear jewellery

c. On Mondays I can go to the library to do homework

d. In my school I can do swimming after school

e. I can never skip lessons

f. I can go to the Spanish club on Fridays

g. I cannot wear make-up

h. I can go to the chess club twice a week

8.2 FULL PRESENT CONJUGATION OF PODER + SE PUEDE + HACER/JUGAR/IR + NOUN/PREPOSITIONAL PHRASE + TIME MARKER

(SAYING WHAT ONE CAN DO AND PLAY AND WHERE ONE CAN GO)

En mi/tu/su/nuestro/vuestro colegio	*in my/your/his/her/our/their school*
En mi/tu/su/nuestro/vuestro instituto	*in my/your/his/her/our/their (secondary) school*

Subject	Poder	Verb	Noun/Prepositional phrase	Time marker
(Yo)	**Puedo** *I can*	**hacer** *(to) do*	**teatro** **natación** **pesas** *weights* **atletismo** **gimnasia** **los deberes**	**a menudo** *often* **de vez en cuando** *from time to time* **los lunes** *on Mondays* **los martes** **los miércoles** **los jueves** **los viernes** **los sábados** **los domingos** **siempre** *always* **todos los días** *every day* **una vez a la semana** *once a week* **después de las clases** *after lessons*
(Tú)	**Puedes** *You can*			
(Él/Ella)	**Puede** *He/she can*	**ir** *(to) go*	**a la biblioteca** **a clases de baile** *to dance lessons* **al club de español** *to the Spanish club* **al club de ciencias** **al club de ajedrez** **ir al taller de teatro** *to the drama workshop*	
(Nosotros)	**Podemos** *We can*			
(Vosotros)	**Podéis** *You guys/ladies can*	**jugar** *(to) play*	**al tenis** **al fútbol** **al rugby**	
(Ellos/Ellas)	**Pueden** *They can*			

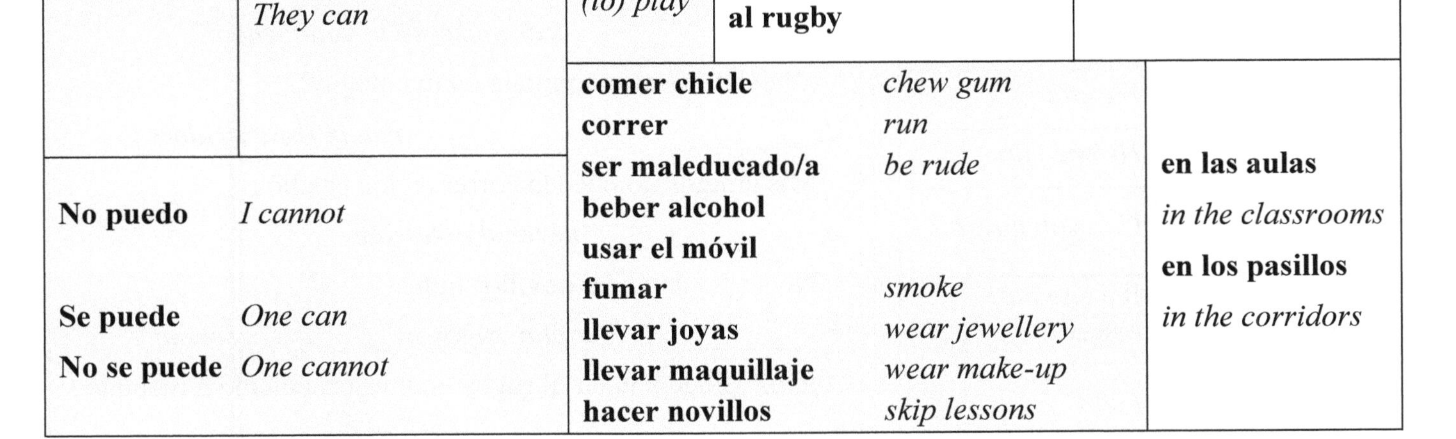

No puedo *I cannot*	**comer chicle**	*chew gum*	**en las aulas** *in the classrooms*
Se puede *One can*	**correr**	*run*	**en los pasillos** *in the corridors*
No se puede *One cannot*	**ser maleducado/a**	*be rude*	
	beber alcohol		
	usar el móvil		
	fumar	*smoke*	
	llevar joyas	*wear jewellery*	
	llevar maquillaje	*wear make-up*	
	hacer novillos	*skip lessons*	

LANGUAGE AWARENESS

PODER: A modal verb…

Poder *(to be able to)* is a modal verb in Spanish. Modal verbs are used to talk about what "we are able to do", what "we should do" or "must do". These verbs are always followed by an infinitive verb.

• **Yo *puedo* comer y beber en clase**
I can eat and drink in class

… and a radical changing verb

Poder is also a Radical Changing verb, like ***jugar***. In this case the "***o***" in ***poder*** changes to "***ue***" in all present tense forms of the verb, **except** for the **we** (*nosotros*) and **you guys** (*vosotros*) forms.

SE PUEDE

Se puede is a great expression to master, it means "One can". Technically, this verb form is called the **Impersonal Passive**.

It is used when we are not specifying the person who does the action, hence the translation as "one".

• **En mi cole no *se puede* fumar**
*In my school **one** cannot smoke*

Poder: Radical Changing Verb

Puedo	*I can*	**Podemos**	*We can*
Puedes	*You can*	**Podéis**	*You (guys) can*
Puede	*He/she can*	**Pueden**	*They can*

Regular ER verb (stem is "BEB")

Bebo	*I drink*	**Bebemos**	*We drink*
Bebes	*You drink*	**Bebéis**	*You guys drink*
Bebe	*He/she drinks*	**Beben**	*They drink*

1. Match

Puedo	*One can't smoke*
Podemos	*I can't skip lessons*
Puede	*Can you?*
Pueden	*One can*
Se puede	*I can't chew gum*
¿Puedes?	*We can*
¿Podéis?	*He/she can*
No puedo comer chicle	*Can you guys?*
No puedo hacer novillos	*We can play tennis*
No se puede fumar	*I can*
Podemos jugar al tenis	*They can*

2. Gapped (English) translation

a. _______________ *do homework after lessons in the* _______________ Puedo hacer los deberes después de las clases en la biblioteca

b. _________________ *do drama on Mondays*
Podemos hacer teatro los lunes

c. _______________ *wear make-up in your school?*
¿Puedes llevar maquillaje en tu colegio?

d. ___________________________ *run in the corridors*
Mis amigos no pueden correr en los pasillos

e. _______________ *never skip lessons*
No se puede hacer novillos nunca

f. ________________ *play rugby in* __________ *school often?* ¿Podéis jugar al rugby en vuestro colegio a menudo?

g. ________________________ *go to the* _____________ ________ *on Tuesdays*
Mi hermano puede ir al club de español los martes

3. Faulty translation: fix the English translation

a. Puedo ir a la biblioteca y hacer los deberes después de las clases

We can go to the library and read after lessons

b. Mi amigo puede hacer atletismo en su colegio los miércoles

My sister can go swimming in our school on Wednesdays

c. ¿Puedes hacer actividades extraescolares en tu colegio?

Can we do extracurricular activities in our school?

d. Se puede ir a clases de baile los jueves después de las clases

I can go to music lessons on Wednesdays after lessons

e. En nuestro colegio podemos jugar al fútbol todos los días

In my school I can play rugby every day

f. ¿Podéis comer chicle en las aulas?

Can they chew gum in the classrooms?

g. No se puede hacer novillos ni fumar en nuestro colegio

One can neither attend lessons nor wear make-up in my school

4. Listen and choose the correct option 

a. Mi amigo **puedo/puede/podemos** hacer teatro en su colegio.

b. No se **puedes/puedo/puede** llevar maquillaje.

c. Nosotros **podéis/podemos/pueden** ir a la biblioteca.

d. ¿Tú **puedes/podéis/puede** usar el móvil en las aulas?

e. ¿Vosotras **pueden/puedes/podéis** llevar maquillaje?

f. Yo no **puedo/podemos/puedes** hacer novillos nunca.

g. Se **pueden/puede/puedo** ir al club de español.

h. Ella no **puedes/puede/pueden** fumar. No lo hace nunca.

5. Translate into English

a. Puedo hacer muchas actividades extraescolares en mi colegio.

b. Después de las clases mi hermano puede hacer los deberes en su colegio. Lo hace a menudo.

c. ¿Podéis llevar maquillaje en vuestro colegio?

d. No se puede hacer novillos o ser maleducado nunca. No lo hago nunca.

e. Se puede ir al taller de teatro y hacer teatro los martes. Lo hago de vez en cuando.

f. Mis amigos y yo podemos jugar al rugby todos los días después de las clases.

g. ¿Se puede jugar al tenis en tu colegio?

6. Spot the mistakes, make corrections; then listen and check 

a. Yo puede ir al club de ciencias. Lo haces siempre.

b. Mi hermano podemos hacer teatro los lunes. Lo hago siempre.

c. No se podemos hacer novillos. Yo no lo hacemos nunca.

d. No se puedo comer chicle en las aulas.

e. Mis amigos podemos ser maleducados a veces.

f. Mi hermana pueden ir a clase de baile. Lo hago siempre.

g. Mis amigos y yo pueden jugar al ajedrez. Lo hago los lunes por la tarde.

h. ¿Tú podéis ir a la biblioteca después de las clases?

7. Tangled translation: translate into Spanish

a. Mi hermano ***can play*** fútbol en ***his*** colegio

b. Mi amigo ***can*** ir ***al science club*** los ***Thursdays***

c. ***I can do drama*** después de las ***lessons***

d. ***One can*** jugar al ***football on*** viernes

e. Mis ***friends*** y ***I can*** ir ***to the*** biblioteca por la ***afternoon***

f. ***One can't*** fumar en ***our school***

g. No se ***can*** beber alcohol en ***our school*** nunca

h. ¿***Can you*** llevar ***jewellery*** o correr ***in*** los ***corridors***?

8. Gapped translation: complete the translation

a. __________ ir a la biblioteca de vez en ___________. *I can go to the library from time to time.*

b. Mis amigos ____________ ir al taller de _____________. ______________ porque es divertido.

My friends can go to the drama workshop. They like it because it is fun.

c. Yo ___________ hacer los deberes en la _____________ después de las _____________. Me gusta porque es __________ .

I can do homework in the library after lessons. I like it because it is useful.

d. ___________ hacer atletismo y ___________ los ____________. _________ porque ____________ .

One can do athletics and gymnastics on Fridays. I go because I like it.

e. Mi hermana ____________ ir a clases de ____________ los jueves por la tarde. ______________ porque es ___________ .

My sister can go to dance lessons on Thursdays in the afternoon. She likes it because it is fun.

9. Listen and underline the words you hear 

a. Mi amigo puede hacer **gimnasia/natación/atletismo** en su colegio. Lo **hace/hacemos/hago** los viernes.

b. Yo **puedo/puede/podemos** ir **a la biblioteca/al club de ciencias/al club de español**. Lo **hacemos/hago/hace** los martes.

c. Se **puedo/puede/podemos** jugar al **fútbol/rugby/tenis** una vez a la semana **los martes/los miércoles/los jueves**.

d. No se puede **fumar/usar el móvil/correr** en las aulas.

e. No se puede **fumar/llevar maquillaje/correr en los pasillos**.

10. Listen and fill in the gaps

a. Mi ____________ puede hacer ____________ en su colegio. Lo _________ los _____________.

b. No se puede ________ en mi colegio __________.

c. Mi hermano _________ hacer los ___________ después de las clases en su ___________.

d. Podemos ________ gimnasia en __________ colegio. Lo ___________ los _____________.

e. ¿Puedes ________ al club de __________ en tu colegio?

f. No ___ ________ fumar ni _________ maquillaje ____________.

11. Staircase translation: translate each sentence from memory

a.	I can	do drama.				
b.	One can	do homework	after lessons.			
c.	We can	play rugby.	We do it	on Thursdays.		
d.	One cannot	wear make-up	or	jewellery	in our school.	
e.	My sister	can	play football	on Wednesdays.	She does it	from time to time.

a. ____

b. ____

c. ____

d. ____

e. ____

8.3 PRESENT OF QUERER (FIRST THREE PERSONS) + NOUN PHRASE
(SAYING WHAT FOOD ONE WANTS)

<table>
<tr><td>(Yo)</td><td>Quiero
I want</td><td colspan="2">agua mineral mineral water
azúcar sugar
arroz rice
café coffee
chocolate chocolate
fruta fruit
una hamburguesa a burger
un helado ice cream</td></tr>
<tr><td rowspan="2">(Tú)</td><td rowspan="2">Quieres
You want</td><td>un helado de…
a … flavoured ice cream</td><td>chocolate
frambuesa raspberry
fresa strawberry
vainilla vanilla</td></tr>
<tr><td colspan="2" rowspan="2">mermelada jam
miel honey
pan bread
patatas fritas chips/crisps
pescado fish
pollo asado roast chicken
(un) pastel (a) cake
queso cheese
té tea
verduras vegetables
zumo de fruta fruit juice
zumo de naranja orange juice</td></tr>
<tr><td>(Él)
(Ella)</td><td>Quiere
He wants
She wants</td></tr>
</table>

LANGUAGE AWARENESS
THE VERB *QUERER*

Quiero literally means *"I want"*. However, in Spanish when we use this verb to ask for something to eat or to drink, for example in a restaurant or bar, the translation is closer to *"I would like"*

- **Quiero pollo asado**
  I want roast chicken / I would like roast chicken

Camarero, quiero miel por favor

¡Enseguida!

1. Match

Queso	*Soup*
Pan	*Water*
Zumo de fruta	*Rice*
Pollo asado	*Tea*
Una hamburguesa	*Fish*
Arroz	*Bread*
Agua	*Cakes*
Té	*A burger*
Pescado	*Fruit juice*
Pasteles	*Vegetables*
Verduras	*Roast chicken*
Sopa	*Cheese*

2. Faulty translation: fix the English translation

a. Quiero queso	*I want fish*
b. ¿Quieres helado?	*Does he want ice cream?*
c. Quiero verduras	*I don't want vegetables*
d. Quiere zumo de fruta	*He/she wants fruit*
e. Mi hermana quiere sopa	*My brother wants soup*
f. Nunca quieres fruta	*You don't want fruit*
g. Quiero pan con miel	*I want bread with jam*
h. ¿Quieres té o café?	*Does he want tea of coffee?*
i. Ella nunca quiere carne	*She never wants fish*
j. Mi madre quiere azúcar	*My mother wants salt*

3. Choose the correct option

a. Mi madre no **quieres/quiere/quiero** pasta

b. Yo **quieres/quiere/quiero** agua

c. Mi hermano **quiero/quieres/quiere** un helado

d. Yo no **quiero/quieres/quiere** pasteles

e. ¿Qué **quiere/quieres/quiero** tú?

f. Mi padre nunca **quiere/quieres/quiere** azúcar

g. Yo no **quieres/quiero/quiere** ni pollo ni pescado

h. Mi amigo Paco **quieres/quiero/quiere** una pera

i. Tu hermana **quiero/quieres/quiere** un café

4. Translate into English

a. No quiero un helado

b. Quiere pollo asado

c. ¿Quieres un café o un té?

d. Quiero un zumo de naranja

e. Quiere una hamburguesa

f. No quiero nada

g. Quiere agua mineral

h. ¿Quiere arroz o pasta?

i. Nunca quiere azúcar en el café

5. Listen and choose the correct word 

a. **Quiere/Quiero/Quieres** patatas fritas y una hamburguesa

b. **Quiere/Quiero/Quieres** arroz y pollo, pero ella **quiero/quieres/quiere** un zumo de naranja

c. **Quiere/Quiero/Quieres** pescado y patatas fritas

d. ¿**Quiere/Quiero/Quieres** azúcar con el té?

e. **Quiere/Quiero/Quieres** un helado de chocolate, pero mi madre **quiero/quieres/quiere** un pastel

f. **Quiere/Quiero/Quieres** agua mineral y un café con leche

6. Gapped translation: complete the translation

a. ________ queso	*I want cheese*
b. Nunca ______ café	*She never wants coffee*
c. No _______ verduras	*I don't want vegetables*
d. Mi padre ______ agua	*My father wants water*
e. ________ pasteles	*He wants cakes*
f. Mi hermano no ________ pescado	*My brother doesn't want fish*
g. ¿Qué _________?	*What do you want?*
h. ¿Qué _________?	*What does he want?*
i. No _________ nada	*I don't want anything*

7. Tangled translation: translate into Spanish

a. Mi hermano ***wants*** arroz con ***chicken***

b. Yo no ***want*** nada, solo un ***ice cream***

c. Ella ***never wants*** azúcar ***in the coffee***

d. ¿Qué ***do you want***?

e. Mi padre no quiere ***nothing***

f. Mi amigo Paco ***wants*** un ***fruit juice***

g. Mi madre ***wants*** té

h. Yo ***want*** un ***ice cream*** de fresa

i. Él ***wants*** pan y ***jam***

j. Yo no ***want*** sopa, yo ***want bread***

8. Translate into Spanish

a. I want bread and cheese

b. What do you want?

c. She never wants sugar in the coffee

d. My father wants nothing

e. Does she want pasta or rice?

f. I want a burger with salad

g. I don't want rice

h. Does he want tea or coffee?

i. Do you want a sandwich?

j. I want an ice cream

k. I don't want soup

l. She wants a fruit juice

8.4 FULL PRESENT CONJUGATION OF QUERER + NOUN PHRASE
(SAYING WHAT ONE WANTS)

(Yo) *I*	**Quiero** *I want*	**agua mineral** *mineral water* **azúcar** *sugar* **arroz** *rice* **café** *coffee* **chocolate** *chocolate* **fruta** *fruit* **una hamburguesa** *a burger* **un helado** *ice cream*	
(Tú) *You*	**Quieres** *You want*		
(Él) *He* **(Ella)** *She*	**Quiere** *He/she wants*	**un helado de...** *a ... flavoured ice cream*	**chocolate** **frambuesa** *raspberry* **fresa** *strawberry* **vainilla** *vanilla*
(Nosotros) *We (m)* **(Nosotras)** *We (f)* **(Mi amigo y yo)** *My friend and I*	**Queremos** *We want*	**mermelada** *jam* **miel** *honey* **pan** *bread* **patatas fritas** *chips/crisps* **pastel** *cake* **pescado** *fish* **pollo asado** *roast chicken* **queso** *cheese* **té** *tea* **verduras** *vegetables* **zumo de fruta** *fruit juice* **zumo de naranja** *orange juice*	
(Vosotros) *You guys* **(Vosotras)** *You girls*	**Queréis** *You guys want*		
(Ellos) *They (m)* **(Ellas)** *They (f)*	**Quieren** *They want*		

LANGUAGE AWARENESS

Querer, *"to want"* is a modal verb in Spanish. This modal is used to talk about what you want to do, as opposed to ***poder*** *(what you are able to do)*. Like ***poder***, it is also a Radical Changing/ Boot verb. See below to see what the **Radical Change** looks like for this boot verb.

TE QUIERO

Please note: if you say ***"te quiero"*** to someone, it means *I love you.*

Te quiero pingüino

Yo también te quiero

Querer: Radical Changing Verb

Quiero	*I want*	**Queremos**	*We want*
Quieres	*You want*	**Queréis**	*You (guys) want*
Quiere	*He/she wants*	**Quieren**	*They want*

1. Match – Part A

Quiero	*We want*
Quiere	*You guys want*
Quieren	*They want*
Quieres	*She/He wants*
Queréis	*I want*
Queremos	*You want*

2. Match – Part B

a.	**Quiero pescado con patatas fritas**	*1.*	*We want chocolate cake*
b.	**Quiero pollo asado con patatas fritas**	*2.*	*I want fish and chips*
c.	**Solo quiere patatas fritas**	*3.*	*We want a white coffee with sugar*
d.	**Queremos un café con leche y azúcar**	*4.*	*I want roast chicken with chips*
e.	**Queremos pastel de chocolate**	*5.*	*He/she wants chips only*

3. Sentence Puzzle

a. quiere Ella hamburguesas dos, pollo yo quiero.	*She wants two burgers, I want chicken.*
b. no Nosotros nada queremos. ¿Qué tú quieres?	*We don't want anything. What do you want?*
c. ¿Qué vosotros queréis? quiero Yo pescado.	*What do you guys want? I want fish.*
d. quiere Él helado un. quiero un Yo pastel.	*He wants an ice cream. I want a cake.*
e. Yo no nada quiero. ¿Qué vosotros queréis?	*I don't want anything. What do you guys want?*
f. Mi agua padre quiere. quiero un Yo café.	*My father wants water. I want a coffee.*
g. queso quieren Ellos. ¿vosotros queréis Qué?	*They want cheese. What do you guys want?*
h. nada no quiere Ella. té Nosotros queremos.	*She doesn't want anything. We want tea.*

4. Faulty translation: fix the English translation

a. Quiero pescado	*We want fish*
b. ¿Queréis pollo?	*Does he want chicken?*
c. Quieren zumo de fruta	*She wants fruit juice*
d. Queremos queso	*You want cheese*
e. ¿Qué quiere?	*What do you want?*
f. ¿Quieres helado?	*I want ice cream*
g. Quiero arroz	*You want rice*
h. ¿Qué quieren?	*What does he want?*
i. Quieren hamburguesas	*We want burgers*

5. Choose the correct option

a. Yo **quiero/quieren/quieres** pescado

b. Él **quiero/quiere/quieres** chocolate

c. Nosotras **queréis/quieren/queremos** café

d. Ella **quieren/quiere/quieres** un helado

e. ¿Qué **quiere/quieres/queréis** tú?

f. ¿Qué **quieres/queréis/quieren** vosostros?

g. Mi amigo Paco **quieren/quiere/quieres** té

h. Ellas no **quiere/queréis/quieren** nada

i. Yo **quieres/quieren/quiero** zumo de fruta

6. Spot and correct the mistakes

a. Mi madre quiero azúcar en el café.

b. ¿Qué quieres vosotros?

c. Yo no quiero nada. ¿Y tú, qué queréis?

d. Mi hermano quiere café. Yo quieres un helado.

e. ¿Qué quieres él?

f. Nosotros quieren pizza.

g. Ellos queremos una hamburguesa.

7. Guided translation

a. Q_ _ _ _ _ p_ _
I want bread

b. N_ q_ _ _ _ _ _ _ _ _ n_ _ _
We don't want anything

c. ¿Q_ _ q_ _ _ _ _ _ _ _?
What do you want?

d. N_ q_ _ _ _ _ _ qu _ _ _
She doesn't want cheese

e. ¿Q_ _ q_ _ _ _ _ _ _ _ ?
What do you guys want?

f. Qu _ _ _ _ hambu _ _ _ _ _ _ _
She wants burgers

g. Quie _ _ pol_ _ c_ _ verdu _ _ _
He wants chicken with vegetables

8. Listen and complete the broken words

a. Y_ quie_ _ fru_ _

b. ¿Qu_ quie_ _ _ t_?

c. Nosot_ _ _ quer_ _ _ _ _ que_ _

d. El_ _ n_ quie_ _ nad_

e. Mi_ amig_ _ quier_ _ u_ hel_ _ _

f. Vosotr_ _, ¿qu_ quer_ _ _?

g. Mi mad_ e qu_ _ _ _ _ u_p_ _ _ _ _ l

h. ¿Qu_ _ _ _ _ _ u_ c_ _ _?

9. Listen and choose the correct word

a. Él quiere pan con **miel/queso/mantequilla**

b. Ella no quiere **pollo/pescado/azúcar**

c. Nosotros queremos **queso/arroz/pescado**

d. ¿Quieres **miel/té/café**?

e. Él quiere un zumo de **naranja/tomate/pera**

f. Yo quiero **té/café/un helado**

g. ¿Vosotros queréis **queso/pan/algo**?

h. Ella quiere **pollo asado/pescado/verduras**

i. Ellos quieren **fruta/arroz/mantequilla**

j. Nosotros queremos **agua/zumo/café**

10. Translate into Spanish

a. I want pizza.

b. We want coffee.

c. She wants tea with sugar.

d. I don't want anything.

e. What do you want?

f. Do you guys want ice cream?

g. They don't want sugar in the coffee.

h. We want water. They want Coca-Cola.

i. I don't want beer. I want fruit juice.

j. My friend Paco wants cheese with wine.

k. She doesn't want chocolate. She wants fruit.

l. We don't want anything. Only water.

8.5 PRESENT OF QUERER + INFINITIVE + NOUN PHRASE
(SAYING WHAT ONE WANTS TO EAT AND DRINK)

QUERER: To want			
(Yo) *I*	**Quiero** *I want*	**beber** *to drink*	**agua mineral** *water*
			azúcar *sugar*
(Tú) *You*	**Quieres** *You want*	**comer** *to eat*	**arroz** *rice*
			café *coffee*
			chocolate *chocolate*
(Él) *He* **(Ella)** *She*	**Quiere** *He/she wants*	**tomar*** *to have*	**fruta** *fruit*
			una hamburguesa *a burger*
			un helado *an ice cream*
(Nosotros) *We* **(Nosotras)** *We (f)* **(Mi amigo y yo)** *My friend and I*	**Queremos** *We want*	**almorzar** *to have for lunch*	**pan** *bread*
			pescado *fish*
			pollo asado *roast chicken*
(Vosotros) *You guys* **(Vosotras)** *You girls*	**Queréis** *You guys/girls want*	**cenar** *to have for dinner*	**patatas fritas** *chips/crisps*
			queso *cheese*
			té *tea*
(Ellos) *They (m)* **(Ellas)** *They (f)*	**Quieren** *They want*	**desayunar** *to have for breakfast*	**una tostada** *toast*
			zumo de fruta *fruit juice*

LANGUAGE AWARENESS

*The verb ***tomar*** works the same as the English 'to have' in the context of 'having something to eat or drink.' You can use it to replace ***beber*** and also ***comer*** in most contexts.

- **Quiero tomar arroz** — *I would like to have rice*
- **Mi amigo quiere tomar café** — *My friend would like to have coffee*

1. Match

Quiero comer arroz	*You guys want to have tea for breakfast*
Quiero desayunar té	*They want to eat fish*
Quiero desayunar café	*We want to have rice*
Quiere beber agua	*I want to eat rice*
Quieren almorzar pescado	*You want to have tea for breakfast*
Quieren comer pescado	*We want to eat rice for dinner*
Queremos cenar arroz	*I want to have tea for breakfast*
Queremos tomar arroz	*I want to have coffee for breakfast*
Quieres desayunar té	*He/she wants to drink water*
Queréis desayunar té	*They want to eat fish for lunch*

2. Categories

Vino – Tostada – Pan – Cerveza – Agua – Pescado – Zumo de pera – Queso – Arroz – Pollo – Carne – Café – Té – Patatas fritas – Helado – Hamburguesas – Limonada – Chocolate caliente

Comida	Bebidas

3. Complete with *BEBER* or *COMER* as appropriate

a. Quiero __________ pescado y patatas fritas

b. Queremos ____________ agua mineral

c. Yo quiero ____________ un zumo de fruta

d. Quieren ____________ pollo asado

e. Tengo hambre. Quiero ____________

f. Tengo mucha sed. Quiero _________ un zumo

g. ¿Queréis _________ una hamburguesa?

h. No tengo hambre. No quiero __________ nada

i. Queremos __________ pan con queso

4. Listen and choose the words you hear

a. **Quiero/queremos tomar/almorzar** pollo asado

b. **Queremos/quiero cenar/almorzar** pescado

c. **Quiere/quiero almorzar/cenar** una hamburguesa

d. **¿Quieres/queréis tomar/beber** un café?

e. **Quieren/quiere cenar/comer** una ensalada

f. **Quiero/quieren desayunar/tomar/beber** té

g. **Queremos/quieren beber/tomar** una cerveza

h. **Quiero/quiere desayunar/beber** zumo de fruta

5. Find the Spanish translation and write it next to the English prompts

q	u	i	e	r	e	d	e	s	a	y	u	n	a	r	c	a	f	é	g	a	t	o	r	q
q	u	i	e	r	o	c	o	m	e	r	p	a	t	a	t	a	s	f	r	i	t	a	s	u
u	n	e	q	u	i	e	r	e	n	d	e	s	a	y	u	n	a	r	c	a	f	é	q	i
i	v	o	r	t	e	c	o	n	p	e	s	c	a	d	o	a	n	a	h	e	d	u	m	e
l	e	a	d	e	s	s	y	u	c	e	n	a	r	q	z	o	l	s	o	s	e	a	o	r
r	o	b	o	t	m	g	a	r	u	c	a	t	e	u	o	n	o	e	i	r	i	a	h	o
q	o	q	p	a	c	o	n	a	g	u	a	q	u	i	r	e	p	l	o	p	a	s	c	p
u	q	u	i	e	r	o	s	c	e	n	a	r	p	e	s	c	a	d	o	c	e	f	u	e
q	u	i	e	r	o	d	e	s	a	y	u	n	a	r	t	é	s	i	d	e	e	r	m	s
t	p	e	s	c	a	d	o	u	i	n	v	t	a	e	c	o	a	y	a	b	s	a	l	c
a	s	r	e	e	s	o	q	r	d	a	e	n	r	t	e	s	a	u	s	e	r	i	u	a
n	e	d	q	s	e	o	s	e	o	s	e	s	e	é	u	q	s	n	e	o	l	e	q	d
i	q	u	i	e	r	o	b	e	b	e	r	a	g	u	a	c	r	a	d	y	l	a	n	o

a. I want to have a tea for breakfast

b. He/she wants to have a coffee for breakfast

c. We want

d. I would like fish

e. I want to eat chips

f. He/she wants tea

g. They want to have coffee for breakfast

h. I want to drink water

6. Tangled translation: translate into Spanish

a. ***I want*** beber ***coffee***

b. Quieren ***to have for lunch*** pescado

c. ¿***Do you want*** tomar algo?

d. No ***we want*** desayunar ***fruit juice***

e. Quiere ***to eat a burger***

f. ***They want to have for dinner*** pollo asado

g. No ***she wants*** beber ***coffee***

h. Quiero ***to eat*** verduras ***and fish***

i. Queremos ***to have*** un helado de ***strawberry***

j. ***They want*** cenar ***fish*** y ***chips***

k. Quiere ***to have*** queso

l. ***We want*** comer ***bread*** y ***cheese***

7. Listen and complete the broken words

a. Qu__________ c__________ una h__________________

b. Qu__________ t__________ un t____

c. Qu_________ p_______ con q__________

d. Qu_________ p__________ y v______________

e. Qu_________ c_________ p___________ f__________

f. Qu_________ a__________ a_________

g. Qu_________ d___________ t__________

h. Qu_________ c___________ p_________ a__________

i. ¿Qu_________ t _________ u____ h________________?

8. Faulty translation: fix the Spanish translation

a. *They want to have tea*	Queremos tomar té
b. *She wants to eat a burger*	Quieren comer una hamburguesa
c. *We want to drink coffee with sugar*	Quiero beber café con azúcar
d. *They want to have fish for lunch*	Quiere almorzar pollo asado
e. *We want to have fish with chips for dinner*	Quiere cenar pescado con patatas fritas
f. *They want to drink fruit juice*	Queréis beber zumo de naranja

9. Sentence Puzzle

a. y Yo verduras almorzar arroz quiero

I want to have rice and vegetables for lunch

b. fruta de beber un zumo café con azúcar y Quiero un

I want to drink a coffee with sugar and a fruit juice

c. ¿Qué vosotros tomar queréis? queremos beber Nosotros té

What do you guys want to have? We want to drink tea

d. chocolate Queremos de helado comer un

We want to eat a chocolate ice cream

e. no yo quiere Ella pero comer nada, quiero una hamburguesa

She doesn't want anything, but I want to eat a burger

f. patatas yo Mi quiere fritas, verduras hermana comer pero quiero

My sister wants to eat chips, but I want vegetables

g. queso, fritas comer Nosotros y pero pan ella queremos quiere patatas

We want to eat bread and cheese, but she wants chips

10. Translate into English

a. Quiero tomar té con azúcar y una tostada

b. Mi hermana quiere comer una hamburguesa

c. Mis padres quieren pescado con patatas fritas

d. ¿Queréis tomar algo? Yo quiero un helado

e. Mis amigos y yo queremos almorzar arroz

f. Ellos quieren comer pan con queso

g. Mi amigo quiere beber agua mineral porque no le gusta el zumo de fruta

11. Translate into Spanish. Then listen and check

a. My parents want to drink tea with sugar 

b. My sister wants to have a burger and chips

c. My brothers and I want to have fish for lunch

d. I want to have a burger for dinner

e. My mother wants to have a strawberry ice cream

f. We don't want to have sugar

g. My parents want to have fish and chips for dinner

8.6 PRESENT OF QUERER + INFINITIVE + NOUN/PREPOSITIONAL PHRASE

(SAYING WHAT ONE WANTS TO EAT AND DRINK, WHAT GAMES ONE WANTS TO DO AND WHAT CHORES ONE WANTS TO DO)

<table>
<tr><td rowspan="5">(Yo)</td><td rowspan="5">Quiero
I want</td><td colspan="2">beber agua</td><td>to drink water</td></tr>
<tr><td colspan="2">cocinar</td><td>to cook</td></tr>
<tr><td colspan="2">comer un bocadillo</td><td>to eat a sandwich</td></tr>
<tr><td colspan="2">cortar el césped</td><td>to cut the grass</td></tr>
<tr><td colspan="2">hacer la cama</td><td>to make the bed</td></tr>
<tr><td rowspan="6">(Tú)</td><td rowspan="6">Quieres
You want</td><td rowspan="3">ir
to go</td><td>al cine</td><td>to the cinema</td></tr>
<tr><td>ir de tiendas</td><td>shopping</td></tr>
<tr><td>ir en bici</td><td>by bike</td></tr>
<tr><td rowspan="3">jugar
to play</td><td>al fútbol</td><td>football</td></tr>
<tr><td>en el ordenador</td><td>on the computer</td></tr>
<tr><td>con mis amigos</td><td>with my friends</td></tr>
<tr><td rowspan="8">(Él)
(Ella)</td><td rowspan="8">Quiere
He/she wants</td><td colspan="2">lavar la ropa</td><td>to do the laundry</td></tr>
<tr><td colspan="2">lavar los platos</td><td>to do the washing up</td></tr>
<tr><td colspan="2">limpiar el suelo</td><td>to clean the floor</td></tr>
<tr><td colspan="2">ordenar la habitación</td><td>to tidy the bedroom</td></tr>
<tr><td colspan="2">pasar la aspiradora</td><td>to do the hoovering</td></tr>
<tr><td colspan="2">sacar fotos</td><td>to take photos</td></tr>
<tr><td colspan="2">sacar la basura</td><td>to take the rubbish out</td></tr>
<tr><td colspan="2">ver una película</td><td>to watch a film</td></tr>
</table>

LANGUAGE AWARENESS

QUERER + INFINITIVE/NOUN

When using the modal verb ***querer***, you can combine it two ways:

Infinitive

- **Quiero <u>ir</u> al parque** *I want to go to the park*

Noun

- **Quiero <u>un café</u>** *I want a coffee*

A COMMON MISTAKE

ILLEGAL COMBINATION!

In Spanish, we never place two conjugated verbs together. Verb structures usually work together with an infinitive:

- **Quiero IR** *I want **<u>to go</u>***
- **Me gusta IR** *I like **<u>to go</u>***

If you use a present tense verb after **quiero (or puedo)**, you create an incorrect structure:

- ***Quiero <u>VOY</u>** *I want **<u>I go</u>***

***Please don't write this**

1. Match

Limpiar el suelo	To take the rubbish out
Ver una película	*To do the laundry*
Ordenar la habitación	*To go by bike*
Cocinar	*To take photos*
Beber agua	*To cook*
Sacar fotos	*To make my bed*
Ir en bici	*To tidy up the room*
Lavar la ropa	*To drink water*
Sacar la basura	*To watch a film*
Hacer mi cama	*To clean the floor*

2. Complete with *QUIERO, QUIERES* or *QUIERE*

a. (Yo) no __________ limpiar el suelo

b. (Él) _________ beber un café

c. Mi madre no __________ cocinar hoy

d. ¿Qué _________ hacer tu?

e. Hoy (yo) __________ ir en bici

f. Mi hermano _________ jugar al futbol

g. Mi hermana no _________ lavar la ropa

h. (Él) no _________ ordenar su habitación

i. Hoy (yo) no _________ salir

3. Complete with the missing verb and translate into English

a. Hoy no quiero __ __ en bici

b. Mi hermana quiere __ __ __ __ __ la basura

c. Mi hermano quiere __ __ __ __ __ su cama

d. ¿Quieres __ __ __ __ __ agua?

e. Mi amigo Paco quiere __ __ __ __ __ al baloncesto

f. Mi padre no quiere __ __ __ __ __ la ropa

g. Hoy no quiero __ __ __ __ __ la basura

h. ¿Quién quiere __ __ al cine conmigo?

4. Break the flow

a. Quierosacarfotosperomihermanaquiereirenbici

b. Noquierehacerlacamanilavarlaropa

c. Quierocomerunbocadillodequesoporquemegusta

d. Quiereiralastiendasenbici

e. Noquieresacarlabasuraporquenolegusta

f. Quieroordenarmihabitaciónelsábadoporlatarde

g. Noquierespasarlaaspiradoratodoslosdías

h. Devezencuandoquiereiralcineconsusamigos

i. Nuncaquiereslavarlosplatosnilimpiarelsuelo

j. Mihermananoquierehacerlacamanilavarlaropa

5. Faulty translation: fix the English translation

a. Quiero limpiar mi habitación	*She wants to clean my room*
b. No quieres cocinar	*He doesn't want to cook*
c. Mi hermano quiere sacar la basura	*My sister wants to take out the rubbish*
d. Quiero jugar con mis amigos	*I want to go out with my friends*
e. ¿Quieres beber agua?	*Does he want to drink water?*
f. Mi amigo Paco quiere jugar al baloncesto	*My friend Paco wants to play on the computer*
g. Hoy no quiero ir en bici	*Today I don't want to walk*
h. Mi padre no quiere lavar los platos	*My father doesn't want to iron the shirts*

6. Insert the missing vowels then listen and check

a. Q__ __ __r__ b__b__r __g__ __	*I want to drink water*
b. N__ q__ __ __r__ __r __n b__c__	*He doesn't want to go cycling*
c. M__ p__dr__ q__ __ __r__ l__v__r __l c__ch __	*My father wants to wash the car*
d. H__y n__ q__ __ __r__ s__l__r	*Today, I don't want to go out*
e. ¿Q__ __ q__ __ __r__s h__c__r h__y?	*What do you want to do today?*
f. N__ q__ __ __r__ s__c__r f__t__s	*He doesn't want to take photos*

7. Split sentences

Quiero sacar la	al cine
Mi hermano no	quiero salir
Tú nunca quieres	agua
Él no quiere ir	basura
Mi padre quiere jugar	el suelo
No	quiere jugar
Ella quiere beber	película
Quiero ver una	hacer tu cama
Tú nunca quieres limpiar	al baloncesto

8. Tick any sentence referring to a house chore

a. Mi padre quiere sacar la basura

b. Yo no quiero jugar en el ordenador

c. ¿No quieres ir en bici?

d. Mi madre quiere cocinar

e. Mi hermano no quiere ordenar su habitación

f. ¿Quieres beber agua?

g. Nunca quiero limpiar la cocina

h. No quiere hacer su cama

9. Translate the following verbs and nouns into English

a. To clean = L__________	f. To make, do = H__________	k. Clothes = R__________
b. To drink = B__________	g. To go = I__________	l. Bed = C__________
c. To wash = L__________	h. To tidy = O __________	m. Room = H__________
d. To cook = C__________	i. To take out = S __________	n. Film = P__________
e. To play = J__________	j. To see, watch = V__________	o. Rubbish = B__________

10. Translate into Spanish, and then listen to check:

a. My father wants to go to the cinema

b. My sister doesn't want to go cycling

c. She doesn't want to clean the floor

d. Do you want to eat?

e. He never wants to go out

f. I don't want to do the hoovering

g. He never wants to take out the rubbish

h. She doesn't want to go out today

i. Today I don't want to go to school

j. My sister doesn't want to play with us

8.7 PRESENT OF QUERER + INFINITIVE + NOUN/PREPOSITIONAL PHRASE
(SAYING WHAT ONE WANTS TO EAT/DRINK OR WHAT ONE WANTS TO DO)

(Yo)	**Quiero** *I want*	**beber agua**		*to drink water*
		cocinar		*to cook*
		comer un bocadillo		*to eat a sandwich*
(Tú)	**Quieres** *You want*	**cortar el césped**		*to cut the grass*
		hacer la cama		*to make the bed*
(Él) (Ella)	**Quiere** *He wants* *She wants*	**ir** *to go*	**al cine**	*to the cinema*
			ir de tiendas	*shopping*
			ir en bici	*by bike*
(Nosotros) (Nosotras) (Mi amigo y yo)	**Queremos** *We (m) want* *We (f) want* *My friend and I want*	**jugar** *to play*	**al fútbol**	*football*
			en el ordenador	*on the computer*
			con mis amigos	*with my friends*
(Vosotros) (Vosotras)	**Queréis** *You guys want* *You girls want*	**lavar la ropa**		*to do the laundry*
		lavar los platos		*to do the washing up*
		limpiar el suelo		*to clean the floor*
		ordenar la habitación		*to tidy the bedroom*
(Ellos) (Ellas)	**Quieren** *They (m) want* *They (f) want*	**pasar la aspiradora**		*to do the hoovering*
		sacar fotos		*to take photos*
		sacar la basura		*to take the rubbish out*
		ver una película		*to watch a film*

1. Match

Yo	**quiere**
Tú	**quieren**
Él / Ella	**queréis**
Nosotros	**quieres**
Vosotros	**quiero**
Ellos /Ellas	**queremos**

2. Choose the correct form of *querer*

a. Mi padre nunca **quieres/quiero/quiere** cocinar

b. Mi hermana no **quiere/quiero/quieren** limpiar el suelo

c. Yo no **quieres/quiero/quieren** ir al cine

d. Mis padres no **quiere/quieren/queremos** jugar

e. Nosotros no **queremos/quieren/quieres** comer ahora

f. Ellas **quiere/quieren/quieres** ir de tiendas

g. ¿Vosotros **quieres/queréis/quieren** sacar la basura?

h. ¿Qué **quieres/queréis/quiere** tú hacer ahora?

i. Mis hermanas **quiere/quieren/quieres** ir en bici

j. Mi padre y yo **queremos/quiero/quiere** jugar al tenis

3. Listen and write the verb you hear

a. Mi padre __________ cocinar

b. Mi hermano no __________ ir de tiendas

c. No ___________ sacar fotos de vosotros

d. No __________ ordenar nuestra habitación

e. No __________ lavar la ropa

f. No ____________ cortar el césped

g. Mis hermanos no __________ sacar la basura

h. Mis padres ___________ ver una película

i. ¿____________ lavar los platos?

j. ¿Qué __________ hacer hoy?

4. Spot and correct the wrong forms of *querer*

a. Mi hermano no quiero jugar al fútbol

b. Mis hermanas no quiere limpiar el suelo

c. Yo no quiere hacer mis deberes

d. Mi hermana quieren ir al cine

e. Mis padres quiere ver una película

f. ¿Qué (tú) queréis hacer?

g. Mi amigo Paco y yo no queréis salir hoy

h. ¡(Vosotros) Nunca quieres trabajar!

i. Mi hermana queremos ir al cine

j. Mis amigos queremos ir a las tiendas

5. Complete with *quiero, quieres, quiere, queremos, queréis* or *quieren* as appropriate

a. Mi madre no ___________ cocinar hoy

b. Mis hermanos ___________ir en bici

c. Paco y yo ___________ comer pizza

d. Mi tío no ___________ planchar sus camisas

e. Yo no ____________ salir contigo

f. Mi hermano menor no __________ sacar la basura

g. Mi amigo Paco no __________ ir al colegio

h. ¿(Tú) ___________ lavar los platos?

i. Ella no _________ limpiar el suelo

j. Nosotras __________ jugar al futbol

k. Él no ___________ hacer sus deberes

l. ¿(Vosotros) __________ salir conmigo?

m. Mi hermana no ________ cocinar hoy

n. Yo no ________ cocinar tampoco

6. Complete the sentences, and then listen to check

a. Yo n__ qui__ __ __ i__ a__ ci__ __

b. Él nun__ __ quie__ __ lim__ __ __ __ __ el sue__ __

c. Mi ami__ __ Paco nun__ __ quie__ __ sal__ __

d. Mi__ padr__ __ qui__ __ __ __ __ i__ d__ tiend__ __

e. Mi__ herma__ __ __ n__ quie__ __ __ coci__ __ __

f. Mi madre y yo quere__ __ __ v__ __ una pelí__ __ __ __

g. Y__ n__ quie__ __ju__ __ __ a__ balonc__ __ __ __

h. Tú n__ q__ __ __ __ __ __ __ sac__ __ l__ bas__ __ __

i. É__ q__ __ __ __ __ __ju__ __ __ en e__ ord__ __ __ __ __ __

7. Translate into Spanish

a. I want

b. She wants

c. You don't want

d. They never want

e. He wants

f. I never want

g. We don't want

h. They want

i. Do you guys want?

j. My mum wants

k. My parents never want

8. Faulty translation: fix the Spanish translation

a. *My cousins do not want to do the hoovering*	Mis hermanos no quieren cortar la aspiradora
b. *Do you guys want to go to the cinema today?*	¿Quieres ir al cine este fin de semana?
c. *She wants to watch a film and have a tea*	Quiero ver una película y comer un bocadillo
d. *They don't want to do the washing up...*	No queremos ordenar los platos…
e. *…on Friday evenings*	…los viernes por la mañana
f. *My parents always want to take the dog out*	Mis padres siempre quieren sacar la basura
g. *We want to make the bed only at weekends*	Ella quiere hacer la cama solo los fines de semana

9. Gapped translation: please complete

a. Nosotros ____________ ir al __________ hoy *We want to go to the cinema today*

b. Mis __________ quieren _________ la ropa mañana *My brothers want to do the laundry tomorrow*

c. Mi amigo __________ comer ___________ de queso *My friend wants to eat a cheese sandwich*

d. Yo no quiero __________ los platos los fines de ____________ *I don't want to do the washing up at weekends*

e. ¿____________ cortar el césped hoy? *Do you want to cut the grass today?*

f. Mi madre quiere _________ pescado y ____________ el ___________ *My mum wants to cook fish and rice on Friday*

10. Translate into English

a. No queremos ordenar nuestra habitación ni lavar la ropa los fines de semana.

b. Quiero ir al cine con mis amigos todos los fines de semana, pero no puedo.

c. Mi hermana quiere ir de tiendas todos los días, pero no puede.

d. Mis amigos no quieren cortar el césped en su jardín.

e. Mis padres quieren ir a la piscina para nadar de vez en cuando.

f. Quiero jugar en el ordenador con mis amigos por las tardes, pero no puedo.

g. Mi madre quiere sacar fotos de mi hermano.

h. Mis padres no quieren ordenar mi habitación.

i. ¿Quieres ir al cine este fin de semana?

11. Translate into Spanish

a. I want to go to the cinema every day with my friends, but I cannot.

b. My sisters don't want to make the bed, they want to go shopping.

c. My mum doesn't want to cut the grass in the garden. She wants to go to the cinema.

d. My sister and I don't want to take the rubbish out every day.

e. Do you want to drink a coffee?

f. I don't want to do the washing up in the evenings.

g. My parents and I want to watch a film on Netflix.

8.8 PUEDO + INFINITIVE + INFINITIVE + NOUN PHRASE +TIME MARKER

(ASKING FOR PERMISSION TO DO THINGS)

¿Puedo *Can I*	**ir** *go*	**a mi clase de música** **al baño** **a casa de Ana** **al cine**	*to my music lesson* *to the toilet* *to Ana's house* *to the cinema*	**ahora?** *now?*
	salir con *go out with*	**mi novio/a** **mis amigos**	*my boyfriend/girlfriend* *my friends*	**mañana?** *tomorrow?*
	jugar con *play with*	**los videojuegos** **mis amigos**	*videogames* *my friends*	**más tarde?** *later?*
	coger este bolígrafo **coger esta goma**		*borrow this pen* *borrow this rubber*	**este fin de semana?** *this weekend?*
	comer más **usar mi móvil**		*eat more* *use my mobile*	

1. Match

Usar mi móvil	*To go to the toilet*
Coger este bolígrafo	*To go out this weekend*
Coger esta falda	*To go to my boyfriend's house*
Ir al cine	*To play videogames*
Jugar con videojuegos	*To use my mobile*
Coger este vestido	*To borrow this pen*
Ir a casa de mi novio	*To borrow this skirt*
Salir este fin de semana	*To borrow this dress*
Ir al baño	*To go to the cinema*

2. Split sentences

a. ¿Puedo usar	1. goma?
b. ¿Puedo coger este	2. casa de Ana?
c. ¿Puedo jugar	3. cine mañana?
d. ¿Puedo salir	4. maquillaje?
e. ¿Puedo ir al	5. bolígrafo?
f. ¿Puedo coger esta	6. mi móvil?
g. ¿Puedo ir a mi	7. con mi móvil?
h. ¿Puedo ir a	8. con mi novio?
i. ¿Puedo ir	9. a casa?
j. ¿Puedo llevar	10. tu vestido?
k. ¿Puedo coger	11. clase?

3. Break the flow

a. ¿PuedoiralcineconMarina?

b. ¿Puedosalirestefindesemana?

c. ¿PuedoiracasadeAnaestatardeparacenar?

d. ¿Puedoiramiclasedemúsicaahora?

e. ¿Puedoiralbaño?

f. ¿Puedocogertulibrodematemáticas?

g. ¿Puedocomermásarroz?

h. ¿Puedocogerestafaldaparamañana?

i. ¿Puedousarmimóvilenclase?

4. Listen and fill in the blanks

a. ¿Puedo _________ al __________?

b. ¿Puedo _________ con mis_________ ________?

c. ¿_________ ir a _______ clase de __________?

d. ¿Puedo ________ tu vestido?

e. ¿Puedo _________esta camisa?

f. ¿__________ comer _________ __________?

g. ¿_________ usar _______ _______en clase?

h. ¿Puedo __________ a los _______________?

i. ¿_________ salir con _____ ____________?

j. ¿Puedo _________ tu libro?

5. Faulty Translation: fix the English translation

a. ¿Puedo salir con mis amigos todos los días? *Can I go to the cinema with my friends this evening?*

b. ¿Puedo usar el móvil en clase? *Can I use my mobile now?*

c. ¿Puedo coger este bolígrafo? *Can I borrow this dress?*

d. ¿Puedo correr en los pasillos? *Can I run in the school?*

e. ¿Puedo ir a casa de mi novia mañana? *Can I go to my boyfriend's house tomorrow?*

6. Complete the translation, then listen to check

a. ¿Puedo ______ al ________?
Can I go to the toilet?

b. ¿_________ salir con _____ ___________?
Can I go out with my friends?

c. ¿_________ jugar con ___ ________ hoy?
Can I play videogames today?

d. ¿Puedo _____ a mi clase de _______?
Can I go to my piano lesson?

e. ¿Puedo ______ tu _______?
Can I borrow your mobile?

f. ¿________ comer más? *Can I eat more?*

g. ¿_______ ir a la _______ de mi ________?
Can I go to my girlfriend's house?

h. ¿Puedo ________ a los ___________?
Can I play videogames?

7. Translate into Spanish

a. Can I go to the toilet?

b. Can I go to Marina's house this evening?

c. Can I go to my music lesson?

d. Can I go out with my friends this weekend?

e. Can I borrow this pen?

f. Can I borrow this book?

g Can I eat more ice cream?

h. Can I eat more vegetables?

i. Can I run in the corridors?

j. Can I play videogames tonight?

k. Can I wear make-up at school?

l. Can I use my mobile here?

m. Can I go to the cinema this weekend?

A

ORAL PING PONG

MODAL VERBS

ENGLISH 1	SPANISH 1	ENGLISH 2	SPANISH 2
I want to eat more vegetables and meat.	Quiero comer más verduras y carne.	I want to eat a cheese sandwich and a cake.	
I want to eat a cheeseburger and chips.	Quiero comer una hamburguesa con queso y patatas fritas.	My friends want to have roast chicken for dinner, but I want fish.	
I can never wear make-up nor run in the corridors.	No puedo llevar maquillaje ni correr en los pasillos nunca.	My friends want to play on the computer in the evening.	
We can't do athletics on Thursdays. We do it at weekends.	No podemos hacer atletismo los jueves. Lo hacemos los fines de semana.	Can I borrow your dress this evening?	
My sister can go to the library every day after school, but I can't.	Mi hermana puede ir a la biblioteca todos los días después del instituto, pero yo no puedo.	I can't chew gum or run in the classrooms.	
I would like to have fish and chips for lunch.	Quiero almorzar pescado y patatas fritas.	We can't be rude in my school.	
My brother never wants to make the bed or cut the grass at home.	Mi hermano nunca quiere hacer la cama o cortar el césped en casa.	Do you want to have a coffee?	
Can I go out tonight with my boyfriend? We want to go to the cinema.	¿Puedo salir esta noche con mi novio? Queremos ir al cine.	I don't want to tidy up my room at weekends, but I do it.	

INSTRUCTIONS - You are **PARTNER A.** Work in pairs. Each of you has two sets of sentences - one set has already been translated for you. You will ask your partner to translate these. The other set of sentences have not been translated. Your partner will ask you to translate these.
HOW TO PLAY - Partner A starts by reading out his/her/their first sentence <u>in English</u>. Partner B must translate. Partner A must check the answer and award the following points: **3 points** = perfect, **2 points** = 1 mistake, **1 point** = mistakes but the verb is accurate. If they cannot translate correctly, Partner A will read out the sentence so that Partner B can learn what the correct translation is.
Then Partner B reads out his/her/their first sentence, and so on.
OBJECTIVE - Try to win more points than your partner by translating correctly as many sentences as possible.

B

ORAL PING PONG

MODAL VERBS

ENGLISH 1	SPANISH 1	ENGLISH 2	SPANISH 2
I want to eat more vegetables and meat.		I want to eat a cheese sandwich and a cake.	Quiero comer un bocadillo de queso y un pastel.
I want to eat a cheeseburger and chips.		My friends want to have roast chicken for dinner, but I want fish.	Mis amigos quieren cenar pollo asado, pero yo quiero pescado.
I can never wear make-up nor run in the corridors.		My friends want to play on the computer in the evening.	Mis amigos quieren jugar en el ordenador por la tarde.
We can't do athletics on Thursdays. We do it at weekends.		Can I borrow your dress this evening?	¿Puedo coger tu vestido esta tarde?
My sister can go to the library every day after school, but I can't.		I can't chew gum or run in the classrooms.	No puedo comer chicle o correr en las aulas.
I would like to have fish and chips for lunch.		We can't be rude in my school.	No podemos ser maleducados en mi instituto.
My brother never wants to make the bed or cut the grass at home.		Do you want to have a coffee?	¿Quieres tomar un café?
Can I go out tonight with my boyfriend? We want to go to the cinema.		I don't want to tidy up my room at weekends, but I do it.	No quiero ordenar mi habitación los fines de semana, pero lo hago.

INSTRUCTIONS - You are **PARTNER B.** Work in pairs. Each of you has two sets of sentences - one set has already been translated for you. You will ask your partner to translate these. The other set of sentences have not been translated. Your partner will ask you to translate these.
HOW TO PLAY - Partner A starts by reading out his/her/their first sentence in English. Partner B must translate. Partner A must check the answer and award the following points: **3 points** = perfect, **2 points** = 1 mistake, **1 point** = mistakes but the verb is accurate. If they cannot translate correctly, Partner A will read out the sentence so that Partner B can learn what the correct translation is.
Then Partner B reads out his/her/their first sentence, and so on.
OBJECTIVE - Try to win more points than your partner by translating correctly as many sentences as possible.

No Snakes No Ladders

MODAL VERBS

SALIDA	1 Puedo ir a la biblioteca	2 ¿Quieres tomar un té?	3 Mis amigos quieren jugar a los videojuegos	4 ¿Puedo ir al cine?	5 Quiero comer pastel	6 Mi madre quiere comer más verduras	7 No puedo ser maleducado
15 Podemos hacer pesas	14 Quiero patatas fritas	13 Quiero salir con mis amigos	12 Mi hermano quiere ir de tiendas	11 Quiero comer arroz	10 Mi hermano quiere un café	9 Quiero salir con mi novio	8 No podemos correr en los pasillos
16 No pueden comer chicle	17 Queremos una hamburguesa	18 No quiere cortar el césped	19 Mis padres quieren ver una película	20 Queremos tomar un café con leche	21 No quiero ir en bici al cine	22 ¿Puedo ir al baño?	23 Quiero desayunar una tostada
LLEGADA	30 Quieren almorzar arroz	29 Mi madre no quiere hacer mi cama	28 Mi amigo quiere almorzar un bocadillo	27 Mis amigos pueden ir de tiendas	26 Quiero pasar la aspiradora esta tarde	25 No podemos comer chicle	24 ¿Quieres un té con leche?

No Snakes No Ladders

MODAL VERBS

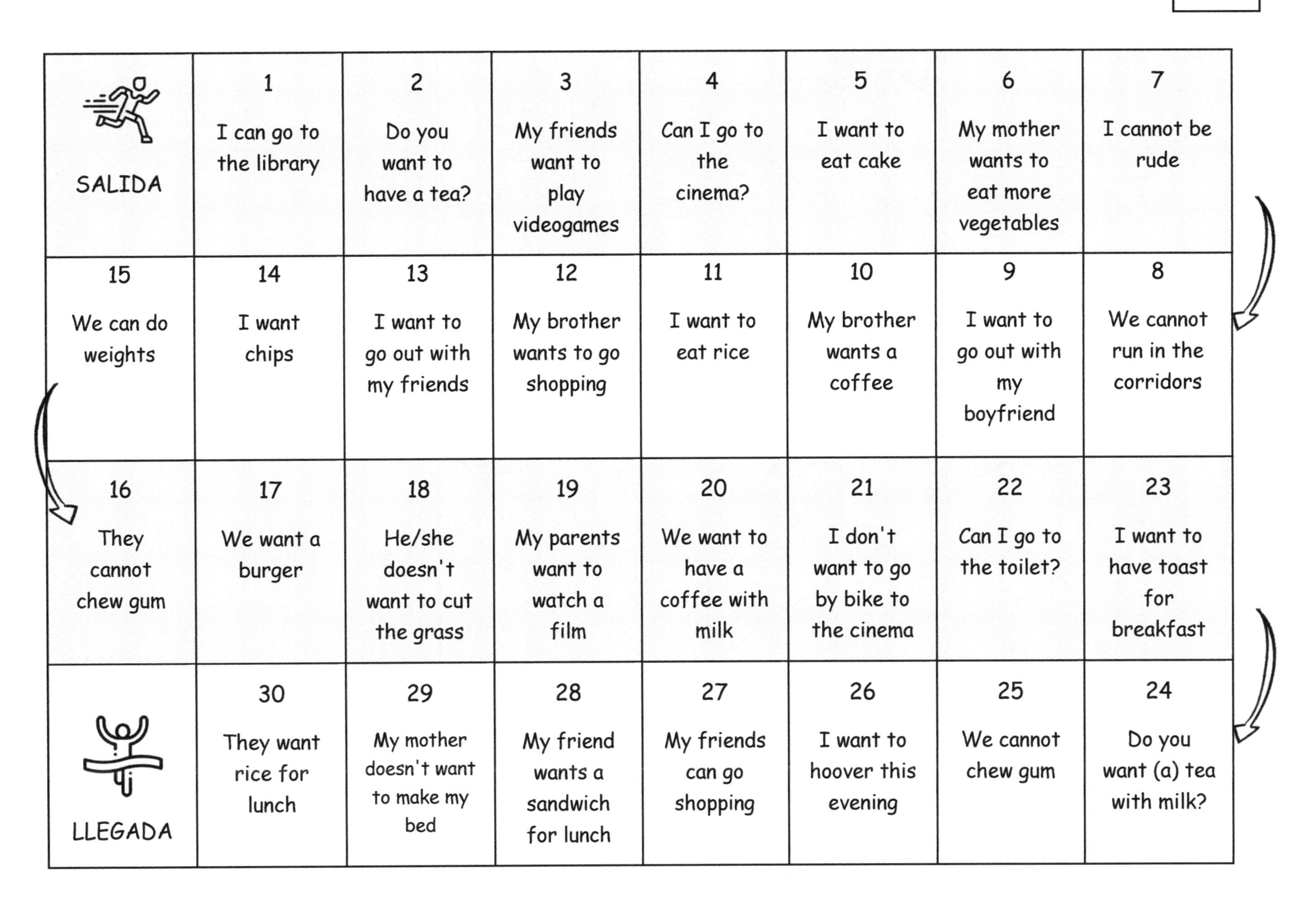

SALIDA	1 I can go to the library	2 Do you want to have a tea?	3 My friends want to play videogames	4 Can I go to the cinema?	5 I want to eat cake	6 My mother wants to eat more vegetables	7 I cannot be rude
15 We can do weights	14 I want chips	13 I want to go out with my friends	12 My brother wants to go shopping	11 I want to eat rice	10 My brother wants a coffee	9 I want to go out with my boyfriend	8 We cannot run in the corridors
16 They cannot chew gum	17 We want a burger	18 He/she doesn't want to cut the grass	19 My parents want to watch a film	20 We want to have a coffee with milk	21 I don't want to go by bike to the cinema	22 Can I go to the toilet?	23 I want to have toast for breakfast
LLEGADA	30 They want rice for lunch	29 My mother doesn't want to make my bed	28 My friend wants a sandwich for lunch	27 My friends can go shopping	26 I want to hoover this evening	25 We cannot chew gum	24 Do you want (a) tea with milk?

PYRAMID TRANSLATION

MODAL VERBS

Translate each part of the pyramid out loud with your partner, then write it into the spaces provided below.

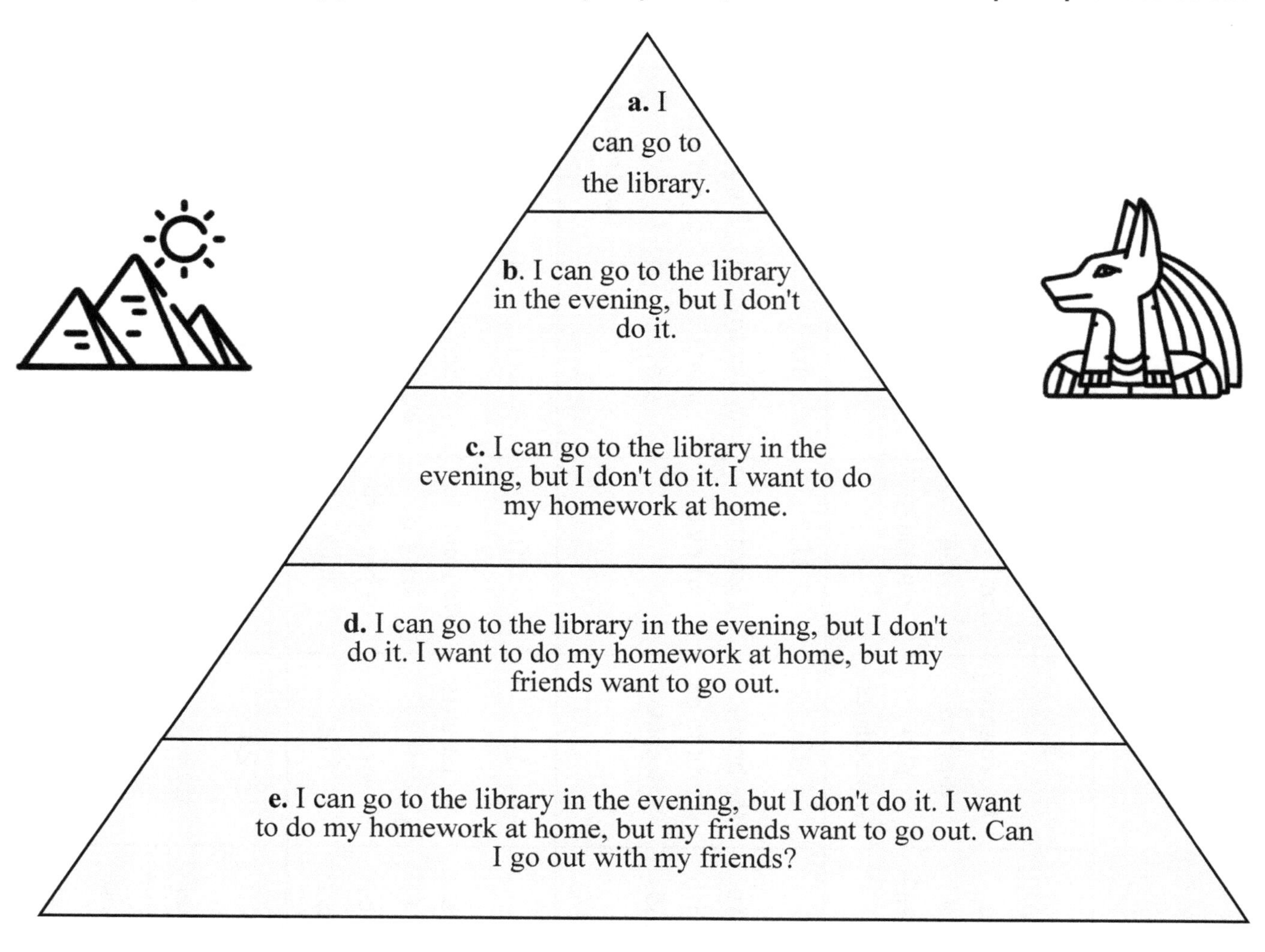

Write your translation here

---------- ✂ -------------- -------------------- ✂ ----------------- ----------------- ✂ ----------

SOLUTION: Puedo ir a la biblioteca por la tarde, pero no lo hago. Quiero hacer mis deberes en casa, pero mis amigos quieren salir. ¿Puedo salir con mis amigos?

Milton Keynes UK
Ingram Content Group UK Ltd.
UKHW030408220724
11UKWH00014B/62